Fibonacci Cubes
with Applications and Variations

Fibonacci Cubes
with Applications and Variations

Ömer Eğecioğlu
University of California at Santa Barbara, USA

Sandi Klavžar
University of Ljubljana, Slovenia

Michel Mollard
CNRS Université Grenoble Alpes, France

World Scientific

NEW JERSEY · LONDON · SINGAPORE · BEIJING · SHANGHAI · HONG KONG · TAIPEI · CHENNAI · TOKYO

Published by

World Scientific Publishing Co. Pte. Ltd.

5 Toh Tuck Link, Singapore 596224

USA office: 27 Warren Street, Suite 401-402, Hackensack, NJ 07601

UK office: 57 Shelton Street, Covent Garden, London WC2H 9HE

British Library Cataloguing-in-Publication Data

A catalogue record for this book is available from the British Library.

FIBONACCI CUBES WITH APPLICATIONS AND VARIATIONS

ISBN 978-981-126-903-5 (hardcover)
ISBN 978-981-126-915-8 (ebook for institutions)
ISBN 978-981-126-916-5 (ebook for individuals)

For any available supplementary material, please visit
https://www.worldscientific.com/worldscibooks/10.1142/13228#t=suppl

We dedicate this book to our colleague and dear friend Yoomi Rho, who shared with us her enthusiasm for Fibonacci strings and related problems. At the height of her career, Yoomi sadly passed away in a car accident in 2016.

For Maja, Martine, and Zeynep for their interest, patience and encouragement that resulted in this book.

Preface

We are living in a world whose technology is largely built on binary numbers. Considering all binary numbers that are represented by a fixed number of bits and encoding them as the vertices of a graph in which two vertices are adjacent if they differ in precisely one bit is thus a most natural idea. This idea is formally realized by the concept of hypercubes which consequently form one of the fundamental graph classes, not only in graph theory but also in theoretical computer science and elsewhere.

To obtain additional graphs with similar appealing properties as hypercubes but without the restriction on their orders to be powers of two, W.-J. Hsu introduced in 1993 the main player of this book—Fibonacci cubes [51]. These graphs live inside the hypercube graphs. Their name comes from the fact that their orders are just Fibonacci numbers. Additionally, Fibonacci cubes are constructed in a way that reflects the recursive construction of the numbers themselves.

It has turned out that Fibonacci cubes give rise to numerous combinatorial questions and have additional beautiful properties, a fine reason to investigate them from different perspectives. In this way, many connections between Fibonacci cubes and concepts from other fields of mathematics have been established and applications in other fields of science have been discovered. We are confident that the contents of the book will easily convince the reader of our assertion.

Furthermore, a number of interesting generalizations to the Fibonacci cube concept itself have also been proposed. As the theory of Fibonacci cubes has matured during the extensive development of the last nearly thirty years, we felt that the time had come for a monograph that would round out the theory, give examples of various approaches, and provide a fundamental reference for further research in the field.

We have tried to make the book as self-contained as possible, but we expect a certain mathematical maturity from the reader. Our aim is to be accessible to advanced students in mathematics and computer science while serving as an archival record of the current state of the field. On the other hand, the Fibonacci cube theory is still very lively, many of the papers we cite are from the last few years. So the story is clearly not yet finished. In the last chapter we outline some possible directions for future investigation, the reader is kindly invited to join our enthusiasm in doing so. Of course, these are just some hints, but it is difficult to predict how things will really develop as the future is unpredictable.

We thank Elif Saygı, Zülfükar Saygı, Andrej Taranenko, and Aleksander Vesel for carefully reading the manuscript of our book and suggesting numerous improvements.

We would also like to thank the artist Petra Paffenholz and the photographer Stefan Aumann for the opportunity to present in this book the sculpture "Fibonacci Cubes," which Petra Paffenholz installed in 2014 near Diepholz in Lower Saxony, Germany. The sculpture can be seen on the front cover of the book as well as on page 12.

Last but not least, we would like to express our sincere thanks to the World Scientific staff: Editors Christopher B. Davis and Steven Patt, and the editorial staff.

Ömer Eğecioğlu
Sandi Klavžar
Michel Mollard
January, 2023

Contents

Chapter 1

Liber Abaci and the Fibonacci Sequence

One of the most fascinating integer sequences in all of mathematics is the so-called *Fibonacci sequence*, the sequence of integers which starts as

$$0, 1, 1, 2, 3, 5, 8, 13, 21, 34, 55, 89, 144, 233, 377, 610, 987, 1597, \ldots \quad (1.1)$$

Here the first two terms are 0 and 1, and after that, each term is the sum of the previous two. For $n \geq 0$, we denote the nth term of this sequence by F_n. F_n is the nth *Fibonacci number*. Formally, the Fibonacci sequence is determined by the recursion

$$F_n = F_{n-1} + F_{n-2} \quad (1.2)$$

for $n \geq 2$ with initial values $F_0 = 0$ and $F_1 = 1$. This again states that for $n \geq 2$, the nth Fibonacci number F_n is obtained as the sum of the previous two, namely the sum of F_{n-1} and F_{n-2}.

The Fibonacci sequence is intrinsically intertwined with the central object of this book, Fibonacci cubes. We will start their investigation in Chapter 3. The reason for this deferral is that in Chapter 1 we first introduce the reader to the fascinating world of the Fibonacci sequence and selected interesting related areas. In Chapter 2 we introduce the basic elements of formal languages and generating functions which are the mathematical tools that will accompany us throughout the book.

1.1 Liber Abaci

Western Europe was introduced to the sequence of numbers (1.1) by the remarkable Italian mathematician Leonardo Pisano, whose seminal work *Liber Abaci* (Book of Calculation) was published in 1202. Leonardo was born in Pisa around the year 1170. He is referred to in many modern treatments as Fibonacci (probably from son of Bonacci), and this is the name we will use. His father was a merchant and a government official of the Holy Roman Empire in Pisa, later posted as a customs clerk to the trading center Béjaïa (Bugia) on the Algerian coast. Leonardo traveled widely in the Middle East all the way to Constantinople, and learned a great deal of ancient mathematics including the Hindu-Arabic numerals.

After settling in Pisa at the end of the 12th century, he disseminated his work in mathematics on number theory and algebraic equations in five books. *Liber Abaci* is his first book published as a manuscript in 1202. No complete copies of this version have survived. *Liber Abaci* came to us by later copies of a 1228 version revised by himself. Fibonacci died about the year 1250.

Roman numerals were still very prevalent in the West during Fibonacci's time. *Liber Abaci* introduced the number system we use today, which is based on Arabic numerals, as well as Greek and Hindu-Arabic mathematicians' previous work, and provided many examples of problems that could be solved with this system of numerals. Some of Leonardo's examples were for commercial applications, but there are surprising variety of problems that are stated in *Liber Abaci* along with their solutions, containing nearly all of the algebraic knowledge of those times. The ideas presented in *Liber Abaci* played a central role in the development of mathematics in the West in the subsequent centuries.

Fibonacci numbers appear in *Liber Abaci* in Chapter 12 in a problem with the Latin title "Quot paria corticulorum in uno anno ex uno pario generentur." Fibonacci assumes that a pair of rabbits requires one month to mature and thereafter reproduces itself once each month. Starting with a single pair, how many pairs will there be in a year? Fibonacci explains the reasoning of his solution in detail, calculating from month to month. The numbers computed are provided in the margin as a table.

There is an English translation of *Liber Abaci* by Sigler [96] which is based on a 1862 Latin edition of the work. A more recent critical Latin edition of *Liber Abaci* was prepared by Giusti [41]. The latter contains an introduction in Italian and in English. This reference edition also includes a full description of the history of the existing copies of the manuscript.

In Sigler's translation, Fibonacci's exposition and his solution to this problem is given as follows[1] [96, Chapter 12, Problem 26]:

---

[1]Reproduced by permission from *Springer Nature*.

"How Many Pairs of Rabbits Are Created by One Pair in One Year

A certain man had one pair of rabbits together in a certain enclosed place, and one wishes to know how many are created from the pair in one year when it is the nature of them in a single month to bear another pair, and in the second month those born to bear also. Because the abovewritten pair in the first month bore, you will double it; there will be two pairs in one month. One of these, namely the first, bears in the second month, and thus there are in the second month 3 pairs; of these in one month two are pregnant, and in the third month 2 pairs of rabbits are born, and thus there are 5 pairs in the month; in this month 3 pairs are pregnant, and in the fourth month there are 8 pairs, of which 5 pairs bear another 5 pairs; these are added to the 8 pairs making 13 pairs in the fifth month; these 5 pairs that are born in this month do not mate in this month, but another 8 pairs are pregnant, and thus there are in the sixth month 21 pairs; to these are added the 13 pairs that are born in the seventh month; there will be 34 pairs in this month; to this are added the 21 pairs that are born in the eighth month; there will be 55 pairs in this month; to these are added the 34 pairs that are born in the ninth month; there will be 89 pairs in this month; to these are added again the 55 pairs that are born in the tenth month; there will be 144 pairs in this month; to these are added again the 89 pairs that are born in the eleventh month; there will be 233 pairs in this month. To these are still added the 144 pairs that are born in the last month; there will be 377 pairs, and this many pairs are produced from the abovewritten pair in the mentioned place at the end of the one year. You can indeed see in the margin how we operated, namely that we added the first number to the second, namely the 1 to the 2, and the second to the third, and the third to the fourth, and the fourth to the fifth, and thus one after another until we added the tenth to the eleventh, namely the 144 to the 233, and we had the abovewritten sum of rabbits, namely 377, and thus you can *in order find it for an unending number of months."*

beginning	*1*
first	*2*
second	*3*
third	*5*
fourth	*8*
fifth	*13*
sixth	*21*
seventh	*34*
eighth	*55*
ninth	*89*
tenth	*144*
eleventh	*233*
end	*377*

This then is the celebrated rabbit problem which is over 800 years old, that gave birth to the Fibonacci numbers.

This sequence is well-known for its apparent representation of certain natural growth phenomena and applications in mathematical sciences. Its properties have been observed as the basis of agreeable forms in architecture, pleasing proportions in paintings and sculptures, and as determining the climactic points in musical compositions. Fibonacci numbers and Fibonacci inspired structures are often used in modern computer science, as a part of number theory, and in expressing a number of interesting properties mathematical objects. They have curious relationships to other families of well-known sequences, such as the binomial coefficients.

Problems involving Fibonacci numbers can be found in many mathematical publications, recreational and otherwise. There is even a quarterly academic journal dedicated to Fibonacci numbers and closely related topics titled *The Fibonacci Quarterly*. From the vast literature on this topic, we cite only a few reference books: [6, 87, 105, 111].

1.2   Fibonacci Numbers in Nature

The number of spirals in the pattern of sunflower seeds turns out to be a Fibonacci number. Similarly, looking at a pinecone from the bottom, the number of spirals going from the center to the outer edge appears to be a

Fibonacci number (see Fig. 1.1 for an example). The number of petals on many flowers are also given by small Fibonacci numbers.

Fig. 1.1 8 spirals of a pinecone when viewed as spreading out counterclockwise from the center; same pinecone has 13 spirals spreading out clockwise from the center

1.3 Fibonacci Identities and Induction

Many relationships between expressions involving Fibonacci numbers can be proved by the method of (strong) mathematical induction, such as the identities

$$\sum_{i=0}^{n} F_i = F_{n+2} - 1,$$

$$F_{n-1}F_{n+1} = F_n^2 + (-1)^n,$$

$$\sum_{i=0}^{n} F_i^2 = F_n F_{n+1},$$

as well as various divisibility properties.

Fibonacci numbers are also related to the binomial coefficients by a simple summation formula. By inspection, the diagonal entries of the Pascal triangle as shown in Fig. 1.2 suggests the identity involving the binomial coefficients

$$F_n = \sum_{i=0}^{n-1} \binom{n-i-1}{i} \tag{1.3}$$

for $n \geq 1$. Once conjectured, this identity immediately follows by induction using (1.2) and elementary properties of the binomial coefficients.

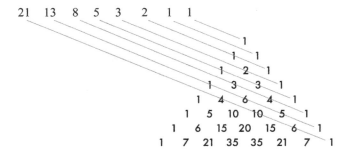

Fig. 1.2 Sums of the diagonal entries in the Pascal triangle are the Fibonacci numbers

1.4   Fibonacci Strings

A binary string of length n is a sequence of n digits (or *letters*), where each digit is a 0 or a 1. We usually write a string as a juxtaposition of its elements, such as $w = 0011101011$. The empty (or null) string with no letters is usually denoted by the special symbol λ, and is assigned length zero.

Of the 2^n binary strings of length n, we consider those in which no two consecutive letters are 1. These are called *Fibonacci strings* of length n. As an example, Fibonacci strings of length $n = 4$ are shown in the first row of Table 1.1.

$\mathcal{F}_4$	0000	0001	0010	0100	1000	0101	1001	1010
$0\,\mathcal{F}_3$	0000	0001	0010	0100		0101		
$10\,\mathcal{F}_2$					1000		1001	1010

Table 1.1   Fibonacci strings of length 4

Fibonacci strings of length $n \geq 2$ can be partitioned into two subsets, first consisting of those that start with 0, and the second, those that start with 1, as shown in the last two rows of Table 1.1 for $n = 4$. In this second subset of Fibonacci strings, the letter following the initial 1 is necessarily a 0.

The first subset is equinumerous with $000, 001, 010, 100, 101$, which are Fibonacci strings of length 3, and the latter subset with $00, 01, 10$, which are Fibonacci strings of length 2. If we let $\mathcal{F}_n$ denote the set of Fibonacci strings of length n, then the decomposition given above can be written symbolically as

$$\mathcal{F}_n = 0\,\mathcal{F}_{n-1} + 10\,\mathcal{F}_{n-2}$$

for $n \geq 2$, analogous to the recursion (1.2). Here $0\,\mathcal{F}_{n-1}$ is the set of all Fibonacci strings of length $n-1$ each prefixed with 0; $10\,\mathcal{F}_{n-2}$ is the set of all Fibonacci strings of length $n-2$ each prefixed with 10, and "+" denotes disjoint union.

Let a_n denote the number of elements in $\mathcal{F}_n$. We see that a_n satisfies

$$a_n = a_{n-1} + a_{n-2}$$

for $n \geq 2$ with $a_0 = 1$ and $a_1 = 2$. Therefore the number of Fibonacci strings of length n is

$$a_n = F_{n+2} \,. \tag{1.4}$$

This has an amusing application. Suppose we flip a fair coin until two consecutive heads are obtained. What is the probability that we flip the coin n times for this event to happen? We easily compute this probability for $n = 1, 2, 3$ as $0, \frac{1}{4}, \frac{1}{8}$, respectively. If we denote the outcome of heads by 1 and tails by 0, for $n \geq 3$ we are looking for the probability of obtaining a Fibonacci string of length $n-3$, followed by a 0, which is then followed by two 1s among all binary strings of length n. Using (1.4) this probability is

$$\frac{F_{n-1}}{2^{n-3}}\frac{1}{2^3} = \frac{F_{n-1}}{2^n} \,.$$

It can be shown that this in turn implies the identity

$$1 = \sum_{n \geq 1} \frac{F_{n-1}}{2^n} \,. \tag{1.5}$$

1.5 Fibonacci Representations

Every positive integer n can be written in terms of Fibonacci numbers as a sum of the form

$$n = F_{k_1} + F_{k_2} + \cdots + F_{k_r} \,,$$

with $k_1 > k_2 > \cdots > k_r \geq 2$. This is a *Fibonacci representation* of n. There may be many different Fibonacci representations of a given integer. However there is a *unique* Fibonacci representation if we impose the additional requirements

$$k_j - k_{j+1} \geq 2, \quad j \in [r-1],$$

where we use the notation $[n] = \{1, \ldots, n\}$ for a given positive integer n. This unique Fibonacci representation of n is called its *canonical* representation (it is also referred to as the *Zeckendorf representation* [124] in the literature).

It is also useful to use binary strings to encode Fibonacci representations by using their Fibonacci indicator "digits," where the rightmost digit corresponds to F_2, the digit to its left to F_3 and so on. F_{i+1} appears as a summand in a Fibonacci representation denoted by a binary string, if and only if the element with index i from the right in the string is 1. In the canonical representation there are no consecutive Fibonacci numbers as summands, and therefore there are no two consecutive 1s in the corresponding binary encoding. We see that the binary encodings of canonical representations of integers are nothing but Fibonacci strings.

n	Canonical representation	Binary encoding
1	F_2	1
2	F_3	10
3	F_4	100
4	$F_4 + F_2$	101
5	F_5	1000
6	$F_5 + F_2$	1001
7	$F_5 + F_3$	1010
8	F_6	10000
9	$F_6 + F_2$	10001
10	$F_6 + F_3$	10010
11	$F_6 + F_4$	10100
12	$F_6 + F_4 + F_2$	10101

Table 1.2 Canonical (Zeckendorf) representation of the integers $1, 2, \ldots, 12$, with their binary encoding

1.6 Compositions

A *composition* of a positive integer n is a way of writing $n = n_1 + n_2 + \cdots + n_k$ for some k, where each summand is a positive integer and the order of the summands is taken into account. Compositions are also called *ordered partitions*. The n_i are called the *parts* of the composition. Let p_n denote the number of compositions of n where each part is ≥ 2. For instance, $n = 6$ has 5 such compositions: 6, 4+2, 3+3, 2+4, 2+2+2, so that $p_6 = 5$. In such a composition with $n_1 \geq 3$, replacing n_1 with $n_1 - 1$ while keeping all other parts the same gives a composition of $n - 1$ of the same type (i.e., parts ≥ 2). If $n_1 = 2$, then $n - 2 = n_2 + \cdots + n_k$, and this is a composition of $n - 2$ of the same type. We see that these are actually one-to-one correspondences. The situation is shown in the array in Table 1.3 for $n = 6$.

Compositions with parts ≥ 2	6	4+2	3+3	2+4	2+2+2
First part ≥ 3	5	3+2	2+3		
First part = 2				4	2+2

Table 1.3   Compositions of 6 with parts ≥ 2

Therefore for $n \geq 3$,

$$p_n = p_{n-1} + p_{n-2}$$

with $p_1 = 0$ and $p_2 = 1$. Consequently $p_n = F_{n-1}$ for $n \geq 1$ [83, p. 134].

A similar argument can be made for the number of compositions of n with parts ≤ 2. These compositions are shown in Table 1.4 for $n = 4$.

Compositions with parts ≤ 2	1+1+1+1	1+1+2	1+2+1	2+1+1	2+2
First part = 1	1+1+1+1	1+1+2	1+2+1		
First part = 2				2+1+1	2+2

Table 1.4   Compositions of 4 with parts ≤ 2

If we denote this number by q_n, then $q_1 = 1$, $q_2 = 2$ and $q_n = q_{n-1} + q_{n-2}$, and therefore this time $q_n = F_{n+1}$.

1.7   Tilings

A *monomer* is a 1×1 rectangle and a *dimer* is a 1×2 rectangle. Let b_n denote the number of monomer-dimer tilings of a $1 \times n$ strip. Monomer-dimer tilings of the 1×4 strip are shown in Fig. 1.3.

Fig. 1.3 Monomer-dimer tilings of the 1×4 strip

There are b_{n-1} tilings in which the leftmost cell of the strip is covered by a monomer, and b_{n-2} tilings in which it is covered by a dimer. It follows that $b_n = b_{n-1} + b_{n-2}$ for $n \geq 3$. We have $b_1 = 1$, $b_2 = 2$ and therefore $b_n = F_{n+1}$ for $n \geq 1$. We can see that these are nothing but compositions of n with parts ≤ 2 in disguise. We also note that monomer-dimer tilings of the $1 \times n$ strip can be thought of as left to right encodings of the Fibonacci strings of length $n - 1$ with a 0 added to the end; a dimer encodes the pair 10 and a monomer encodes a 0 which is not preceded by a 1.

Let us also consider the dimer-only tilings of the $2 \times n$ rectangle. Dimer-only tilings of the 2×4 rectangle is shown in Fig. 1.4. If c_n denotes the number of such tilings then $c_n = c_{n-1} + c_{n-2}$ for $n \geq 3$. This is because the number of tilings in which the leftmost dimer is vertical is counted by c_{n-1}, and those in which it is a pair of horizontal dimers is counted by c_{n-2}. Since $c_1 = 1$ and $c_2 = 2$, we again have $c_n = F_{n+1}$.

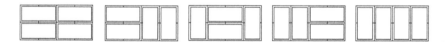

Fig. 1.4 Dimer-only tilings of the 2×4 strip

Dimer-only tilings are also called tilings with dominoes. At the end of Section 3.8 we will consider a variation of this problem, enumeration of distinct tilings with dominoes of the $2 \times n$ rectangle.

1.8 The Golden Mean

The ratio F_{n+1}/F_n of successive Fibonacci numbers converges to the *golden ratio*; or the *golden mean* φ, given by

$$\varphi = \frac{1 + \sqrt{5}}{2} = 1.61803398874989...$$

The golden mean is the positive root of the equation $x^2 - x - 1 = 0$. In fact this quadratic polynomial factors as $(x - \varphi)(x + \varphi^{-1})$.

Let us divide a line segment in two parts as shown in Fig. 1.5 in such a way that the ratio of the larger part to the smaller is the same as the ratio of the length of the whole line segment to the larger part. In other words we would like to have $A/B = (A + B)/A$, where the two parts have lengths $A > B$. Then this common ratio is φ, and the point x is called the *golden section* (see Fig. 1.5). It appears that the properties of the golden ratio were already studied in antiquity for their pleasurable properties, independently of its connection with the Fibonacci sequence.

Fig. 1.5 The *golden section* is defined by the property: $A/B = (A + B)/A$

A closely related object, the *golden rectangle*, is a special rectangle the ratio of the length of whose longer side to the shorter one is φ. In terms of the labels of the golden section of Fig. 1.5, its base is $A + B$ and side length is A, as shown in Fig. 1.6. The rectangle which shares a side with the $A \times A$ square itself is a golden rectangle. Continuing this way, we obtain a sequence of self-similar rectangles as shown in Fig. 1.6. By a geometric construction as shown in Fig. 1.6, we also obtain an approximation to the logarithmic spiral curve observed in nature.

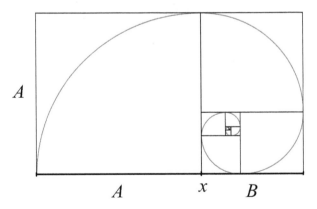

Fig. 1.6 Repeated divisions by the golden section φ and the approximation to the logarithmic spiral with quarter arcs of circles inscribed in the squares

It is interesting that Fibonacci numbers and the golden ratio φ have been observed as defining agreeable forms in architecture, painting, sculpture, and as the basis of diverse natural phenomena. There are many observed examples in nature in which the number φ magically appears, from snail shells to the angular location of leaves on a plant stem.

Among the Fibonacci inspired structures, one of particular interest to us is the one consisting of nine iron Fibonacci cubes designed by the artist Petra Paffenholz. In addition to its pleasing proportions, this piece of art shares with this book the phrase "Fibonacci Cube," albeit with a somewhat different intended meaning.

Paffenholz's work was erected in 2014 in the flat land near Diepholz in Lower Saxony as a part of a sculpture walk. The largest of the cubes is almost 7 meters tall. The dimensions of the cubes are given by the Fibonacci sequence, so that the side length of the 7th cube, for instance, is the sum of the side lengths of the 6th and the 5th cubes.

Fig. 1.7   Petra Paffenholz's sculpture titled Fibonacci Cubes in Diepholz (Photo: Stefan Aumann, used by permission)

Paffenholz explains her personal philosophy behind this beautiful structure with the words "When it comes to mathematics, I really was a terrible pupil. But nevertheless, I am fascinated by the simplicity of the Fibonacci sequence, which can be calculated forever, symbolizing the infinite universe. Well, we do not know if the universe is infinite, but imagination of mankind has problems to think either way; if there is an end or not, both ways blow our minds. That is the idea, the reason why I choose to design this artwork."

Fibonacci Cubes sculpture brings to mind the following version, which we may this time call *Fibonacci squares*. Starting with two initial squares of unit area corresponding to $n = 1$ and $n = 2$, this time we require that the *area* of each succeeding square should be the sum of the areas of the two preceding ones. Fig. 1.8 illustrates this.

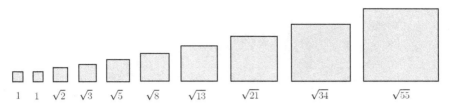

$$1 \quad 1 \quad \sqrt{2} \quad \sqrt{3} \quad \sqrt{5} \quad \sqrt{8} \quad \sqrt{13} \quad \sqrt{21} \quad \sqrt{34} \quad \sqrt{55}$$

Fig. 1.8 Starting with two unit squares, the area of each square is the sum of the areas of the previous two

We easily see that the side length of the nth square in this sequence is $\sqrt{F_n}$. Also, any three consecutive side lengths forms a *Pythagorian real triple*, meaning

$$\left(\sqrt{F_n}\right)^2 = \left(\sqrt{F_{n-1}}\right)^2 + \left(\sqrt{F_{n-2}}\right)^2. \tag{1.6}$$

This means that these quantities are the side lengths of a right triangle. Of course the identity (1.6) is nothing but the defining recursion of the Fibonacci sequence.

This allows for a pleasing construction which starts with the right triangle with vertices $(0,0)$, $(1,0)$, and $(0,1)$. This triangle has side lengths $\sqrt{F_2}$, $\sqrt{F_1}$, and $\sqrt{F_3}$, starting from $(0,0)$ and proceeding counterclockwise. In the next step we use the hypotenuse of length $\sqrt{F_3}$ of this triangle as the base and construct a new right triangle with side lengths $\sqrt{F_3}$, $\sqrt{F_2}$, and $\sqrt{F_4}$, again proceeding counterclockwise from $(0,0)$. The construction continues in the manner indicated in Fig. 1.9. We note that the resulting shape is much like the outline of an ordinary spiral seashell.

1.9 Binet Formula

For $n \geq 0$, there is a closed form expression for F_n, namely

$$F_n = \frac{1}{\sqrt{5}}\left[\left(\frac{1+\sqrt{5}}{2}\right)^n - \left(\frac{1-\sqrt{5}}{2}\right)^n\right]. \tag{1.7}$$

This is called the *Binet formula* for F_n. Even though it is a fairly standard calculation in the study of recurrence relations that yields (1.7), the appearances of $\sqrt{5}$ always leaves the uninitiated stunned as they must all disappear after carrying out the calculations indicated on the right, leaving an integer behind; i.e., F_n.

In terms of the golden ratio φ, (1.7) can be written as

$$F_n = \frac{1}{\sqrt{5}}\left[\varphi^n - (-\varphi)^{-n}\right].$$

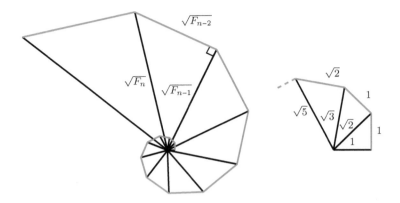

Fig. 1.9   The construction with the sequence of numbers $(\sqrt{F_n})_{n \geq 1}$

Note also that the identity (1.5) can be obtained following a straight-forward calculation if we use the closed form expression (1.7).

As we will see below, Binet's formula is very important and applicable, but on the other hand it is not practical for the calculation of the Fibonacci numbers themselves.

1.10   Lucas Numbers

The Fibonacci sequence as well as variations modeled on it were studied in detail by Édouard Lucas (1842-1891) in his 1891 treatise *Théorie des nombres* [72].

The so-called *Lucas numbers* L_n are defined by the same recurrence relation as (1.2) for $n \geq 2$, i.e., they satisfy

$$L_n = L_{n-1} + L_{n-2} \text{ for } n \geq 2, \tag{1.8}$$

but with different initial values, given by $L_0 = 2$ and $L_1 = 1$. The Lucas sequence thus starts with

$$2, 1, 3, 4, 7, 11, 18, 29, 47, 76, 123, 199, 322, 521, 843, 1364, 2207, 3571, \ldots$$

It can be shown that the Binet formula for Lucas numbers is

$$L_n = \left(\frac{1 + \sqrt{5}}{2}\right)^n + \left(\frac{1 - \sqrt{5}}{2}\right)^n = \varphi^n + (-\varphi)^{-n}. \tag{1.9}$$

The Lucas numbers can be expressed in terms of the Fibonacci numbers. Indeed by an immediate induction one can prove the identity

$$L_n = F_{n-1} + F_{n+1} \tag{1.10}$$

as well as the companion identity

$$F_n = \tfrac{1}{5}(L_{n-1} + L_{n+1})$$

for $n \geq 1$, relating the two sequences to one another.

Chapter 2

Formal Languages and Generating Functions

Fibonacci cubes, our main objects of study in this book, have as their underlying building blocks strings of 0s and 1s of a given length, with certain restrictions imposed on them. In our studies, these strings are broken up into smaller pieces, which are more or less of the same kind as the original ones. This allows us to study our objects by studying smaller and smaller ones, and also to try and figure out the properties that are preserved in this process. The study of strings which obey certain restrictions is the area of *formal languages*. However we only need the very basic constructs of the theory of formal languages for our approach.

Perhaps just as important for the techniques we use frequently is the study of *generating functions*. These are in general more familiar mathematical objects. There is a very useful interplay between sets of strings under consideration and generating functions, which keep track of the number of strings with certain properties. This interplay can either be viewed as keeping track of a whole sequence of numbers that we are interested in, or perhaps as looking at a myopic version of our set of strings, where we disregard some of the properties that define them. In this way we can use techniques from calculus and elementary algebra to discover numerical behavior of a number of parameters of our graphs.

2.1 Generating Functions

Given a sequence of numbers $a_0, a_1, a_2, \ldots$, which we can denote by $(a_n)_{n \geq 0}$ for short, we can keep track of all of the numbers in the sequence simultaneously. This is done by passing to the *generating function* of the sequence.

Definition 2.1. The generating function of a sequence $(a_n)_{n \geq 0}$ is the formal power series

$$\sum_{n \geq 0} a_n t^n = a_0 + a_1 t + a_2 t^2 + a_3 t^3 + \cdots. \tag{2.1}$$

Note that we are using various powers of the symbol t merely as place holders, and in this formulation a generating function is not really a function but only a formal series. Nevertheless, this terminology is used for historical reasons. Usually we are interested in closed form expressions for generating functions on which we can use algebraic techniques.

The generating function of the sum of two sequences is the sum of their generating functions. In particular, if two sequences have the same generating function, then they are identical. Equality of two generating functions is the equality of all of their coefficients. Given two generating functions

$$f(t) = a_0 + a_1 t + a_2 t^2 + \cdots, \qquad g(t) = b_0 + b_1 t + b_2 t^2 + \cdots,$$

$$h(t) = f(t)g(t) = c_0 + c_1 t + c_2 t^2 + \cdots + c_n t^n + \cdots$$

is the generating function of the *convolution* of the two sequences, whose terms are defined by

$$c_n = \sum_{k=0}^{n} a_k b_{n-k}.$$

Newton's expansion formula is a very useful tool when working with generating functions:

$$(1+t)^\alpha = 1 + \sum_{k \geq 1} \frac{\alpha(\alpha-1)\cdots(\alpha-k+1)}{k!} t^k. \tag{2.2}$$

This series is convergent for $|t| < 1$ for arbitrary complex number α, but we will not be evaluating it for any numerical value of t. We note that when α is a positive integer, (2.2) reduces to the binomial theorem.

2.2   Elements of Formal Languages

Here we review some basic constructs from the theory of formal languages and their relation to generating functions. It turns out that a number of properties of Fibonacci cubes and their variants that we are interested in are sometimes expressed in terms of elementary properties of formal languages and then passing on to the generating functions.

The basic terms we use are *alphabet, letter, word, string* and *language*.

An alphabet Σ is any finite non-empty collection of symbols called *letters*. For example $\Sigma = \{a\}$, $\Sigma = \{0,1\}$, $\Sigma = \{a,b,c\}$, $\Sigma = \{x_1, x_2, x_3, \ldots, x_9\}$ are alphabets. $\Sigma = \{0,1\}$ is called the *binary alphabet*. We reserve the symbol $\mathcal{B}$ for the binary alphabet.

In most cases, the letters of the alphabet have a natural order on them such as for $\Sigma = \{a,b,c\}$ we have $a < b < c$; and for $\Sigma = \{x_1, x_2, x_3, \ldots, x_9\}$ we have $x_1 < x_2 < \cdots < x_9$.

If w is a juxtaposition of any number of letters from an alphabet Σ, then w is called a Σ-*word* or equivalently a Σ-*string*. When the alphabet is fixed or when it is clear from the context, we drop the Σ- and talk about *words* or *strings* over Σ. So the terms string and word may be used interchangeably.

A *language* $\mathcal{L}$ over Σ is a finite or infinite collection of words over Σ.

Length

If w is a word, the number of letters of w is the *length* of w, denoted by the symbol $|w|$.

The Null-Word

The special word consisting of no letters is usually referred to as the *empty string* or the *null-word* and it is assigned zero length. The null-word is often denoted by the symbol λ.

Concatenation

If u and v are words, by $u \cdot v$ or by simply uv we mean the word of length $|u| + |v|$ obtained by placing u and v one after the other. Thus if $u = abba$ and $v = bb$ then $uv = abbabb$. This operation is referred to as *concatenation*. In fact, the same term is used when we juxtapose any number of words.

Note that concatenation has the mathematical character of multiplication. Indeed, any triplet of words u, v, w we have $(u \cdot v) \cdot w = u \cdot (v \cdot w)$. This is the *associativity* of concatenation.

Concatenating the null-word with any other word w gives w back: $w \cdot \lambda = \lambda \cdot w = w$. Thus λ behaves with respect to concatenation very much in the same manner the number 1 behaves with respect to multiplication. Thus an alternate and appropriate notation for the null-word could be the symbol

"1" itself, assuming that it is not one of the letters of the alphabet we are working with.

We note however that concatenation is not in general a commutative operation. As an example, $u \cdot v \neq v \cdot u$ for the words $u = a$ and $v = b$ over the alphabet $\{a, b\}$.

Prefixes and Suffixes

If w can be written in the form $w = u \cdot v$, then we shall say that u is a *prefix* of w and v is a *suffix* of w. Note that the null-word λ and w itself are always prefixes of w. They are also suffixes of w.

The Languages Σ^*, Σ^+, Σ_n

The collection consisting of all Σ-words (including the null-word) is denoted by Σ^*. The collection of non-null Σ-words is denoted by Σ^+. For $n \geq 0$ we define

$$\Sigma_n = \{w \in \Sigma^* : |w| = n\}.$$

Of particular interest is the language $\mathcal{B}^*$ which is the set of all binary words, (or binary strings) including the null-word. The language of words over $\mathcal{B}$ of length n is denoted by $\mathcal{B}_n$. Thus for $n \geq 0$,

$$\mathcal{B}_n = \{w \in \mathcal{B}^* : |w| = n\}.$$

Subwords and Complements

A word s is a *subword* or *substring* of a word w if w can be written as $w = usv$ for some $u, v \in \Sigma^*$. Note that s is a contiguous part of w. A substring s of w is referred to as a *factor* of w in some treatments.

A *run* in a word is a maximal length subword consisting of a single repeated letter. For instance in the word $w = 001111000$, there are two runs of 0s of lengths 2 and 3, and a single run of 1s of length 4. Runs are sometimes referred to as *blocks*.

The symbol $|w|_s$ denotes the number of occurrences of s as a subword in w. So for example if $w = 01010$; $|w|_0 = 3$, $|w|_1 = 2$ and $|w|_{010} = 2$.

For a given alphabet Σ and a word f over Σ, we define $\Sigma_n(f)$ to be the set of strings of length n over Σ in which f *does not* appear as a subword. In other words

$$\Sigma_n(f) = \{w \in \Sigma_n : \nexists\, u, v \in \Sigma^* \text{ with } w = ufv\}$$
$$= \{w \in \Sigma_n : |w|_f = 0\}.$$

In particular, given a word over the binary alphabet $\mathcal{B} = \{0,1\}$ we have

$$\mathcal{B}_n(f) = \{w \in \mathcal{B}_n : \not\exists\, u, v \in \{0,1\}^* \text{ with } w = ufv\}$$
$$= \{w \in \mathcal{B}_n : |w|_f = 0\}.$$

When we deal with a binary string f, it makes sense to talk about its *complement* $\overline{f}$, defined by replacing each bit in f by the complementary bit. So for example $\overline{1001} = 0110$.

Reverses and Palindromes

Given a word $w = w_1 w_2 \ldots w_n$ of length n over an alphabet Σ, its *reverse* is the word $w^R = w_n w_{n-1} \ldots w_1$. Thus w^R is the word w written backwards. Clearly $(w^R)^R = w$. A *palindrome* is a word w with $w = w^R$. A palindrome is also referred to as a *palindromic word* or a *palindromic string*.

Series and Algebraic Operations

Certain basic operations involving words and languages can be translated into algebraic operations. To do this, it is convenient to represent languages as a formal sum of words and write $\mathcal{L} = \sum_{w \in \mathcal{L}} w$. This is merely a convenient way to deal with all the words of $\mathcal{L}$ at the same time. For instance if $\mathcal{L}$ is the language of all words of length 2 over the binary alphabet $\mathcal{B} = \{0,1\}$ then we write

$$\mathcal{L} = 00 + 01 + 10 + 11. \tag{2.3}$$

We can think of this as a shorthand for $\mathcal{L} = \{00\} \cup \{01\} \cup \{10\} \cup \{11\}$ where "+" in (2.3) denotes disjoint union and we ignore the curly brackets.

Concatenating Languages

One of the most basic operations which can be used to produce further languages from given ones is *concatenation*. Given two languages $\mathcal{L}_1$ and $\mathcal{L}_2$ we define

$$\mathcal{L}_1 \mathcal{L}_2 = \{uv : u \in \mathcal{L}_1, v \in \mathcal{L}_2\}.$$

This definition can easily be extended to the concatenation of an arbitrary number of languages. In particular for any language $\mathcal{L}$ and positive integer n, we can talk about the language $\mathcal{L}^n$, which is the concatenation of n copies of $\mathcal{L}$. For convenience we put $\mathcal{L}^0 = \lambda$. We see that with the concatenation operation the language Σ_n of words of length n over Σ can be written as

Σ^n. Similarly, $\mathcal{B}_n$ is the n-fold concatenation $\mathcal{B}^n$.

The simplest alphabet is one consisting of a single letter. For $\Sigma = \{a\}$ we have $\Sigma^* = \{\lambda, a, aa, aaa, \ldots\}$ so we may write

$$\Sigma^* = 1 + a + a^2 + a^3 + \cdots$$

Note that the notation 1 for the null-word is consistent with the mathematical convention that $a^0 = 1$. Thus we can use the shorthand notation

$$\Sigma^* = \frac{1}{1-a}.$$

Let us now consider the alphabet $\Sigma = \{a, b\}$. Let Σ_n denote the language consisting of all Σ-words of length n. It is easy to show that $\Sigma_n = (a+b)^n$, i.e., the concatenation of n copies of $a+b$, which we can write as Σ^n. Since

$$\Sigma^* = 1 + \Sigma + \Sigma^2 + \Sigma^3 + \cdots, \tag{2.4}$$

we may again write

$$\Sigma^* = \frac{1}{1-(a+b)}. \tag{2.5}$$

We can observe the advantage of the formalism of writing a language as the sum of its words when we pass to the generating function. As an example, writing the language of words of length 3 over $\Sigma = \{a, b\}$ as

$$(a+b)^3 = aaa + aab + aba + abb + baa + bab + bba + bbb.$$

Replacing each a by 1 and each b by some variable t in both sides of this identity yields the polynomial identity

$$(1+t)^3 = 1 + t + t + t^2 + t + t^2 + t^2 + t^3 = 1 + 3t + 3t^2 + t^3,$$

which is of course a special case of the binomial theorem.

As another example for $\Sigma = \{a, b\}$, consider the generating function

$$g(t) = \sum_{w \in \Sigma^*} t^{|w|}.$$

The coefficient of t^n on the right is the number of words of length n over Σ, that is 2^n. Replacing each letter by t in both sides of (2.4) gives

$$g(t) = 1 + (2t) + (2t)^2 + \cdots = \frac{1}{1-2t},$$

which is what we would obtain from the formal expression (2.5) for Σ^* by replacing both a and b by t.

Enumerator Polynomials

Sometimes we find it of interest to count a set of objects by classifying them according to some parameter. For example, of the 2^n strings of length n over the alphabet $\Sigma = \{a, b\}$, there are $\binom{n}{k}$ with exactly k occurrences of a. The polynomial

$$\sum_{k=0}^{n} \binom{n}{k} x^k \qquad (2.6)$$

which keeps track of these numbers as the coefficients of the powers of a variable (x in this case), is called their *enumerator polynomial*. For a given n, (2.6) is precisely the generating function of the sequence of numbers

$$\binom{n}{0}, \binom{n}{1}, \ldots, \binom{n}{n}$$

in the variable x. For this example the binomial theorem says that the enumerator polynomial (2.6) is simply $(1+x)^n$. We shall at times refer to enumerator polynomials as *counting polynomials*.

In various instances we will be interested in the generating function of the enumerator polynomials themselves. For the above example, denoting (2.6) by $e_n(x)$, we have

$$\sum_{n\geq 0} e_n(x) t^n = \sum_{n\geq 0} (1+x)^n t^n = \frac{1}{1 - (1+x)t}.$$

2.3 Generating Functions for Fibonacci and Lucas Numbers

Let

$$F(t) = F_0 + F_1 t + F_2 t^2 + \cdots$$

denote the generating function of the Fibonacci sequence. Details of the computation of $F(t)$ from the recursion defining the Fibonacci sequence are as follows. We multiply (1.2) by t^n and sum for $n \geq 2$. This gives

$$\sum_{n\geq 2} F_n t^n = \sum_{n\geq 2} F_{n-1} t^n + \sum_{n\geq 2} F_{n-2} t^n$$

$$= t \sum_{n\geq 1} F_n t^n + t^2 \sum_{n\geq 0} F_n t^n$$

$$= t(F(t) - F_0) + t^2 F(t).$$

Therefore

$$F(t) - F_0 - F_1 t = t(F(t) - F_0) + t^2 F(t). \qquad (2.7)$$

Using the initial values $F_0 = 0$ and $F_1 = 1$, and then solving (2.7) for $F(t)$, we find

$$F(t) = \frac{t}{1 - t - t^2} \, . \tag{2.8}$$

We can think of (2.8) as keeping track of all Fibonacci numbers at once.

We note that another technique that is frequently made use of when working with generating functions is partial fractions expansion. Since $1 - t - t^2 = (1 - \varphi t)(1 + \varphi^{-1} t)$, partial fractions expansion gives

$$\frac{t}{1 - t - t^2} = \frac{1}{\sqrt{5}} \left(\frac{1}{1 - \varphi t} \right) - \frac{1}{\sqrt{5}} \left(\frac{1}{1 + \varphi^{-1} t} \right)$$

$$= \frac{1}{\sqrt{5}} \left(\sum_{n \geq 0} \varphi^n t^n \right) - \frac{1}{\sqrt{5}} \left(\sum_{n \geq 0} (-\varphi^{-1})^n t^n \right),$$

from which the Binet formula (1.7) for F_n immediately follows by extracting the coefficient of t^n.

To calculate the generating function of the Lucas numbers, we proceed in exactly the same way as the case of the Fibonacci numbers until we reach identity (2.7). The initial values for the Lucas sequence are $L_0 = 2$ and $L_1 = 1$, which results in

$$L(t) - 2 - t = t(L(t) - 2) + t^2 L(t) \, ,$$

and consequently

$$L(t) = \frac{2 - t}{1 - t - t^2} \, .$$

2.4   Further Examples on Generating Functions

The recursive definition of the Fibonacci numbers allows us to construct the generating functions of various sequences obtained from them in a relatively straightforward manner. For example, let

$$C(t) = \sum_{n \geq 0} F_n F_{n+1} t^n \quad \text{and} \quad S(t) = \sum_{n \geq 0} F_n^2 t^n \, .$$

We can relate the quantities $F_n F_{n+1}$ and F_n^2 using the recursive definition of F_n and obtain a system of equations which we can then solve.

For $n \geq 1$,

$$F_n F_{n+1} = F_n (F_n + F_{n-1}) = F_n^2 + F_{n-1} F_n \, . \tag{2.9}$$

Multiplying (2.9) by t^n and summing for $n \geq 1$, we obtain

$$C(t) = S(t) + t C(t) \, . \tag{2.10}$$

Similarly, for $n \geq 2$ we have

$$F_n^2 = (F_{n-1} + F_{n-2})^2 = F_{n-1}^2 + 2F_{n-2}F_{n-1} + F_{n-2}^2 . \qquad (2.11)$$

Multiplying (2.11) by t^n and summing for $n \geq 2$, we obtain

$$S(t) - t = tS(t) + 2t^2 C(t) + t^2 S(t) . \qquad (2.12)$$

Solving the system of the pair of equations (2.10) and (2.12) for $C(t)$ and $S(t)$, we find

$$C(t) = \frac{t}{(1+t)(1-3t+t^2)} \quad \text{and} \quad S(t) = \frac{(1-t)t}{(1+t)(1-3t+t^2)} .$$

2.5 Exponential Generating Functions

In certain situations, in particular when the objects of interest to be enumerated are labeled, a variant of the generating function called the *exponential generating function* of a sequence is used.

Definition 2.2. Using the variable t, the exponential generating function of the sequence $(a_n)_{n \geq 0}$ is defined to be the formal power series

$$\sum_{n \geq 0} \frac{a_n}{n!} t^n = \frac{a_0}{0!} + \frac{a_1}{1!} t + \frac{a_2}{2!} t^2 + \frac{a_3}{3!} t^3 + \cdots .$$

As examples, the exponential generating function of the constant sequence $(1)_{n \geq 0}$ is e^t and that of $(n!)_{n \geq 0}$ is $(1-t)^{-1}$. The exponential generating function of the Fibonacci sequence is given by

$$\frac{1}{\sqrt{5}} \left(e^{\varphi t} - e^{-\varphi^{-1} t} \right) .$$

We will have the opportunity to consider certain exponential generating functions which turn out to be familiar trigonometric functions in Section 4.4.1 when we consider the enumeration of a certain family of paths in Fibonacci cubes.

We remark that when there may be confusion as to which type of generating function is under consideration, (2.1) is referred to as the *ordinary generating function* of the sequence $(a_n)_{n \geq 0}$.

2.6 Fibonacci Polynomials

The classical Fibonacci polynomials $F_n(x)$ are defined by a recursion similar to the one that defines the Fibonacci numbers. We set $F_0(x) = 0$, $F_1(x) = 1$, and for $n \geq 2$ define

$$F_n(x) = xF_{n-1}(x) + F_{n-2}(x) . \qquad (2.13)$$

Clearly $F_n(1) = F_n$ for $n \geq 0$. First few Fibonacci polynomials are

$$F_2(x) = x\,,$$
$$F_3(x) = x^2 + 1\,,$$
$$F_4(x) = x^3 + 2x\,,$$
$$F_5(x) = x^4 + 3x^2 + 1\,,$$
$$F_6(x) = x^5 + 4x^3 + 3x\,.$$

The properties of these polynomials have been extensively studied. We only note the following interpretation. We can assign to each Fibonacci string $w \in \mathcal{F}_n$ a *weight* $W(w)$ by setting $W(w) = x^{n+1-2|w|_1}$. Then for $n \geq 0$,

$$F_n(x) = \sum_{w \in \mathcal{F}_{n-2}} W(w)\,.$$

This is because of our basic identity

$$\mathcal{F}_n = 0\mathcal{F}_{n-1} + 10\mathcal{F}_{n-2}\,, \tag{2.14}$$

which implies that if $w = 0w'$, then $W(w) = x \cdot W(w')$, and if $w = 10w'$, then $W(w) = W(w')$. Keeping in mind the rule of exponents, this is nothing but the recurrence (2.13) defining the Fibonacci polynomials.

The generating function of the sequence of Fibonacci polynomials is

$$\sum_{n \geq 0} F_n(x)t^n = \frac{t}{1 - xt - t^2}\,.$$

In addition to the classical Fibonacci polynomials, there are other generalizations, or *q-analogues* (in this case perhaps more appropriately called *x-analogues*) of the Fibonacci numbers. These would be polynomials defined analogously to (2.14) which evaluate to the Fibonacci numbers when the argument is set to 1. For example, if we decide to classify Fibonacci strings of length n by the number of subwords 10 they contain, then for $w \in \mathcal{F}_n$ we could set $W(w) = y^{|w|_{10}}$, where $|w|_{10}$ is the number of occurrences of 10 in w. Set

$$G_n(y) = \sum_{w \in \mathcal{F}_{n-2}} W(w)$$

for $n \geq 2$.

We obtain $G_2(y) = 1$, $G_3(y) = 2$ and for $n \geq 4$,

$$G_n(y) = G_{n-1}(y) + yG_{n-2}(y)$$

directly from the recurrence (2.14). This gives

$$G_4(y) = y + 2,$$
$$G_5(y) = 3y + 2,$$
$$G_6(y) = y^2 + 5y + 2,$$

with $G_n(1) = F_n$ for $n \geq 2$. Setting $G_0(y) = F_0 = 0$, $G_1(y) = F_1 = 1$, the generating function of the sequence $G_n(y)$ is

$$\sum_{n \geq 0} G_n(y)t^n = \frac{t + (1-y)t^3}{1 - t - yt^2}.$$

We shall have plenty of occasion in this book to make use of formulations and manipulations of this kind. Sometimes the details will be given explicitly and sometimes the intermediate calculations will be omitted all together.

Chapter 3

Structure of Fibonacci Cubes

In this chapter we come (finally) to the Fibonacci cubes themselves. We first give the basic definitions from graph theory that we need in the following. A reader who is familiar with graph theory can easily skip this section. Then we formally introduce Fibonacci cubes, present their fundamental decomposition, and determine their order and size. After that we present the Greene and Wilf theory which allows us to derive several formulae of interest in closed form. In the subsequent section we enumerate the number of vertices of Fibonacci cubes of an arbitrary given degree as well as of an arbitrary given degree and a given Hamming weight. After this we determine the connectivity and the edge connectivity of Fibonacci cubes and conclude the chapter with a detailed description of the symmetry properties of these graphs.

3.1 Glossary of Graph Theory

A graph G is an ordered pair $(V(G), E(G))$, where $V(G)$ is the *vertex set* of G and $E(G)$ the *edge set* of G which contains unordered pairs of vertices of G. The *order* of G is the number of its vertices and will be denoted by $n(G)$. That is, $n(G) = |V(G)|$. The *size* of G is the number of its edges and will be denoted by $m(G)$, that is, $m(G) = |E(G)|$.

The *complete graph* K_n, $n \geq 1$, is the graph of order n and all possible edges. In other words K_n has size $m(K_n) = \binom{n}{2}$. The path graph of order n will be denoted by P_n and the cycle of order n by C_n.

If $\{x, y\} \in E(G)$ we will simplify the notation to $xy \in E(G)$ and say that y is a *neighbor* of x (and that x is a neighbor of y), or that x and y are adjacent. The *degree* of a vertex $u \in V(G)$ is the number of its neighbors and is denoted by $\deg_G(u)$. The *minimum degree* and the *maximum degree* of

G are denoted by $\delta(G)$ and $\Delta(G)$, respectively. If all vertices of a graph G have the same degree, then G is a *regular graph*. If the degree in question is r, then we may also say that G is an *r-regular graph*. The set of all neighbors of a vertex $u \in V(G)$ is the *open neighborhood* of u, denoted by $N_G(u)$. The *closed neighborhood* of u is $N_G[u] = N_G(u) \cup \{u\}$.

The *distance* $d_G(u,v)$ between two vertices u and v of a connected graph G is the number of edges on a shortest u, v-path. The *eccentricity* $\mathrm{ecc}_G(u)$ of $u \in V(G)$ is the maximum distance between u and any other vertex of G. We may shortly write $d(u,v)$ and $\mathrm{ecc}(u)$ when G is clear from the context. The *diameter* $\mathrm{diam}(G)$ of a connected graph G is the maximum distance between pairs of vertices of G or equivalently the maximum eccentricity $\mathrm{ecc}(x)$ among vertices x of G. The *radius* $\mathrm{rad}(G)$ is the minimum eccentricity. A subgraph H of a graph G is *isometric* if $d_H(u,v) = d_G(u,v)$ holds for any $u, v \in V(H)$. In addition, H is *convex* if for every $u, v \in V(H)$, and every shortest u, v-path P in G, the path P lies completely in H. Clearly, each convex subgraph is isometric but not necessarily the other way around.

Even more basic notion that the isometric subgraph is the one of an *induced subgraph*. If $X \subseteq V(G)$, then the subgraph of G induced by X is the maximal subgraph of G with the vertex set X and is denoted by $G[X]$. In other words, $G[X]$ has X as its vertex set, and its edge set consists of all edges in $E(G)$ that have both endpoints in X. In particular, if $G[X]$ is a path graph, then we say it is an *induced path*. Complete subgraphs which are addressed to also as *cliques* clearly have the above properties, that is, cliques are induced and convex subgraphs. If $v \in V(G)$, then $G - v$ denotes the induced subgraph $G[V(G) \setminus \{v\}]$, that is, the graph obtained from G by removing the vertex v and all the edges incident to it. Finally, an ordinary *subgraph* of a graph G is a graph H such that $V(H) \subseteq V(G)$ and $E(H) \subseteq E(G)$. The distance between subgraphs H_1 and H_2 of a graph G is the minimum distance in G between a vertex of H_1 and a vertex of H_2. In particular, the distance between a subgraph H of G and a vertex $v \in V(G)$ is $\min\{d_G(x,v) \mid x \in V(H)\}$.

The notion of graph products is essential in graph theory. We mention that an entire book [46] is dedicated to this concept. The structure of hypercubes derives from one of the most important, the Cartesian product. The *Cartesian product* $G \,\square\, H$ of graphs G and H has the vertex set $V(G) \times V(H)$, and (g,h) is adjacent to (g',h') if either $g = g'$ and $hh' \in E(H)$, or $gg' \in E(G)$ and $h = h'$. The construction is illustrated in Fig. 3.1 on the Cartesian product $G \,\square\, H$, where $G = H = K_2$ with $V(G) = \{g, g'\}$ and $V(H) = \{h, h'\}$. The example also explains why the box label is chosen for the Cartesian product operation of graphs.

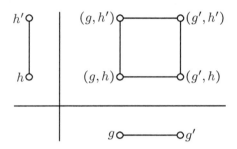

Fig. 3.1 The Cartesian product $K_2 \mathbin{\square} K_2$

The *line graph* of G is defined by taking $E(G)$ as the vertex set, and making two edges adjacent if they share an endpoint in G.

If G is a graph, then $S \subseteq V(G)$ is a *separating set* of G if $G \smallsetminus S$ has more than one component. The *connectivity* $\kappa(G)$ of G is the minimum cardinality of $S \subseteq V(G)$ such that $G \smallsetminus S$ is disconnected or a single vertex. By the definition, $\kappa(K_n) = n - 1$ for $n \geq 1$. In particular, $\kappa(K_1) = 0$, even though K_1 is connected. We also say that for each $k \leq \kappa(G)$ the graph G is *k-connected*. Similarly, $S \subseteq E(G)$ is a *disconnecting set* if $G \smallsetminus S$ has more than one component. G is *k-edge-connected* if every disconnecting set consists of at least k edges, and the *edge-connectivity* $\kappa'(G)$ of G is the maximum k for which G is k-edge-connected.

An *isomorphism* from G to H is a bijective mapping $\alpha : V(G) \to V(H)$ which preserves edges and non-edges, that is, $uv \in E(G)$ if and only if $\alpha(u)\alpha(v) \in E(H)$ holds for each pair of vertices u and v of G. If an isomorphism exists between two graphs, then the graphs are called *isomorphic* and denoted as $G \cong H$. An *automorphism* of a graph G is an isomorphism from G onto itself. The set of all automorphisms of a graph G equipped with the composition operation forms a group called the *automorphism group* of G, denoted by $\mathrm{Aut}(G)$.

Let G be a connected graph. A *Hamiltonian path* in G is a path that visits every vertex of G exactly once. A *Hamiltonian cycle* in G is a cycle that visits every vertex of G exactly once. A graph that contains a Hamiltonian cycle is called a *Hamiltonian graph*.

A set of vertices $S \subseteq V(G)$ is *independent*, if no two vertices from S are adjacent. The cardinality of a largest independent set of G is the *independence number* of G denoted by $\alpha(G)$. A set of edges $M \subseteq E(G)$ is a *matching*, if no two different edges from M share a common end-vertex. That is, a matching is a set of independent edges. The matching M is *perfect* if each vertex of G is an end-vertex of some edge from M. Clearly, if a graph admits a perfect matching, then its order is even.

The *complement* $\overline{G}$ of a graph G has the same vertex set as G, and uv is an edge of $\overline{G}$ if and only if uv is not an edge of G. For instance, the complement of the complete graph on n vertices is the graph with n vertices and no edges, while $\overline{P_4} \cong P_4$.

If G is a graph, then $D \subseteq V(G)$ is a *dominating set* if every vertex from $V(G) \setminus D$ has a neighbor in D. The *domination number* $\gamma(G)$ of G is the cardinality of a smallest dominating set of G. Furthermore, $D \subseteq V(G)$ is a *total dominating set* if every vertex from $V(G)$ has a neighbor in D. The *total domination number* $\gamma_t(G)$ of G is the cardinality of a smallest total dominating set of G.

3.2   Fibonacci Cubes

Fibonacci cubes were introduced in 1993 by Hsu as a model for interconnection networks [51], but as we will demonstrate throughout the book, these graphs have found numerous applications elsewhere and are also extremely interesting in their own right. In 2013, a review article on Fibonacci cubes was written by Klavžar [59].

As already mentioned in the preface to this book, the modern world is powered by computers which are based on binary numbers. These numbers are in turn constructed from bits, that is, the values 0 and 1. Recall that we use the notation $\mathcal{B} = \{0, 1\}$ for the binary alphabet and $\mathcal{B}_n$ for the binary strings of length n. $\mathcal{B}_n$ can be used to encode all (decimal) numbers between 0 and $2^n - 1$. If $b = b_1 \ldots b_n \in \mathcal{B}_n$, then we say that b_i is the ith *coordinate* of b. For $j \in [n]$ the string $b + \delta_j$ will be the string c such that $c_j \neq b_j$ and $c_i = b_i$ for all $i \neq j$.

Clearly, $|\mathcal{B}_n| = 2^n$. The *n-cube* Q_n, $n \geq 1$, is the graph with $V(Q_n) = \mathcal{B}_n$, in which two vertices $b = b_1 \ldots b_n$ and $b' = b'_1 \ldots b'_n$ are adjacent if $b_i \neq b'_i$ holds for exactly one $i \in [n]$, i.e., if $b' = b + \delta_i$. The order and the size of Q_n is given by $n(Q_n) = 2^n$ and $m(Q_n) = n2^{n-1}$. In Fig. 3.2 the 3-cube is drawn. For convenience we also define the *0-cube* Q_0 as the complete graph on a single vertex, that is, $Q_0 = K_1$. The family of all n-cubes is called *hypercubes*.

Since two vertices of the n-cube Q_n corresponding to strings u, v are adjacent if and only if $u_i \neq v_i$ holds for exactly one $i \in [n]$, we easily infer

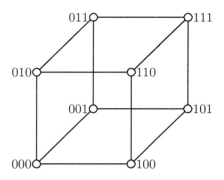

Fig. 3.2 The 3-cube Q_3

that $d_{Q_n}(u,v)$ is equal to the number of indices i such that $u_i \neq v_i$. Defining the *Hamming distance* $H(x,y)$ between two binary strings x and y of the same length to be the number of coordinates in which x and y differ, we have thus seen that if $u,v \in V(Q_n)$, then

$$d_{Q_n}(u,v) = H(u,v). \qquad (3.1)$$

Let $k \in [n]$ and let $f = f_1 \ldots f_k \in \mathcal{B}_k$. Recall from Section 2.2 that by $\mathcal{B}_n(f)$ we denote the set of strings from $\mathcal{B}_n$ which do not contain f as a substring. Using this notation, Fibonacci strings of length n are

$$\mathcal{F}_n = \mathcal{B}_n(11).$$

This simply means that a binary string $b_1 \ldots b_n$ is a Fibonacci string if it does not contain two consecutive 1s. More precisely, for every $i \in [n-1]$, at most one of the bits b_i and b_{i+1} is 1. Hence another useful way to define the set of Fibonacci strings of length n is:

$$\mathcal{F}_n = \{b_1 \ldots b_n : b_i b_{i+1} = 0, i \in [n-1]\}.$$

In this set notation $b_i b_{i+1}$ is the algebraic product of the values of the two bits. Note that if $x \in \mathcal{F}_n$ and $x_j = 1$ it is immediate that $x + \delta_j$ is a Fibonacci string.

The stars of our book are defined as follows. The 0-*dimensional Fibonacci cube* Γ_0 is K_1. That is, $\Gamma_0 = Q_0 = K_1$. For $n \geq 1$, the n-*dimensional Fibonacci cube* Γ_n has

$$V(\Gamma_n) = \mathcal{F}_n,$$

and two vertices are adjacent if they differ in exactly one coordinate. See Fig. 3.3 for the smallest four Fibonacci cubes and Fig. 3.4 for Γ_{10}. The

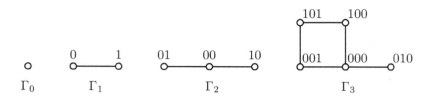

Fig. 3.3   Small Fibonacci cubes

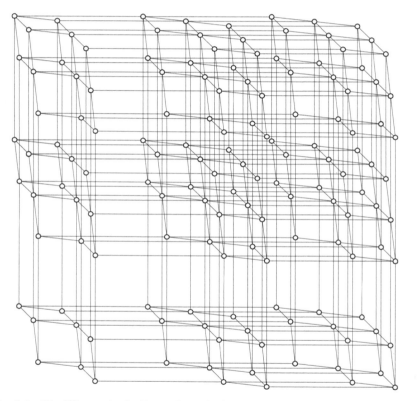

Fig. 3.4   The Fibonacci cube Γ_{10} as drawn by Eppstein. He used some custom software to draw it, based on the work reported in his paper [28]

drawings of the Fibonacci cubes Γ_7 through Γ_{10} as rendered by Mathematica can be found in Appendix A.

An equivalent definition of the Fibonacci cube Γ_n is that it is the graph obtained from Q_n by removing all vertices whose binary labels contain at least two consecutive 1s.

3.3   Fundamental Decomposition

Let n be a positive integer and let $f \in \mathcal{B}_k$ for some $k \in [n]$. For $\mathcal{C}_n \subseteq \mathcal{B}_n$, we define by $\mathcal{C}_n^{f\bullet}$ the set of all strings from $\mathcal{C}_n$ which have f as a prefix, and by $\mathcal{C}_n^{\bullet f}$ those strings from $\mathcal{C}_n$ which have f as a suffix. That is

$$\mathcal{C}_n^{f\bullet} = \{c \in \mathcal{C}_n : c = fy \text{ for some } y \in \mathcal{B}_{n-k}\}$$
$$\mathcal{C}_n^{\bullet f} = \{c \in \mathcal{C}_n : c = xf \text{ for some } x \in \mathcal{B}_{n-k}\} \,.$$

We will use the convention that the empty string belongs to $\mathcal{B}_0^{0\bullet}$, $\mathcal{B}_0^{\bullet 0}$, $\mathcal{F}_0^{0\bullet}$ and $\mathcal{F}_0^{\bullet 0}$. Then for any $n \geq 0$, the vertex sets of Q_n and Γ_n, naturally partition as

$$\mathcal{B}_n = \mathcal{B}_n^{0\bullet} + \mathcal{B}_n^{1\bullet} \,,$$
$$\mathcal{F}_n = \mathcal{F}_n^{0\bullet} + \mathcal{F}_n^{1\bullet} \,,$$

where we recall that the symbol + stands for the disjoint union. Since a Fibonacci string of $\mathcal{F}_n^{1\bullet}$ cannot start with 11, this can equivalently be written for $n \geq 2$, as

$$\mathcal{F}_n = 0\mathcal{F}_{n-1} + 10\mathcal{F}_{n-2} \,.$$

If uv is an edge of Q_n, then we have exactly three possibilities:

(i) u and v belong to $\mathcal{B}_n^{0\bullet}$,

(ii) u and v belong to $\mathcal{B}_n^{1\bullet}$, or

(iii) $u = 0x$ and $v = 1x$ where $x \in \mathcal{B}_{n-1}$.

In the first two cases the edge uv belongs to the subgraphs of Q_n induced by $\mathcal{B}_n^{0\bullet}$ or $\mathcal{B}_n^{1\bullet}$, respectively. Both of these graphs are isomorphic to Q_{n-1}. In the last case uv belongs to a perfect matching between $\mathcal{B}_n^{1\bullet}$ and $\mathcal{B}_n^{0\bullet}$. Therefore, for $n \geq 1$, the n-cube Q_n can be represented as the Cartesian product graph as follows:

$$Q_n = Q_{n-1} \,\square\, K_2 = Q_{n-1} \,\square\, Q_1 \,.$$

This fact is illustrated in Fig. 3.5 for $n = 4$. Many properties of hypercubes are derived from this recursive construction.

The intrinsic recursive structure for Fibonacci cubes, parallel with the recursive structure of hypercubes via the Cartesian product operation, is the following *fundamental decomposition* of Γ_n.

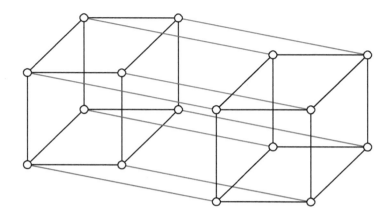

Fig. 3.5　The 4-cube $Q_4 = Q_3 \square K_2 = Q_3 \square Q_1$

Consider the partition $\mathcal{F}_n = \mathcal{F}_n^{0\bullet} + \mathcal{F}_n^{10\bullet}$ for $n \geq 2$. Since 10 ends with a 0 the set $\mathcal{F}_n^{10\bullet}$ induces a subgraph of Γ_n isomorphic to Γ_{n-2}. Similarly, $\mathcal{F}_n^{0\bullet}$ induces a subgraph of Γ_n isomorphic to Γ_{n-1}. Moreover, each vertex $10x$ of $\mathcal{F}_n^{10\bullet}$ has exactly one neighbor in $\mathcal{F}_n^{0\bullet}$, which is the vertex $00x$. These latter edges form a matching, analogous to the case of the hypercube graph. They are sometimes referred to as *link edges*. The recursive structure of Γ_n described is illustrated in Fig. 3.6, where Γ_6 is decomposed into Γ_4 (left), Γ_5 (right), and the matching edges between them drawn in red.

The *Hamming weight* of a binary string b is $|b|_1$, that is the number of occurrences of 1 in b. It is immediate that the number of strings in $\mathcal{B}_n$ of Hamming weight k is $\binom{n}{k}$.

In this book we use the combinatorial definition of binomial coefficients given in [42]. In particular $\binom{n}{0} = 1$ and $\binom{n}{k} = 0$ for all $n, k \in \mathbb{Z}$ with $k < 0$. Some computer algebra systems use a generalization to negative arguments of binomial coefficients coming from the Gamma function which result in non-zero values for $k < 0$. Our conventions simplify the issues that arise with summation bounds.

Let $u \in \mathcal{F}_n$ with Hamming weight w. In the string $u0$ of $\mathcal{F}_{n+1}$ every 1 is followed by a 0. Replace every substring 10 in $u0$ by the character x. In this way we obtain a string $\theta(u)$ over the alphabet $\{0, \text{x}\}$ of length $n+1-w$ which uses exactly w characters x. It is immediate that θ is a bijection. Thus we have

Proposition 3.1. *The number of strings in $\mathcal{F}_n$ of Hamming weight w is*

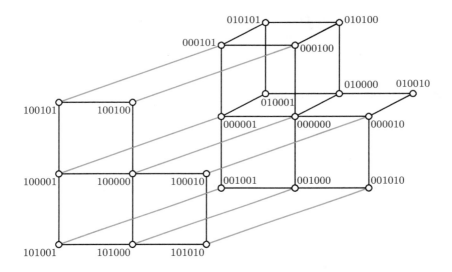

Fig. 3.6   The Fibonacci cube Γ_6

$\binom{n-w+1}{w}$.

As a corollary we obtain a combinatorial interpretation of the expression of Fibonacci numbers as sum of diagonal entries in the Pascal triangle as already stated in (1.3), see also Fig. 1.2.

3.4   Order and Size

Since the vertex set of Γ_n is the set of Fibonacci strings of length n it is clear that

$$n(\Gamma_n) = F_{n+2} \,,$$

as given in (1.4). This fact will be used either explicitly or implicitly many times in the rest of the book.

From the fundamental decomposition of Γ_n, $n \geq 2$, the edge set partitions into three subsets:

(i)   the edges of the Γ_{n-1} induced by $\mathcal{F}_n^{0\bullet}$,
(ii) the edges of Γ_{n-2} induced by $\mathcal{F}_n^{10\bullet}$, and
(iii) the edges of the matching between $\mathcal{F}_n^{10\bullet}$ and $\mathcal{F}_n^{00\bullet}$.

Therefore the size of Γ_n satisfies

$$m(\Gamma_n) = m(\Gamma_{n-1}) + m(\Gamma_{n-2}) + F_n \tag{3.2}$$

for $n \geq 2$, with the initial conditions $m(\Gamma_0) = 0$, $m(\Gamma_1) = 1$. It is immediate to verify by induction that the expression given in Proposition 3.2 satisfies (3.2). This result was first reported by Munarini, Perelli Cippo, and Zagaglia Salvi.

Proposition 3.2. [81, Proposition 4] *For any positive integer n, the size of Γ_n is*

$$m(\Gamma_n) = \tfrac{1}{5}\left(nF_{n+1} + 2(n+1)F_n\right).$$

An alternative expression for $m(\Gamma_n)$ due to Klavžar reads as follows.

Proposition 3.3. [58, Proposition 3] *The size of Γ_n, $n \geq 0$, is*

$$m(\Gamma_n) = \sum_{i=1}^{n} F_i F_{n-i+1}. \tag{3.3}$$

Proof. This is immediate for $n = 0$ and $n = 1$. Let $n \geq 2$ and assume the identity for $n-1$ and $n-2$. Then by (3.2),

$$
\begin{aligned}
m(\Gamma_n) &= \sum_{i=1}^{n-1} F_i F_{n-i} + \sum_{i=1}^{n-2} F_i F_{n-i-1} + F_n \\
&= \sum_{i=1}^{n-2} F_i F_{n-i} + \sum_{i=1}^{n-2} F_i F_{n-i-1} + F_{n-1}F_1 + F_n.
\end{aligned}
$$

Since $F_{n-i} + F_{n-i-1} = F_{n-i+1}$ and $F_{n-1}F_1 + F_n = F_{n-1} + F_n = F_{n-1}F_2 + F_n F_1$, the result follows by induction. $\square$

Say that an edge between vertices x and $x + \delta_i$ uses the *direction i*. In Proposition 6.6, or as the case $k = 1$ of Corollary 5.4, we prove that for any $i \in [n]$, $F_i F_{n-i+1}$ counts the number of edges using the direction i. This gives an alternative combinatorial proof of Proposition 3.3.

3.5   Digression: Greene and Wilf Theory

It is not difficult to check that the expression

$$\tfrac{1}{5}\left(nF_{n+1} + 2(n+1)F_n\right) \tag{3.4}$$

satisfies recursion (3.2) of $m(\Gamma_n)$, but how is it possible to guess that an expression like this is the solution in the first place?

On the other hand, the formula (3.3) has a combinatorial interpretation and thus Proposition 3.3 can be obtained directly without mathematical induction. Therefore one could ask oneself if it is possible to derive a formula like (3.4) from an expression such as (3.3).

This is precisely the object of the theory of Greene and Wilf presented in [44]. They studied the existence of closed formulas for expressions of the form

$$\sum_{j=0}^{n-1} G_1(a_1 n + b_1 j + c_1) G_2(a_2 n + b_2 j + c_2) \cdots G_k(a_k n + b_k j + c_k),$$

where each sequence $(G_i(n))_{n \geq 0}$ satisfies a finite linear recurrence with constant coefficients. Fibonacci numbers are of course such a sequence where the recurrence relation has order 2.

Rewriting the right hand side of (3.3) in the form

$$\sum_{j=0}^{n-1} F_{j+1} F_{n-j}, \tag{3.5}$$

it follows from [44, Theorem 2] that the sum (3.5) can be expressed as a linear combination of the four terms nF_n, F_n, nF_{n+1} and F_{n+1}. Furthermore, [44, Theorem 3] implies that if a rational linear combination of these four terms and the sum (3.5) agree for $n = 0, 1, 2, 3$, then they agree for all n.

Since the values of (3.5) for $n = 0, 1, 2, 3$ are $0, 1, 2, 5$, the coefficients of the linear combination $a\, nF_n + b\, F_n + c\, nF_{n+1} + d\, F_{n+1}$ must satisfy the system

$$\begin{pmatrix} 0 & 0 & 0 & 1 \\ 1 & 1 & 1 & 1 \\ 2 & 1 & 4 & 2 \\ 6 & 2 & 9 & 3 \end{pmatrix} \begin{pmatrix} a \\ b \\ c \\ d \end{pmatrix} = \begin{pmatrix} 0 \\ 1 \\ 2 \\ 5 \end{pmatrix}$$

whose solution is $(a, b, c, d) = (\frac{2}{5}, \frac{2}{5}, \frac{1}{5}, 0)$.

When the generating function of the sequence is known, another approach is possible, we will explain it in details illustrating again the power of the concept of the generating function.

Indeed consider the expression of $m(\Gamma_n)$ given by Proposition 3.3. Since $F_0 = 0$, this sum can be rewritten as $m(\Gamma_n) = \sum_{i=0}^{n} F_i F_{n+1-i}$. Therefore, the sequence $(m(\Gamma_n))_{n \geq 0}$ is the convolution of the sequences $(F_n)_{n \geq 0}$ and $(F_{n+1})_{n \geq 0}$. Since the generating functions of these sequences are

$$\sum_{n \geq 0} F_n t^n = \frac{t}{1 - t - t^2} \quad \text{and} \quad \sum_{n \geq 0} F_{n+1} t^n = \frac{1}{1 - t - t^2}, \tag{3.6}$$

the generating function of $m(\Gamma_n)$ is their product

$$\sum_{n \geq 0} m(\Gamma_n) t^n = \frac{t}{(1 - t - t^2)^2}. \tag{3.7}$$

Can we rewrite the right hand side of (3.7) as a linear combination of generating functions of sequences for which we know a closed formula?

The first two candidates, those of F_n and F_{n+1} can be rewritten as

$$\sum_{n\geq 0} F_n t^n = \frac{t - t^2 - t^3}{(1 - t - t^2)^2} \quad \text{and} \quad \sum_{n\geq 0} F_{n+1} t^n = \frac{1 - t - t^2}{(1 - t - t^2)^2},$$

therefore we have to add two generating functions

$$\frac{P(t)}{(1 - t - t^2)^2} \quad \text{and} \quad \frac{Q(t)}{(1 - t - t^2)^2},$$

distinct or not, where $P(t)$ and $Q(t)$ are polynomials of degree at most 3, such that the numerator t can be written as a linear combination of $t - t^2 - t^3$, $1 - t - t^2$, $P(t)$, and $Q(t)$.

There are two natural candidates. By differentiation of the formal series in (3.6) we obtain

$$\sum_{n\geq 0} n F_n t^n = \frac{t + t^3}{(1 - t - t^2)^2} \quad \text{and} \quad \sum_{n\geq 0} n F_{n+1} t^n = \frac{t + 2t^2}{(1 - t - t^2)^2}.$$

Solving

$$t = a(t + t^3) + b(t - t^2 - t^3) + c(t + 2t^2) + d(1 - t - t^2)$$

gives also $(a, b, c, d) = (\frac{2}{5}, \frac{2}{5}, \frac{1}{5}, 0)$.

Since the generating functions of the sequences $(m(\Gamma_n))_{n\geq 0}$ and $(\frac{1}{5}(nF_{n+1} + 2(n+1)F_n))_{n\geq 0}$ are the same, the coefficients of x^n for any integer n are equal, and therefore the sequences are identical.

Further applications of the above described theory will be presented in Section 7.2 and Section 7.3.1. These techniques are implicit in many other results we present whose proofs are only sketched or omitted.

3.6 Sequence of Degrees

In this section we will study the number of vertices of Γ_n of a given degree, a fundamental parameter of a family of graphs.

As observed in the seminal paper [51, Lemma 6], the Fibonacci cube Γ_n ($n \geq 2$) is not regular. The vertex 0^n is a vertex of maximum degree n and $(010)^\delta$, $(010)^\delta 0$ or $(010)^\delta 01$ are examples of vertices of minimum degree $\lfloor (n+2)/3 \rfloor$. That is, $\Delta(\Gamma_n) = n$ and $\delta(\Gamma_n) = \lfloor (n+2)/3 \rfloor$. This arises from the observation that changing a 1 to 0 in a string of $\mathcal{F}_n$ gives a string in $\mathcal{F}_n$, while a 0 can be changed to 1 only if it is not adjacent to some 1. Therefore the minimal degree is obtained for a string with a maximum number of adjacent blocks 010.

A first approach for computing the sequence of degrees is to use the fundamental decomposition of Γ_n. It will be convenient to set $A_n = \mathcal{F}_n^{1\bullet}$ and $B_n = \mathcal{F}_n^{0\bullet}$. For any $n \geq 1$ and any $0 \leq k \leq n$, let $a_{n,k}$ and $b_{n,k}$, be the number of vertices of degree k of A_n and B_n, respectively. Consider a vertex $x \in A_n$ of degree k. Then it is of degree $k - 1$ in the subgraph Γ_{n-2} of Γ_n induced by A_n. Since x lies in exactly one of the sets A_{n-2} or B_{n-2}, we get

$$a_{n,k} = a_{n-2,k-1} + b_{n-2,k-1}\,.$$

Similarly, a vertex $y \in B_n$ has a neighbor in A_n if it starts with 00 or has no neighbor in A_n. In the first case, it is a vertex of the corresponding set B_{n-1}, in the second case, a vertex of A_{n-1}. Therefore,

$$b_{n,k} = b_{n-1,k-1} + a_{n-1,k}\,.$$

Hence the degree sequences in the subgraphs induced by A_n and B_n satisfy the following system of linear recurrences and initial conditions

$$
\begin{aligned}
a_{n,k} &= a_{n-2,k-1} + b_{n-2,k-1} && (n \geq 2, k \geq 1)\,, \\
b_{n,k} &= b_{n-1,k-1} + a_{n-1,k} && (n \geq 1, k \geq 1)\,, \\
a_{0,k} &= a_{n,0} = 0 && (n \geq 0, k \geq 0)\,, \\
b_{0,k} &= b_{n,0} = 0 && (n \geq 1, k \geq 1)\,, \\
a_{1,k} &= 0 && (k \geq 2)\,, \\
a_{1,1} &= b_{0,0} = 1\,.
\end{aligned}
$$

Their generating functions

$$a(x,y) = \sum_{n,k \geq 0} a_{n,k} x^n y^k \quad \text{and} \quad b(x,y) = \sum_{n,k \geq 0} b_{n,k} x^n y^k$$

therefore satisfy the system of linear algebraic equations

$$
\begin{aligned}
a(x,y) - xy &= x^2 y a(x,y) + x^2 y b(x,y), \\
b(x,y) - 1 &= xy b(x,y) + x a(x,y)
\end{aligned}
$$

whose solution is

$$a(x,y) = \frac{xy(1 + x - xy)}{(1 - xy)(1 - x^2 y) - x^3 y}\,,$$

$$b(x,y) = \frac{1}{(1 - xy)(1 - x^2 y) - x^3 y}\,.$$

The sum $a(x,y) + b(x,y)$ is the generating function of the number of vertices in Γ_n of degree k. By a standard but rather technical manipulation of this generating function we arrive at the following result of Klavžar, Mollard, and Petkovšek.

Theorem 3.4. [65, Theorem 1.1] *If $n \geq k \geq 0$, then the number of vertices in Γ_n of degree k is*

$$\sum_{i=0}^{k} \binom{n-2i}{k-i}\binom{i+1}{n-k-i+1}.$$

Note that the summation can be restricted to the interval between $\lceil (n-k)/2 \rceil$ and $\min(k, n-k)$ since the other terms vanish.

We will give a combinatorial interpretation of the expression under the summation sign. Let us first recall the following basic result about compositions of integers into k parts, whose proof is omitted.

Lemma 3.5. *Let $k, m \geq 0$. The number of solutions of $x_1 + x_2 + \cdots + x_k = m$, with $x_1, x_2, \ldots, x_k$ (strictly) positive integers, is $\binom{m-1}{k-1} = \binom{m-1}{m-k}$.*

Let u be a vertex of Γ_n of Hamming weight w. In the Fibonacci string $u0$ every 1 is followed by a 0, therefore $u0$ can be uniquely decomposed as

$$u0 = 0^{\alpha_1}(10)0^{\alpha_2}(10)\ldots 0^{\alpha_w}(10)0^{\alpha_{w+1}},$$

where $\alpha_i \geq 0$ for all $i \in [w+1]$ and $\alpha_1 + \cdots + \alpha_{w+1} = n + 1 - 2w$. Furthermore every such decomposition can be obtained from some u.

In every block $0^{\alpha_i}, i \in [w]$, only the $\alpha_i - 1$ first 0s are not adjacent to some 1. Therefore any such block contributes $\alpha_i - 1$ to $\deg_{\Gamma_n}(u)$ if $\alpha_i \geq 1$, and zero otherwise. Consider now the last block $0^{\alpha_{w+1}}$. If $\alpha_{w+1} = 0$ then u ends with 1. Otherwise u ends with exactly α_{w+1} 0s but only the last $\alpha_{w+1} - 1$ are not adjacent to a 1, therefore in any case $0^{\alpha_{w+1}}$ also contributes like the previous blocks to $\deg_{\Gamma_n}(u)$. Therefore any block $0^{\alpha_i}, i \in [w+1]$, contributes $\alpha_i - 1$ to $\deg_{\Gamma_n}(u)$ if $\alpha_i \geq 1$, and zero otherwise. Let $J = \{i \in [w+1] : \alpha_i = 0\}$ and $K = [w+1] \setminus J$. Since a 1 can be changed into 0, the degree of u in Γ_n is thus

$$\deg_{\Gamma_n}(u) = w + \sum_{i \in K}(\alpha_i - 1) = w + \sum_{i \in K}\alpha_i - |K|$$

$$= w + \sum_{i \in [w+1]}\alpha_i - |K| = n - w - |K| + 1.$$

Therefore we have constructed a one-to-one mapping from vertices of Γ_n of Hamming weight w and degree k to $(w+1)$-tuples of non-negative integers $(\alpha_1, \alpha_2, \ldots, \alpha_{w+1})$ whose sum is $n + 1 - 2w$ with the additional constraint that exactly $n - w - k + 1$ of the α_is are strictly positive.

There is $\binom{w+1}{n-w-k+1}$ ways to choose the subset $K \subseteq [w+1]$ of this non-zero α_is. The set K chosen, by Lemma 3.5, the number of choices of the α_is, $i \in K$, is $\binom{n-2w}{k-w}$. We have thus the following refinement of Theorem 3.4.

Theorem 3.6. [65, Theorem 4.6] *For all integers k, n, w with $k, w \leq n$ the number of vertices of Γ_n having degree k and Hamming weight w is*

$$\binom{n-2w}{k-w}\binom{w+1}{n-w-k+1}.$$

3.7 Connectivity

The connectivity of a graph is one of its most basic properties. For practical and theoretical reasons, it is of interest to measure how connected a graph is. In this section we will first prove that the vertex connectivity as well as the edge connectivity of Fibonacci cubes is as high as theoretically possible. Of course, this is another nice structural feature of Fibonacci cubes.

A basic property of connectivity is that for any graph G the inequalities

$$\kappa(G) \leq \kappa'(G) \leq \delta(G) \tag{3.8}$$

hold, cf. [120, Theorem 4.1.9]. As explained in Section 3.6, for $n \geq 1$ we have

$$\delta(\Gamma_n) = \left\lfloor \frac{n+2}{3} \right\rfloor. \tag{3.9}$$

Hence, in view of (3.8), the best we can hope is that the connectivity of Γ_n is $\lfloor (n+2)/3 \rfloor$. We will next prove that this is indeed the case! The result is due to Azarija, Klavžar, Lee, and Rho.

Theorem 3.7. [7, Theorem 2.2] *If $n \geq 1$, then*

$$\kappa(\Gamma_n) = \kappa'(\Gamma_n) = \left\lfloor \frac{n+2}{3} \right\rfloor.$$

Proof. In view of (3.8) and (3.9) if suffices to prove that $\kappa(\Gamma_n) \geq \delta(\Gamma_n) = \lfloor (n+2)/3 \rfloor$.

The result can be checked for $n \leq 5$ by inspection. Suppose now that the result is true for $n \leq 3k+2$, $k \geq 1$. By induction we will prove the result for $n = 3k+3$, $n = 3k+4$, and $n = 3k+5$. Before that, recall the fundamental decomposition of Γ_n consisting of the partition $\mathcal{F}_n = \mathcal{F}_n^{0\bullet} + \mathcal{F}_n^{10\bullet}$, where $\mathcal{F}_n^{10\bullet}$ induces a subgraph isomorphic to Γ_{n-2}, and $\mathcal{F}_n^{0\bullet}$ induces a subgraph isomorphic to Γ_{n-1}. Moreover, each vertex $10x$ of $\mathcal{F}_n^{10\bullet}$ has exactly one neighbor in $\mathcal{F}_n^{0\bullet}$, the vertex $00x$. It will be again convenient to set $A_n = \mathcal{F}_n^{1\bullet}$ and $B_n = \mathcal{F}_n^{0\bullet}$.

We now start the induction proof for $n = 3k+3$. Let $X_{3k+1} = \Gamma_{3k+3}[A_{3k+3}] \cong \Gamma_{3k+1}$ and let $X_{3k+2} = \Gamma_{3k+3}[B_{3k+3}] \cong \Gamma_{3k+2}$. By the induction hypothesis, $\kappa(X_{3k+1}) = \kappa(X_{3k+2}) = k + 1$. We claim that $\kappa(\Gamma_{3k+3}) \geq k+1$. Suppose on the contrary that Γ_{3k+3} contains a separating set S with $|S| = k$. If $S \subseteq A_{3k+3}$, then $X_{3k+1} \smallsetminus S$ is connected and hence Γ_{3k+3} is connected. Similarly Γ_{3k+3} is connected if $S \subseteq B_{3k+3}$. So some vertices of S necessarily lie in A_{3k+3} and some in B_{3k+3}. But then both $X_{3k+1} \smallsetminus S$ and $X_{3k+2} \smallsetminus S$ are connected. Moreover, as $k = |S| < |A_{3k+3}| = F_{3k+3}$, there exists an edge that connects a vertex of $X_{3k+1} \smallsetminus S$ with a vertex of $X_{3k+2} \smallsetminus S$. We have thus proved that $\kappa(\Gamma_{3k+3}) \geq k + 1$ holds, hence by (3.8) and (3.9) we have $\kappa(\Gamma_{3k+3}) = k + 1$.

Let $n = 3k + 4$. We need to show that $\kappa(\Gamma_{3k+4}) \geq k + 2$. Let $X_{3k+2} = \Gamma_{3k+4}[A_{3k+4}] \cong \Gamma_{3k+2}$, and let $X_{3k+3} = \Gamma_{3k+4}[B_{3k+4}] \cong \Gamma_{3k+3}$. By the induction hypothesis and the already proved case of $n = 3k + 3$, we have $\kappa(X_{3k+2}) = k + 1$ and $\kappa(X_{3k+3}) = k + 1$. Suppose that Γ_{3k+4} contains a separating set S with $|S| = k + 1$. If $S \subseteq A_{3k+4}$, then since any vertex of $A_{3k+4} \smallsetminus S$ has a neighbor in B_{3k+4}, the graph $\Gamma_{3k+4} \smallsetminus S$ is connected. Similarly, if both A_{3k+4} and B_{3k+4} contain some vertices of S, then $X_{3k+2} \smallsetminus S$ and $X_{3k+3} \smallsetminus S$ are both connected and so is $\Gamma_{3k+4} \smallsetminus S$. Assume finally that $S \subseteq B_{3k+4}$ and consider the fundamental decomposition of X_{3k+3}. It decomposes X_{3k+3} into $Y \cong \Gamma_{3k+1}$ and $Z \cong \Gamma_{3k+2}$ that are (by induction) both of connectivity $k+1$. Since S disconnects X_{3k+3} and $|S| = k+1$, every vertex of S, considered as a vertex of Z, begins with 0. It follows that any vertex of S is considered as a vertex of X_{3k+3} starts with 00. Now, the subgraph of X_{3k+3} induced by the vertices starting with 01 is connected. Moreover, since there are $n(\Gamma_{3k+1}) = F_{3k+3} > k + 1$ independent edges between the vertices of X_{3k+3} starting with 010 and the vertices starting with 000, there is a vertex of X_{3k+3} starting with 01 that has a neighbor starting with 00 in the graph $\Gamma_{3k+4} \smallsetminus S$. This vertex has in turn a neighbor in X_{3k+2}. Recalling that $A_{3k+4} \cap S = \varnothing$ and using the fact that any vertex of $X_{3k+2} \smallsetminus S$ has a neighbor in X_{3k+3}, we conclude that $\Gamma_{3k+4} \smallsetminus S$ is connected.

The last case to consider is $n = 3k + 5$. Let A_{3k+5}, B_{3k+5}, $X_{3k+3} \cong \Gamma_{3k+3}$, and $X_{3k+4} \cong \Gamma_{3k+4}$ have the same meaning as in the previous cases. By the already proved previous cases, $\kappa(X_{3k+3}) = k + 1$ and $\kappa(X_{3k+4}) = k + 2$. We need to show that $\kappa(\Gamma_{3k+5}) \geq k + 2$. Assume that Γ_{3k+5} contains a separating set S with $|S| = k+1$. But now S cannot lie completely in X_{3k+4} (as $\kappa(X_{3k+4}) = k + 2$), while in the other cases we can argue again as we did in the first paragraph to conclude that S cannot be a separating set. □

3.8 Symmetry

In this section we will look at symmetry properties of Fibonacci cubes.

We note that the reverse b^R of a Fibonacci string b is also a Fibonacci string. Hence, for each $n \geq 1$ we can define the *reverse map* $r : V(\Gamma_n) \to V(\Gamma_n)$ by setting $r(b) = b^R$. It is clear that r is one-to-one and onto since $r(b^R) = b$. Thus r is a bijection. It is equally easy to observe that if b and c are Fibonacci strings, then $bc \in E(\Gamma_n)$ if and only if $r(b)r(c) \in E(\Gamma_n)$. We thus conclude that $r \in \mathrm{Aut}(\Gamma_n)$. We now prove that besides the identity map, r is the only other automorphism of Γ_n.

We first prove a lemma, for which we need the following definition. Let $u \in V(\Gamma_n)$ be a vertex with the Hamming weight $|u|_1 = k$. If $uv \in E(\Gamma_n)$, where $|v|_1 = k - 1$, then we say that v is a *down-neighbor* of u and that u in an *up-neighbor* of v.

Lemma 3.8. *If $n \geq 3$ and $u, v \in V(\Gamma_n)$ are different vertices with $|u|_1 = |v|_1 \geq 2$, then u and v have different sets of down-neighbors.*

Proof. Set $k = |u|_1 = |v|_1$. Then $k \geq 2$ and $d_{\Gamma_n}(u, v) \geq 2$. Assume first that $d_{\Gamma_n}(u, v) \geq 3$. Let i be an arbitrary index such that $u_i \neq v_i$ and assume without loss of generality that $u_i = 1$. Then the vertex obtained from u by changing its ith coordinate to 0 is a down-neighbor of u but is not a down-neighbor of v. Suppose now that $d_{\Gamma_n}(u, v) = 2$ and let i and j be the coordinates in which u and v differ. We may assume without loss of generality that $u_i = v_j = 1$ and $u_j = v_i = 0$. Since $k \geq 2$, there exists an index $\ell \notin \{i, j\}$ such that $u_\ell = v_\ell = 1$. But then the vertex obtained from u by changing its ℓth coordinate to 0 is a down-neighbor of u but is not a down-neighbor of v. $\qquad\square$

Now we can state and prove the following result of Castro, Klavžar, Mollard, and Rho.

Theorem 3.9. [20, Theorem 2.2] *If $n \geq 1$, then $\mathrm{Aut}(\Gamma_n) \simeq \mathbb{Z}_2$.*

Proof. The assertion is clear for $\Gamma_1 \cong K_2$ and $\Gamma_2 \cong P_3$, hence assume in the rest that $n \geq 3$. For $k \geq 0$ set $X_k = \{u \in V(\Gamma_n) : |u|_1 = k\}$.

Let $\alpha \in \mathrm{Aut}(\Gamma_n)$. Since 0^n is the only vertex of degree n and automorphisms preserve degrees, $\alpha(0^n) = 0^n$. It follows that α maps X_1 onto X_1. Let $X'_1 = \{10^{n-1}, 0^{n-1}1\}$ and $X''_1 = X_1 \setminus X'_1$. Since 10^{n-1} and $0^{n-1}1$ are the only vertices of degree $n - 1$, α maps X'_1 onto X'_1, and hence also maps X''_1 onto X''_1. We distinguish two cases with respect to how α maps X'_1.

Case 1: $\alpha(10^{n-1}) = 10^{n-1}$.

In this case we then have $\alpha(0^{n-1}1) = 0^{n-1}1$. Among the vertices of X_1'', only 010^{n-2} has no common up-neighbor with 10^{n-1}. Therefore, $\alpha(010^{n-2}) = 010^{n-2}$. Among the remaining vertices of X_1'', only 0010^{n-3} has no common up-neighbor with 010^{n-2}. Therefore $\alpha(0010^{n-3}) = 0010^{n-3}$. Inductively proceeding with the same argument, α fixes X_1'' pointwise and hence fixes the whole set X_1 pointwise. Applying Lemma 3.8 and the induction hypothesis, we infer that α fixes X_k pointwise for all k. Therefore α is the identity.

Case 2: $\alpha(10^{n-1}) = 0^{n-1}1$.

In this case $\alpha(0^{n-1}1) = 10^{n-1}$. Now, among the vertices of X_1'', only 010^{n-2} has no common up-neighbor with 10^{n-1}. Thus $\alpha(010^{n-2}) = 0^{n-2}10$, which is in turn the only vertex from X_1'' with no common up-neighbor together with $\alpha(10^{n-1}) = 0^{n-1}1$. By proceeding with the same argument, α reverses all the elements of X_1'', that is, restricted to X_1'' we have $\alpha = r$. Consecutively $\alpha = r$ holds on the whole set X_1. Applying Lemma 3.8 once more and using the induction hypothesis, we conclude that in this case $\alpha = r$. $\quad\square$

For any graph G, the action of its automorphism group $\mathrm{Aut}(G)$ on $V(G)$ partitions $V(G)$ into *orbits*. If $x \in V(G)$, then the orbit in which x lies is the set of vertices y such that there exists $\alpha \in \mathrm{Aut}(G)$ with $\alpha(x) = y$. Let $o(G)$ denote the number of orbits of G under the action of $\mathrm{Aut}(G)$ on $V(G)$. It follows from Theorem 3.9 that each orbit of Γ_n, $n \geq 1$, contains either one or two vertices. Let $o(\Gamma_n, 1)$ be the number of orbits of Γ_n with one element, and $o(\Gamma_n, 2)$ the number of orbits of Γ_n with two elements. Then we have the following result due to Ashrafi, Azarija, Fathalikhani, Klavžar, and Petkovšek.

Theorem 3.10. [5, Theorem 4.2] *If* $n \geq 2$, *then*

$$o(\Gamma_n, 1) = F_{\lfloor \frac{n-(-1)^n}{2} \rfloor + 2},$$

$$o(\Gamma_n, 2) = \frac{1}{2} \left(F_{n+2} - F_{\lfloor \frac{n-(-1)^n}{2} \rfloor + 2} \right),$$

$$o(\Gamma_n) \quad = \frac{1}{2} \left(F_{n+2} + F_{\lfloor \frac{n-(-1)^n}{2} \rfloor + 2} \right).$$

Proof. The orbits of cardinality 1 correspond to the fixed points of the reverse map r, that is, to the palindromic Fibonacci strings of length n.

Let $u \in V(\Gamma_n)$ be palindromic. Suppose first that $n = 2k$. If u begins with 0, then u is of the form $u = 0v00v^R0$, where $v \in V(\Gamma_{k-2})$. Hence there are F_k such Fibonacci strings. If u starts with 1, then $u = 10v00v^R01$, where $v \in V(\Gamma_{k-3})$, and so there are F_{k-1} such strings. Hence there are $F_k + F_{k-1} = F_{k+1}$ palindromic Fibonacci strings of length $n = 2k$. Now suppose that $n = 2k + 1$. If u starts with 0, then u is of the form $u = 0v0v^R0$ with $v \in V(\Gamma_{k-1})$, or $u = 0v010v^R0$ with $v \in V(\Gamma_{k-2})$. If u starts with 1, then $u = 10v0v^R01$ with $v \in V(\Gamma_{k-2})$, or $u = 10v010v^R01$ with $v \in V(\Gamma_{k-3})$. Hence there are $(F_{k+1} + F_k) + (F_k + F_{k-1}) = F_{k+2} + F_{k+1} = F_{k+3}$ palindromic Fibonacci strings of length $n = 2k + 1$.

We have thus shown that there are F_{k+1} palindromic Fibonacci strings of length $n = 2k$ and F_{k+3} palindromic Fibonacci strings of length $n = 2k+1$. This can be combined into $o(\Gamma_n, 1) = F_{\lfloor \frac{n-(-1)^n}{2} \rfloor + 2}$.

The remaining two assertions of the theorem follow from

$$o(\Gamma_n, 1) + o(\Gamma_n, 2) = o(\Gamma_n),$$
$$o(\Gamma_n, 1) + 2o(\Gamma_n, 2) = F_{n+2},$$

where the first equality follows by the fact that orbits of Γ_n are only of cardinalities 1 and 2, and the second equality is obtained by counting the number of vertices of Γ_n in two different ways. $\square$

Table 3.1 gives the first few values of $o(\Gamma_n)$, $o(\Gamma_n, 1)$ and $o(\Gamma_n, 2)$.

n	1	2	3	4	5	6	7	8	9	10	11	12	13	14
$n(\Gamma_n)$	2	3	5	8	13	21	34	55	89	144	233	377	610	987
$o(\Gamma_n)$	1	2	4	5	9	12	21	30	51	76	127	195	322	504
$o(\Gamma_n, 1)$	0	1	3	2	5	3	8	5	13	8	21	13	34	21
$o(\Gamma_n, 2)$	1	1	1	3	4	9	13	25	38	68	106	182	288	483

Table 3.1   The numbers of vertices, orbits, orbits of cardinality 1 and orbits of cardinality 2 of Γ_n, $n \in [14]$

The mathematician of our internet age can use a wonderful tool, the On-line Encyclopedia of Integers Sequences (OEIS for short) [98]. The sequence $(o(\Gamma_n))_{n \geq 3}$ is the sequence A001224 from it. It has different interpretations. Let us consider here a tiling problem of Patten and Golomb [85] and give a bijective proof that the tiling problem and the number of orbits of Γ_n yields the same sequence.

Patten and Golomb asked in how many ways can a $2 \times (n + 1)$ rectangle be tiled with dominoes (i.e., rectangles of dimensions 2×1 and 1×2)? More precisely, the problem asks for the number of *distinct* tilings, where two tilings are considered distinct if one cannot be obtained from the other by reflections and rotations. We are going to show that the answer is $o(\Gamma_n)$.

If $n = 1$, then 2×2 square has a single distinct tiling; there are two tilings, but one can be obtained from the other by the 90° rotation. Suppose now that $n \geq 2$.

Let $u \in V(\Gamma_n)$ and $v = u0 \in V(\Gamma_{n+1})$. Assign to v a tiling of the $2 \times (n+1)$ rectangle with dominoes as follows. Going through v from left to right, assign to each 0 a vertical domino and to each 10 a pair of horizontal dominoes. Conversely, to each tiling of the $2 \times (n+1)$ rectangle assign $v \in V(\Gamma_{n+1})$ by going through the tiling from left to right, coding vertical dominoes with 0 and pairs of horizontal dominoes with 10. Then v ends with 0; let $u \in V(\Gamma_n)$ be v without the final 0. This establishes a bijection between $V(\Gamma_n)$ and the set of all tilings of the $2 \times (n+1)$ rectangle which preserves palindromes in both directions.

To conclude the section, we consider also the edge orbits. Let $o_E(G)$ denote the number of orbits of G under the action of $\mathrm{Aut}(G)$ on $E(G)$. Further let $o_E(G,1)$ be the number of edge orbits of G containing one edge, and $o_E(G,2)$ the number of edge orbits of G containing two edges.

Theorem 3.11. [5, Theorem 4.3] *If $n \geq 0$, then*

$$o_E(\Gamma_n, 1) = \frac{1-(-1)^n}{2} F_{\lfloor \frac{n+1}{2} \rfloor},$$

$$o_E(\Gamma_n, 2) = \frac{1}{10}\left(nF_{n+1} + 2(n+1)F_n\right) - \frac{1-(-1)^n}{4}F_{\lfloor \frac{n+1}{2} \rfloor},$$

$$o_E(\Gamma_n) = \frac{1}{10}\left(nF_{n+1} + 2(n+1)F_n\right) + \frac{1-(-1)^n}{4}F_{\lfloor \frac{n+1}{2} \rfloor}.$$

Proof. The formulas hold for $n \in \{0,1\}$ by direct inspection, hence we can assume that $n \geq 2$. The edge orbits of cardinality 1 correspond to the fixed points of the reverse map r, that is, to edges $uv \in E(\Gamma_n)$ for which $\{r(u), r(v)\} = \{u, v\}$. This can happen only when $r(u) = u$ and $r(v) = v$. Hence u and v are Fibonacci palindromes of length n differing in a single position. This is only possible if $n = 2k+1$ with $u = x000r(x)$ and $v = x010r(x)$ (or vice versa), for some $x \in V(\Gamma_{k-1})$. Hence

$$o_E(\Gamma_n, 1) = \begin{cases} n(\Gamma_{k-1}) = F_{k+1} & \text{if } n = 2k+1, \\ 0 & \text{if } n = 2k. \end{cases}$$

This can in turn be written as $\frac{1-(-1)^n}{2}F_{\lfloor \frac{n+1}{2} \rfloor}$. The remaining two asserted formulas can now be deduced from this using the identities $o_E(\Gamma_n, 1) + o_E(\Gamma_n, 2) = o_E(\Gamma_n)$ and $o_E(\Gamma_n, 1) + 2o_E(\Gamma_n, 2) = m(\Gamma_n)$. □

Table 3.2 lists the first few values of $o_E(\Gamma_n)$, $o_E(\Gamma_n, 1)$ and $o_E(\Gamma_n, 2)$.

n	1	2	3	4	5	6	7	8	9	10	11	12	13	14
$m(\Gamma_n)$	1	2	5	10	20	38	71	130	235	420	744	1308	2285	3970
$o_E(\Gamma_n)$	1	1	3	5	11	19	37	65	120	210	376	654	1149	1985
$o_E(\Gamma_n,1)$	1	0	1	0	2	0	3	0	5	0	8	0	13	0
$o_E(\Gamma_n,2)$	0	1	2	5	9	19	34	65	115	210	368	654	1136	1985

Table 3.2 The numbers of edges, edge orbits, edge orbits of cardinality 1 and edge orbits of cardinality 2 in $E(\Gamma_n)$, $n \le 14$

3.9 Linear Permutations

In the context of routing permutations on Γ_n, Ramras [88] introduced and solved the problem of the identification of invertible binary matrices which preserve Fibonacci strings. In this section we present the solution.

Consider the binary strings of length n as vectors of $\mathbb{F}^n$, the vector space of dimension n over the field $\mathbb{F} = \mathbb{Z}_2$, that is, associate to a string $x = x_1x_2\ldots x_n$ the vector $x = (x_1, x_2, \ldots, x_n) \in \mathbb{F}^n$. We can thus interpret permutations of $\mathcal{B}_n$ as permutations of $\mathbb{F}^n$ and vice versa. A *linear permutation* of $\mathcal{B}_n$ is a permutation θ on $\mathcal{B}_n$ such that there exists some $n \times n$ binary matrix A with $\theta(x) = xA^\top$ for any $x \in \mathcal{B}_n$. Denote by $\mathcal{F}_n^\top$ the set of column vectors $\{x^\top : x \in \mathcal{F}_n\}$, and by $e_1, \ldots, e_n$ the canonical basis of $\mathbb{F}^n$.

Definition 3.12. [88] A linear permutation, or equivalently an invertible binary matrix A is Γ_n-*good* if the image of any Fibonacci string of $\mathcal{F}_n$ is a Fibonacci string, that is $\forall x \in \mathcal{F}_n$, $Ax^\top \in \mathcal{F}_n^\top$.

A Γ_n-good permutation is thus a permutation on $V(\Gamma_n)$ that is linear on $\mathbb{F}^n$.

As usual, let I_n be the identity matrix and let C_n be the anti-diagonal matrix defined by $C_{ij} = 1$ when $i + j = n + 1$ and $C_{ij} = 0$ otherwise. Note that C_n is the matrix of the reverse map and thus I_n and C_n are Γ_n-good since they define two automorphisms of Γ_n. The set of Γ_n-good permutations is stable for composition and thus form a group.

To formulate the next result, we need to recall the *dihedral group* on n elements which we denote by D_{2n}. For $n \ge 3$, the group D_{2n} can be viewed as the group of symmetries of a regular n-gon, so that it contains n rotations and n reflections. Abstractly, D_{2n} can be represented in group theory notation as $\langle x, y : x^2 = 1, y^n = 1, (xy)^2 = 1 \rangle$. Ramras proved that for $n \ge 4$ the group of Γ_n-good permutations is the dihedral group of the regular 4-gon.

Let $A = (A_{ij})$ be a Γ_n-good $n \times n$ binary matrix and let $A_{.j}$ and $A_{i.}$ denote its jth column and i^{th} row, respectively. Note that all rows and columns of A are non-zero.

Proposition 3.13. *Suppose A is Γ_n-good and let i, j with $A_{ij} = 1$. Then, $A_{(i-1)j} = 0$ if $i \geq 2$, and $A_{(i+1)j} = 0$ if $i \leq n - 1$.*

Proof. Let e_j be the jth basis vector of $\mathbb{F}^n$. By definition $Ae_j^{\top} = A_{.j}$ does not have adjacent 1s. Thus $A_{(i-1)j} = A_{(i+1)j} = 0$. $\qquad \square$

Lemma 3.14. [88, Lemma 1] *Suppose A is Γ_n-good and let i, j with $A_{ij} = 1$. Then a 1 in row $i - 1$ or $i + 1$ can only occur in columns $j - 1$ or $j + 1$.*

Proof. Suppose by way of contradiction that $A_{(i-1)k} = 1$ or $A_{(i+1)k} = 1$ with $|k - j| > 1$. Then $e_j + e_k$ belongs to $\mathcal{F}_n$. Assume first $A_{(i-1)k} = 1$. From Proposition 3.13, $A_{ik} = 0$ and $A_{(i-1)j} = 0$. Therefore $A_{ik} + A_{ij} = A_{(i-1)k} + A_{(i-1)j} = 1$ and thus $A(e_j + e_k)^{\top} = A_{.j} + A_{.k}$ has adjacent 1's, contradicting the assumption that A is Γ_n-good. The case $A_{(i+1)k} = 1$ is similar. We have thus $|k - j| = 1$. $\qquad \square$

Lemma 3.15. [88, Lemma 2] *Suppose A is Γ_n-good, where $n \geq 3$. If row i of A has two 1s, occurring in columns j and k, with $j < k$, then $k = j + 2$ and $i = 1$ or n.*

Proof. Assume $i \geq 2$. Because $A_{ij} = 1$, by Lemma 3.14, a 1 in row $i - 1$ must occur in either column $j - 1$ or column $j + 1$. Similarly, because $A_{ik} = 1$ it must occur in column $k - 1$ or column $k + 1$. By the invertibility of A there exists a 1 in row $i - 1$. Since $j < k$, to satisfy both conditions, this 1 must be unique. Therefore $j + 1 = k - 1$, and thus $k = j + 2$. Furthermore the row $i - 1$ must be e_{j+1}. For $i \leq n - 1$ the same argument holds for row $i + 1$ and gives also that this row is e_{j+1}, and that $k = j + 2$. So for $2 \leq i \leq n - 1$, rows $i - 1$ and $i + 1$ are equal, contradicting the assumption that A is invertible. Therefore $i = 1$ or $i = n$, and $k = j + 2$. $\qquad \square$

Lemma 3.16. *If $n \geq 4$ and A is Γ_n-good, then the following hold.*

    (i) *Any 1 in column 1 must occur in row 1 or row n. Similarly, a 1 in column n must occur in row 1 or row n.*

    (ii) *There exist exactly one 1 in columns 1 and n. Moreover, either*

    (iii) *For all i with $2 \leq i \leq n - 1$ the ith row is $A_{i.} = e_i$ or* *(iii')* for all i with $2 \le i \le n-1$ the ith row is $A_{i.} = e_{n-i+1}$.

Proof. (i): Suppose $A_{i1} = 1$ and $2 \le i \le n-1$. Since $A_{.1} \in \mathcal{F}_n^\top$, $A_{(i-1)1} = A_{(i+1)1} = 0$. By Lemma 3.14 we infer the existence of a unique 1 in row $i-1$ and a unique 1 in row $i+1$, both occurring in the second column. Thus $A_{(i-1).} = A_{(i+1).} = e_2$, contradicting the invertibility of A. Since $A_{.1}$ is non-zero, either $A_{11} = 1$ or $A_{n1} = 1$. The argument for column $A_{.n}$ is similar.

(iii) and (iii'): Assume $A_{11} = 1$. Then, by Lemma 3.14, $A_{2.} = e_2$. Since $A_{31} = 0$ we obtain again by Lemma 3.14, that $A_{3.} = e_3$. Let k be the greatest integer such that for all m in $\{2, \ldots, k\}$, $A_{m.} = e_m$. If $k \le n-2$ then, by Lemma 3.15, there exists a unique 1 in row $k+1$ and, by Lemma 3.14, this 1 is in column $k-1$. Therefore $A_{(k+1).} = e_{k-1} = A_{(k-1).}$, contradicting the invertibility of A. Thus $k \ge n-1$ and we obtain (iii). If we assume $A_{n1} = 1$ then we obtain similarly (iii').

(ii): If $A_{11} = 1$ then $A_{22} = 1$ and thus by (iii), $A_{(n-1)(n-1)} = 1$. Therefore, by Lemma 3.14, $A_{n1} = 0$. The proof is similar for the nth column. $\square$

$$
\begin{pmatrix}
1&0&0&0&0&0\\
0&1&0&0&0&0\\
0&0&1&0&0&0\\
0&0&0&1&0&0\\
0&0&0&0&1&0\\
0&0&0&0&0&1
\end{pmatrix}
\begin{pmatrix}
1&0&1&0&0&0\\
0&1&0&0&0&0\\
0&0&1&0&0&0\\
0&0&0&1&0&0\\
0&0&0&0&1&0\\
0&0&0&0&0&1
\end{pmatrix}
\begin{pmatrix}
1&0&0&0&0&0\\
0&1&0&0&0&0\\
0&0&1&0&0&0\\
0&0&0&1&0&0\\
0&0&0&0&1&0\\
0&0&0&1&0&1
\end{pmatrix}
\begin{pmatrix}
1&0&1&0&0&0\\
0&1&0&0&0&0\\
0&0&1&0&0&0\\
0&0&0&1&0&0\\
0&0&0&0&1&0\\
0&0&0&1&0&1
\end{pmatrix}
$$

$$
\begin{pmatrix}
0&0&0&0&0&1\\
0&0&0&0&1&0\\
0&0&0&1&0&0\\
0&0&1&0&0&0\\
0&1&0&0&0&0\\
1&0&0&0&0&0
\end{pmatrix}
\begin{pmatrix}
0&0&0&0&0&1\\
0&0&0&0&1&0\\
0&0&0&1&0&0\\
0&0&1&0&0&0\\
0&1&0&0&0&0\\
1&0&1&0&0&0
\end{pmatrix}
\begin{pmatrix}
0&0&0&1&0&1\\
0&0&0&0&1&0\\
0&0&0&1&0&0\\
0&0&1&0&0&0\\
0&1&0&0&0&0\\
1&0&0&0&0&0
\end{pmatrix}
\begin{pmatrix}
0&0&0&1&0&1\\
0&0&0&0&1&0\\
0&0&0&1&0&0\\
0&0&1&0&0&0\\
0&1&0&0&0&0\\
1&0&1&0&0&0
\end{pmatrix}
$$

Fig. 3.7 The eight Γ_6-good matrices

Theorem 3.17. [88, Theorem 1] *For $n > 3$, there are precisely eight Γ_n-good linear permutations and they form the dihedral group D_8. For $n = 3$, (i.e., for Γ_3) there are exactly six Γ_3-good linear permutations and they form the symmetric group S_3.*

Proof. Denote by E^{ij} the $n \times n$ binary matrix whose single non-zero entry is in row i and column j. Suppose that $n \geq 4$. We claim that the following set of eight matrices constitutes the set of all Γ_n-good matrices:

$$\{I_n, I_n + E^{13}, I_n + E^{n(n-2)}, I_n + E^{13} + E^{n(n-2)}\} \bigcup$$
$$\{C_n, C_n + E^{n3}, C_n + E^{1(n-2)}, C_n + E^{n3} + E^{1(n-2)}\}.$$

Indeed, assume A is a Γ_n-good matrix, $n \geq 4$. From Lemma 3.16 we have only two possibilities for the submatrix defined by the rows with indices in $\{2, \ldots, n-1\}$.

Assume first $A_{2.} = e_2$. Then $A_{n-1.} = e_{n-1}$, thus, by Proposition 3.13, $A_{n1}=0$ and, by Lemma 3.16, $A_{11} = 1$. We infer that the row 1 must be e_1 or $e_1 + e_3$. From $A_{n-1.} = e_{n-1}$ we deduce similarly that the row n must be e_n or $e_n + e_{n-2}$.

Assuming $A_{2.} = e_{n-1}$ we obtain that the first row must be e_n or $e_n + e_{n-3}$, and the last one must be e_1 or $e_1 + e_3$. Therefore A is one of the eight matrices. Conversely it is easy to check that any of them is Γ_n-good. For example consider $A = I_n + E^{13}$ and let $x = (x_1, x_2, \ldots, x_n)$. We have $Ax^\top = (x_1 + x_3, x_2, x_3, \ldots, x_n)^\top$. Since $x \in \mathcal{F}_n$, if $Ax^\top \notin \mathcal{F}_n^\top$ the only non-trivial possibility is $x_1 + x_3 = 1$ and $x_2 = 1$. For $x_1 + x_3 = 1$ one of x_1, x_3 is 1, contradicting $x_2 = 1$.

Setting $A = C_n + E^{1(n-2)}$ and $B = I_n + E^{13}$, it is immediate that $A^2 \neq I_n$ and that $A^4 = I_n$. Furthermore $B^2 = I_n$ and $BAB = A^3$. It follows that the group of Γ_n-good matrices is D_8.

For $n = 3$, the matrix $I_n + E^{13} + E^{n(n-2)} = C_n + E^{n3} + E^{1(n-2)}$ is not invertible. Then the order of the group is 6, and furthermore the group is non-Abelian since

$$(I_3 + E^{13})(I_3 + E^{31}) \neq (I_3 + E^{31})(I_3 + E^{13}).$$

The group is thus $S_3 = D_6$. $\qquad\qquad\qquad\qquad\qquad\qquad\qquad\qquad\square$

Chapter 4

Paths and Cycles in Fibonacci Cubes

In this chapter we consider distance related topics in Fibonacci cubes. In the initial short section, we present the basic metric properties of Fibonacci cubes. It is a fundamental result that Fibonacci cubes belong to a family of partial cubes, which have been well-studied. This fact significantly simplifies calculations. After that we focus on the eccentricity of vertices in Γ_n. This property is approached in two different ways. One of these is connecting Fibonacci cubes with Fibonacci trees which in turn form an important data structure in computer science. In the third section we characterize Fibonacci cubes that are Hamiltonian and among those that are not, characterize their vertex-deleted Hamiltonian subgraphs. Following that we prove that the sequence of the numbers of diametral shortest paths in Fibonacci cubes is the sequence of Euler numbers. In the final section of the chapter we focus on the exact enumeration of short paths and short cycles in Fibonacci cubes.

4.1 Distance and Related Concepts

In (3.1) we observed that $d_{Q_n}(u,v) = H(u,v)$ holds for arbitrary vertices u and v of the n-cube Q_n. We now show that the same property holds for Γ_n. We record this property as a lemma.

Lemma 4.1. *For any two vertices (Fibonacci strings) u and v of Γ_n,*

$$d_{\Gamma_n}(u,v) = d_{Q_n}(u,v) = H(u,v). \tag{4.1}$$

Proof. Let w be the binary string defined by $w_i = u_i$ if $u_i = v_i$ and $w_i = 0$ otherwise. It is clear that $w \in \mathcal{F}_n$. We can construct a u,w-path in Γ_n changing the coordinates i such that $u_i = 1$ and $w_i = 0$ one by one. Similarly we can construct a w,v-path in Γ_n changing the coordinates i such that

$w_i = 0$ and $v_i = 1$ one by one. The concatenation of these two paths is a u, v-path in Γ_n whose length is the Hamming distance $H(u, v)$ between u and v. Thus $d_{\Gamma_n}(u, v) \le d_{Q_n}(u, v)$. Since Γ_n is a subgraph of Q_n the converse inequality also holds. □

A graph G is a *partial cube* if G is an isometric subgraph of some hypercube. Thus (4.1) implies the following.

Proposition 4.2. *Fibonacci cubes are partial cubes.*

As noted by Hsu [51], $\mathrm{diam}(\Gamma_n) = n$ since $d_{\Gamma_{2k}}((01)^k, (10)^k) = 2k$ and $d_{\Gamma_{2k+1}}(1(01)^k, 0(10)^k) = 2k + 1$. Munarini and Zagaglia Salvi [82] proved that the radius of Γ_n is $\lfloor \frac{n+1}{2} \rfloor$. The eccentricity of a vertex in Γ_n lies between these bounds. In the next section we will determine the number of vertices with a given eccentricity.

4.2 Eccentricity Sequence and Fibonacci Trees

We first describe an easy way of computing the eccentricity of a vertex x of Γ_n. Our starting point is that x has a unique factorization as the concatenation of particular strings.

Proposition 4.3. *A Fibonacci string x of Hamming weight p can be uniquely factored as*

$$x = 0^{l_0} 10^{l_1} \ldots 10^{l_{p-1}} 10^{l_p}$$

where $l_0, l_p \ge 0$ and $l_i \ge 1$ for all $i \in [p-1]$.

In this section, by the eccentricity of a string we mean its eccentricity in the Fibonacci cube of the corresponding dimension. The main tool is the following observation.

Proposition 4.4. *If $z = xy \in \mathcal{F}_n$, where $x \in \mathcal{F}_{n_1}$ and $y \in \mathcal{F}_{n_2}$, then*

$$\mathrm{ecc}(z) \le \mathrm{ecc}(x) + \mathrm{ecc}(y).$$

Proof. Let $c \in \mathcal{F}_n$ be such that $d(z, c) = \mathrm{ecc}(z)$. Then $c = ab$ with $a \in \mathcal{F}_{n_1}$ and $b \in \mathcal{F}_{n_2}$. By definition of eccentricity, $d(x, a) \le \mathrm{ecc}(x)$ and $d(y, b) \le \mathrm{ecc}(y)$. Therefore $\mathrm{ecc}(z) = d(xy, ab) = d(x, a) + d(y, b) \le \mathrm{ecc}(x) + \mathrm{ecc}(y)$. □

The eccentricity of 0^l is the largest number of 1s in a string of $\mathcal{F}_l$, i.e., $\lfloor \frac{l+1}{2} \rfloor$. Let w_l be a vertex at maximum distance from 0^l. Then 10^l is a

Fibonacci string and $d(10^l, 0w_l) = 1 + \text{ecc}(0^l)$. Thus from Proposition 4.4 we obtain the following result.

Proposition 4.5. *If* $l \geq 0$, *then*

$$\text{ecc}(10^l) = \left\lceil \frac{l+1}{2} \right\rceil + 1.$$

We are now ready for the following result due to Castro and Mollard.

Theorem 4.6. [21, Theorem 3.7] *If* $x = 0^{l_0} 10^{l_1} 10^{l_2} \cdots 10^{l_p} \in \mathcal{F}_n$, *where* $p, l_0, l_p \geq 0$ *and* $l_1, \ldots, l_{p-1} \geq 1$, *then*

$$\text{ecc}(x) = p + \sum_{i=0}^{p} \left\lceil \frac{l_i+1}{2} \right\rceil.$$

Proof. Using the same idea as the previous proof, for all i let w_{l_i} be a string farthest from 0^{l_i}. The string $y = w_{l_0} 0 w_{l_1} \ldots 0 w_{l_p}$ is a Fibonacci string and

$$d(x, y) = \left\lceil \frac{l_0+1}{2} \right\rceil + \sum_{i=1}^{p} \left(\left\lceil \frac{l_i+1}{2} \right\rceil + 1 \right) = p + \sum_{i=0}^{p} \left\lceil \frac{l_i+1}{2} \right\rceil.$$

By Proposition 4.4 the result follows. $\qquad\square$

Using Theorem 4.6, it is possible to obtain the generating function of the eccentricity sequence.

Theorem 4.7. [21, Theorem 4.3]. *Let* $f_{n,k}$ *be the number of vertices of* Γ_n *having eccentricity* k. *Then*

$$\sum_{n,k \geq 0} f_{n,k} x^k t^n = \frac{1 + xt}{1 - xt(t+1)}. \tag{4.2}$$

Consequently, if $n \geq k \geq 1$, *then*

$$f_{n,k} = \binom{k}{n-k} + \binom{k-1}{n-k}.$$

Proof. From Theorem 4.6 it is possible to find a recurrence relation satisfied by the $f_{n,k}$. We omit this rather long and technical computation and give the proof of the second part. We have the expansion

$$\frac{1}{1 - xt(t+1)} = \sum_{i \geq 0} (xt(1+t))^i \tag{4.3}$$

$$= \sum_{i \geq 0} \left[x^i t^i \sum_{j=0}^{i} t^j \binom{i}{j} \right] = \sum_{i \geq 0} \sum_{j=0}^{i} x^i t^{i+j} \binom{i}{j}$$

$$= \sum_{n \geq 0} \sum_{k=0}^{n} x^k t^n \binom{k}{n-k}.$$

The proof follows by noting that the coefficient of $x^k t^n$ for $n, k \geq 1$ in the development of $\frac{xt}{1-xt(t+1)}$ is the coefficient of $x^{k-1} t^{n-1}$ in (4.3). $\qquad\square$

We will establish the generating function of the eccentricity in another way using an a priori mysterious connection. Consider the first values of the eccentricity sequence $(f_{n,k}, 0 \le k \le n)_{n \ge 0}$ and arrange them into a triangular array where the first row corresponds to $n = 0$:

$$
\begin{array}{ccccc}
1 \\
0 & 2 \\
0 & 1 & 2 \\
0 & 0 & 3 & 2 \\
0 & 0 & 1 & 5 & 2
\end{array}
$$

Reading the entries by rows we obtain an integer sequence that starts

$$1, 0, 2, 0, 1, 2, 0, 0, 3, 2, 0, 0, 1, 5, 2, \ldots$$

In the OEIS [98] this beginning matches with the start of the sequence A178524. The latter sequence, described in our notation, is "the triangular array, read by rows, of the number $t_{n+1,k}$ of leaves at depth k in the Fibonacci tree of order $n + 1$." The two sequences indeed coincide since they have the same generating function. We will establish the generating function of $t_{n+1,k}$ and give a bijective proof that the two sequences coincide. As a corollary this will give an alternative proof of Theorem 4.7 without the need of calculate the generating function of the $f_{n,k}$.

So what is a Fibonacci tree? Consider a rooted binary tree. The depth of a leaf is the distance from the root, and the height of a rooted tree is the maximum depth. Now, *Fibonacci trees* T_n, $n \ge 0$, are binary trees defined recursively as follows:

(i) T_0 and T_1 are trees with a single vertex—the root.
(ii) For $n \ge 2$, T_n is the rooted tree whose left subtree is T_{n-1} and whose right subtree is T_{n-2}.

As an example, Fig. 4.1 illustrates how T_4 is obtained from T_3 and T_2.

Proposition 4.8. *Let $d_{n,k}$ be the number of leaves at depth k in T_n. The generating function of the $d_{n+1,k}$ is*

$$G(x,t) = \sum_{n,k \ge 0} d_{n+1,k}\, x^k t^n = \frac{1 + xt}{1 - xt(t+1)}. \qquad (4.4)$$

Proof. The depth of a leaf of T_n is one more that its depth as a leaf of the right or left subtree. We have thus

$$d_{n+1,k} = d_{n,k-1} + d_{n-1,k-1}. \qquad (4.5)$$

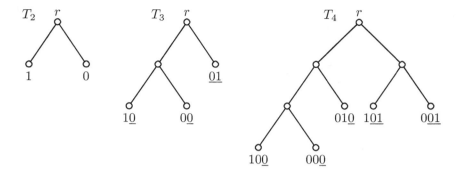

Fig. 4.1 Fibonacci trees equipped with the standard labeling

Passing to the generating function from the recursion, we take (4.5) for $n, k \geq 1$, multiply by $x^k t^n$ and sum. This gives

$$G(x,t) - 2xt - 1 = xt(G(x,t) - 1) + xt^2 G(x,t),$$

from which (4.4) follows. $\square$

Clearly, for any n the number of leaves of T_n is $F_{n+1} = |\mathcal{F}_{n-1}|$. We can recursively construct a labeling of the leaves of T_n with distinct Fibonacci strings of length $n-1$ as follows. Let $\mathcal{F}_n^{\bullet 0}$ and $\mathcal{F}_n^{\bullet 1}$ be the sets of Fibonacci strings ending with 0 and 1. We then have

$$\mathcal{F}_n = \mathcal{F}_n^{\bullet 0} + \mathcal{F}_n^{\bullet 1} = \{s0 : s \in \mathcal{F}_{n-1}\} + \{s01 : s \in \mathcal{F}_{n-2}\}$$

for $n \geq 2$. First label T_1 and T_2 and assume $n \geq 3$. We append 01 to the labels of the right leaves already labeled as leaves of T_{n-2}, and 0 to the labels of the left leaves already labeled as leaves of T_{n-1}. In Fig. 4.1 this construction is presented for the first three non-trivial Fibonacci trees, where the currently attached strings are underlined.

This standard labeling of Fibonacci trees does not respect the correspondence between depth and eccentricity. For example, the depth of the leaf of T_3 labeled 01 is 1, but $\mathrm{ecc}_{\Gamma_2}(01) = 2$. Nevertheless, the depth sequence of leaves of T_3 is $0, 1, 2$ and thus coincides with the third line of the triangular array of eccentricity. We next construct a labeling that respects the equality vertex by vertex.

Notice first that, for $n \geq 2$,

$$\mathcal{F}_n = \{s00 : s \in \mathcal{F}_{n-2}\} + \{s0 : s \in \mathcal{F}_{n-1}^{\bullet 1}\} + \{s1 : s \in \mathcal{F}_{n-1}^{\bullet 0}\}.$$

Label T_1 with the null-word and T_2 according to Fig. 4.2. Assume that $n \geq 3$ and that the leaves of T_{n-1} and T_{n-2} were already labeled. We append 00 to the label of the right leaves. For the left leaves append 0 to the label of a leaf with a label ending with 1; otherwise append label 1. Let θ denote this labeling of the leaves of T_n by vertices of Γ_{n-1}. It is shown in Fig. 4.2, again for the first three non-trivial Fibonacci trees.

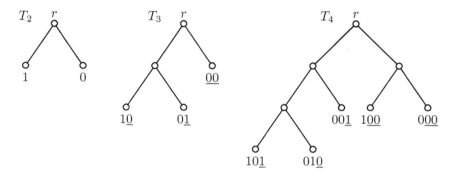

Fig. 4.2   Fibonacci trees equipped with the labeling θ

The main result of this section which is due to Klavžar and Mollard reads as follows.

Theorem 4.9. [63, Theorem 3.1] *If $n \geq 1$ and $u \in V(\Gamma_n)$, then*

$$\mathrm{ecc}_{\Gamma_n}(u) = \mathrm{depth}_{T_{n+1}}(\theta^{-1}(u)).$$

Proof. We proceed by induction on n, the cases $n \in [2]$ being trivial. Let $n \geq 3$ and let $u \in V(\Gamma_n)$. Consider the following three cases.

Case 1: Suppose first that $u = v00$, where $v \in \mathcal{F}_{n-2}$. Then we claim that $\mathrm{ecc}_{\Gamma_n}(u) = \mathrm{ecc}_{\Gamma_{n-2}}(v) + 1$. Let u' be a vertex of Γ_n with $d_{\Gamma_n}(u, u') = \mathrm{ecc}(u)$. Let $u' = wab$, where $w \in \mathcal{F}_{n-2}$. Since $ab \neq 11$, $d_{\Gamma_n}(u, u') \neq d_{\Gamma_{n-2}}(v, w) + 2$. Then

$$\mathrm{ecc}_{\Gamma_n}(u) = d_{\Gamma_n}(u, u') \leq d_{\Gamma_{n-2}}(v, w) + 1 \leq \mathrm{ecc}_{\Gamma_{n-2}}(v) + 1.$$

Conversely, let $w \in \mathcal{F}_{n-2}$, such that $d_{\Gamma_{n-2}}(v, w) = \mathrm{ecc}(v)$. Then $w01 \in \mathcal{F}_n$ and $d_{\Gamma_n}(u, w01) = \mathrm{ecc}_{\Gamma_{n-2}}(v) + 1$. It follows that $\mathrm{ecc}_{\Gamma_n}(u) \geq \mathrm{ecc}_{\Gamma_{n-2}}(v) + 1$. This proves the claim.

Case 2: Suppose next that $u = v1$, where $v \in \mathcal{F}_{n-1}^{\bullet 0}$. Now we claim that $\mathrm{ecc}_{\Gamma_n}(u) = \mathrm{ecc}_{\Gamma_{n-1}}(v) + 1$. The inequality $\mathrm{ecc}_{\Gamma_n}(u) \leq \mathrm{ecc}_{\Gamma_{n-1}}(v) + 1$ follows by an argument similar as in the first case. Conversely, let $w \in \mathcal{F}_{n-1}$, such that $d_{\Gamma_{n-1}}(v, w) = \mathrm{ecc}(v)$. Then $w0 \in \mathcal{F}_n$ and $d_{\Gamma_n}(u, w0) = \mathrm{ecc}_{\Gamma_{n-1}}(v) + 1$. If follows that $\mathrm{ecc}_{\Gamma_n}(u) \geq \mathrm{ecc}_{\Gamma_{n-1}}(v) + 1$.

Case 3: Suppose finally that $u = v0$, where $v \in \mathcal{F}_{n-1}^{\bullet 1}$. We claim again that $\mathrm{ecc}_{\Gamma_n}(u) = \mathrm{ecc}_{\Gamma_{n-1}}(v)+1$. Again, the inequality $\mathrm{ecc}_{\Gamma_n}(u) \leq \mathrm{ecc}_{\Gamma_{n-1}}(v)+1$ follows as above. Conversely, let $w \in \mathcal{F}_{n-1}$, such that $d_{\Gamma_{n-1}}(v, w) = \mathrm{ecc}_{\Gamma_{n-1}}(v)$. Then w ends with 0, because otherwise w would not be an eccentric vertex of v. Indeed, if w ended with 1, then the string w' obtained from w by changing its last bit to 0 would lie in $\mathcal{F}_{n-1}$ and hence $d_{\Gamma_{n-1}}(w', v) > d_{\Gamma_{n-1}}(w, v) = \mathrm{ecc}_{\Gamma_{n-1}}(v)$, a contradiction. It follows that $w1 \in \mathcal{F}_n$ and $d_{\Gamma_n}(u, w1) = d_{\Gamma_{n-1}}(w, v) + 1 = \mathrm{ecc}_{\Gamma_{n-1}}(v) + 1$.

We have thus proved that for any $u \in \mathcal{F}_n$, $\mathrm{ecc}_{\Gamma_n}(u)$ increases by 1 with respect to the string v to which a suffix has been added to obtain u. By the construction of T_n and by the induction hypothesis,

$$\mathrm{depth}_{T_{n+1}}(\theta^{-1}(u)) = \mathrm{depth}_{T_{n-1}}(\theta^{-1}(v)) + 1 = \mathrm{ecc}_{\Gamma_{n-2}}(v) + 1 = \mathrm{ecc}_{\Gamma_n}(u)$$

in the first case, and

$$\mathrm{depth}_{T_{n+1}}(\theta^{-1}(u)) = \mathrm{depth}_{T_n}(\theta^{-1}(v)) + 1 = \mathrm{ecc}_{\Gamma_{n-1}}(v) + 1 = \mathrm{ecc}_{\Gamma_n}(u)$$

in the last two cases. $\qquad\square$

4.3 Hamiltonicity

It is well-known that the n-cube Q_n, $n \geq 2$, is Hamiltonian. For example, the reflected binary code of length n defines a Hamiltonian cycle in Q_n.

The *reflected binary code of length* n is the sequence S_n of the binary strings $\mathcal{B}_n$ defined recursively by

$$S_0 = \lambda,$$
$$S_{n+1} = 0S_n, 1S_n^R \qquad (n \geq 0),$$

where S_n^R denotes the sequence S_n written in reverse order of its elements.

The first few sequences are thus

$$S_1 = 0, 1$$
$$S_2 = 00, 01, 11, 10$$
$$S_3 = 000, 001, 011, 010, 110, 111, 101, 100.$$

It is immediate by induction that S_n is a Hamiltonian path in Q_n with endpoints 0^n and 10^{n-1}. Furthermore, for $n \geq 2$, there exists an edge between its endpoints not used by this path. Adding this edge to S_n we obtain a Hamiltonian cycle in Q_n (Fig. 4.3, left).

The reflected binary sequence is often called *Gray code* after Frank Gray who used them for communication purposes. However they were applied to

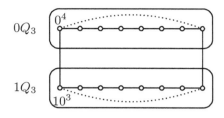 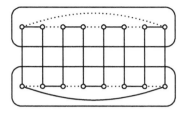

Fig. 4.3   Two recursive construction of Hamiltonian cycles in Q_4

mathematical puzzles long before they became known to engineers. They appear for example in the description of solutions of the Chinese ring puzzle and the Tower of Hanoi game; see the books by Hinz, Klavžar, and Petr [49] and by Knuth [70] for more details and the historical point of view.

There exist many other constructions of Hamiltonian cycles in Q_n. The number of Hamiltonian cycles in Q_n is only known for $n \leq 6$ and Q_6 itself has 777739016577752714 equivalence classes of Hamiltonian cycles as reported by Haanpää and Östergård in [45]!

Another example of recursive construction of a Hamiltonian cycle in Q_n for $n \geq 2$ is illustrated in Fig. 4.3. Let $C_{n-1} = x_1, x_2, \ldots, x_{2^{n-1}}, x_1$ be a Hamiltonian cycle of Q_{n-1}. Interleaving the edges of $0C_{n-1}$ and $1C_{n-1}$ with the edges of the perfect matching between $0Q_{n-1}$ and $1Q_{n-1}$ we obtain the following Hamiltonian cycle C_n in Q_n:

$$0x_1, 0x_2, 1x_2, 1x_3, 0x_3, \ldots, 0x_{2i-1}, 0x_{2i}, 1x_{2i}, 1x_{2i+1}, \ldots,$$

$$0x_{2^{n-1}-1}, 0x_{2^{n-1}}, 1x_{2^{n-1}}, 1x_1, 0x_1.$$

Using the fundamental decomposition of Fibonacci cubes a construction inspired by that of Fig. 4.3 (left) was used by Cong, Zheng, and Sharma in [24] for constructing a Hamiltonian path in Γ_n. When $n(\Gamma_n)$ is even, by a modification of this path using the interleaving construction of Fig. 4.3 (right), one can construct a Hamiltonian cycle in Γ_n.

Let V_n be the sequence of strings in $\mathcal{F}_n$ defined recursively by

$$V_0 = \lambda$$

$$V_1 = 0, 1$$

$$V_n = 0V_{n-1}^R, 10V_{n-2}^R, \qquad (n \geq 2).$$

We have thus

$$V_2 = 01, 00, 10$$

$$V_3 = 010, 000, 001, 101, 100$$

$$V_4 = 0100, 0101, 0001, 0000, 0010, 1010, 1000, 1001.$$

It follows from the fundamental decomposition $\mathcal{F}_n = \mathcal{F}_n^{0\bullet} + \mathcal{F}_n^{10\bullet}$ that every vertex of Γ_n appears exactly once in V_n. Furthermore, it can be proved by by induction that V_n is a Hamiltonian path in Γ_n with endpoints

$$
\begin{array}{lll}
(010)^m \text{ and } (100)^m & \text{for } & n = 3m\,, \\
(010)^m 0 \text{ and } (100)^m 1 & \text{for } & n = 3m + 1\,, \\
(010)^m 01 \text{ and } (100)^m 10 & \text{for } & n = 3m + 2\,.
\end{array}
$$

We have therefore constructively demonstrated the following result.

Theorem 4.10. [24] *There exists a Hamiltonian path in Γ_n for any $n \geq 0$.*

Since Γ_n is bipartite, using Theorem 4.10 and the orders of the bipartition, we easily find its independence number $\alpha(\Gamma_n)$.

Corollary 4.11. [82, Theorem 1] *If $n \geq 0$, then $\alpha(\Gamma_n) = \left\lceil \frac{1}{2} F_{n+2} \right\rceil$.*

Note that if a graph G is bipartite and Hamiltonian, then $n(G)$ must be even. A graph G is *pancyclic* if G contains cycles of all lengths from 3 up to $n(G)$. A bipartite graph cannot be pancyclic, because it does not contain odd length cycles, but it is said to be *bipancyclic* if it contains cycles of all even lengths from 4 to $n(G)$.

Since F_0 is even and F_1 is odd, the recurrence $F_m = F_{m-1} + F_{m-2}$ immediately implies that F_m is even if and only if $m \equiv 0 \,(\mathrm{mod}\, 3)$. Therefore, $n(\Gamma_n)$ is even if and only if $n \equiv 1 \,(\mathrm{mod}\, 3)$.

One can easily verify that Γ_4 is Hamiltonian and bipancyclic, and that Γ_3 and Γ_5 are not Hamiltonian but are bipancyclic. We now give a simple proof that Γ_n is bipancyclic for any $n \geq 3$.

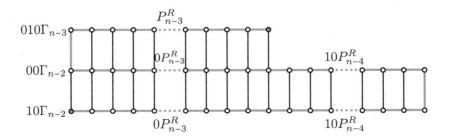

Fig. 4.4 H_n with V_n in red

Using recursively the construction of V_n, we obtain successively:

$$V_n = 0V_{n-1}^R, 10V_{n-2}^R$$
$$= 010V_{n-3}, 00V_{n-2}, 1010V_{n-4}, 100V_{n-3}$$
$$= 010V_{n-3}, 000V_{n-3}^R, 0010V_{n-4}^R, 1010V_{n-4}, 100V_{n-3}\,.$$

Consider the subgraph H_n of Γ_n (Fig. 4.4) defined by the three paths

$$010V_{n-3}^R$$
$$000V_{n-3}^R, 0010V_{n-4}^R$$
$$100V_{n-3}^R, 1010V_{n-4}^R$$

with the addition of the edges of the two perfect matchings between $010V_{n-3}^R$ and $000V_{n-3}^R$ on one hand, and between $000V_{n-3}^R$, $0010V_{n-4}^R$ and $100V_{n-3}^R$, $1010V_{n-4}^R$ on the other.

Note that V_n is a subgraph of H_n and since $V(H_n) = V(\Gamma_n)$ if H_n is bipancyclic, then Γ_n will have the same property.

Consider first the cycle $C = 000V_{n-3}^R, 0010V_{n-4}^R, 1010V_{n-4}, 100V_{n-3}$ and the path $010V_{n-3}^R$. Note that $000V_{n-3}^R$ is a sub-path of C, and $010V_{n-3}^R$ is disjoint of C.

If $|V_{n-3}|$ is even, interleaving the edges of $010V_{n-3}^R$ or $000V_{n-3}^R$ with those of the matching between them we obtain a Hamiltonian cycle in H_n thus in Γ_n (Fig. 4.5).

If $|V_{n-3}|$ is odd, we can only interleave the first $|V_{n-3}|-1$ edges of $010V_{n-3}^R$ or $000V_{n-3}^R$ with those of the matching. We obtain therefore a cycle of length $n(\Gamma_n) - 1$ (Fig. 4.6).

In both cases using edges of the matching as a shortcut we can embed cycles of arbitrary smaller even length. The parities of $n(V_{n-3})$ and $n(V_n) = n(\Gamma_n)$ are the same.

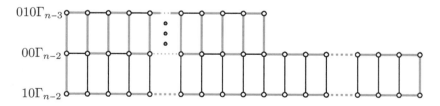

Fig. 4.5 Case $|V_{n-3}|$ even, in red a Hamiltonian cycle in H_n

Therefore H_n, $n \geq 3$, and thus Γ_n are bipancyclic. As a corollary we obtain:

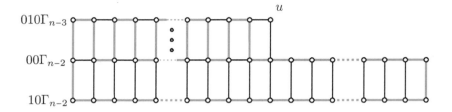

Fig. 4.6   Case $|V_{n-3}|$ odd, in red a Hamiltonian cycle in $H_n - u$

Corollary 4.12. *If $n = 3m + 1$ and $m \geq 1$, then Γ_n is Hamiltonian.*

This result was mentioned without proof in [24]. Later Zelina provided a proof in [125]. However, the result is actually a corollary of the following earlier theorem of Zagaglia Salvi, proving a property stronger than bipancyclicity.

Theorem 4.13. [123, Theorem 1] *Let $n \geq 5$ and let m be an even integer with $4 \leq m \leq n(\Gamma_n)$. Then for any edge e of Γ_n there exists a cycle of length m containing e.*

Let $\mathcal{E}_n$ and $\mathcal{O}_n$ be the set of strings in $\mathcal{F}_n$ of even and odd Hamming weight, respectively.

Proposition 4.14.

$$
\begin{aligned}
|\mathcal{E}_n| = |\mathcal{O}_n| + 1 \quad & if \ n \equiv 0, 5 \, (\mathrm{mod} \, 6), \\
|\mathcal{E}_n| = |\mathcal{O}_n| \quad & if \ n \equiv 1, 4 \, (\mathrm{mod} \, 6), \\
|\mathcal{O}_n| = |\mathcal{E}_n| + 1 \quad & if \ n \equiv 2, 3 \, (\mathrm{mod} \, 6).
\end{aligned}
$$

Proof. This is true for $n \leq 3$ and immediate by induction since, by the fundamental decomposition,

$$
\begin{aligned}
|\mathcal{E}_n| = |\mathcal{E}_{n-1}| + |\mathcal{O}_{n-2}|, \\
|\mathcal{O}_n| = |\mathcal{O}_{n-1}| + |\mathcal{E}_{n-2}|,
\end{aligned}
$$

and thus $|\mathcal{E}_n| - |\mathcal{O}_n| = -(|\mathcal{E}_{n-3}| - |\mathcal{O}_{n-3}|)$.   □

Assume $n \not\equiv 1 \, (\mathrm{mod} \, 3)$. One of the two sets $\mathcal{O}_n$, $\mathcal{E}_n$ has one more vertex than the other. Let $\mathcal{M}_n$ be this set. A path alternately passes through a vertex in $\mathcal{O}_n$ then a vertex in $\mathcal{E}_n$. Since a cycle in a bipartite graph has even length, if $\Gamma_n - u$ is Hamiltonian then u must be in $\mathcal{M}_n$. The converse is true for $n \geq 5$ as proved by Castro.

Theorem 4.15. [19, Theorem 3.1.10] *If $n \geq 5$ and $n \not\equiv 1 \,(\mathrm{mod}\,3)$, then $\Gamma_n - u$ is Hamiltonian if and only if u belongs to $\mathcal{M}_n$.*

4.4   Diametral Shortest Paths in Γ_n

Recall from Section 3.1 that the diameter $\mathrm{diam}(G)$ of a connected graph G is the maximum distance between its vertices. Vertices $u, v \in V(G)$ with $d_G(u, v) = \mathrm{diam}(G)$ are *diametrically opposite vertices*. Shortest paths between diametrically opposite vertices are referred to as *diametral paths*. It is of interest to consider the cardinality of diametral paths in G.

It is well-known and easy to verify that $\mathrm{diam}(Q_n) = n$ and that diametrically opposite vertices are pairs $u, \overline{u}$, where u is an arbitrary vertex of Q_n. Hence there are exactly 2^{n-1} diametrically opposite pairs in Q_n, and for every such pair, the number of diametral paths between them is $n!$.

In this section we calculate the number of diametral paths in Γ_n. The material we present is based on the treatment of Eğecioğlu, E. Saygı and Z. Saygı in [38]. First we need to consider seemingly remote combinatorial objects called *alternating permutations* and their enumerator, which are the *Euler numbers*.

4.4.1   *Alternating Permutations and Euler Numbers*

Following Stanley [101], a permutation $\sigma = \sigma_1 \sigma_2 \ldots \sigma_n$ of $[n]$ is *alternating* if $\sigma_1 > \sigma_2 < \sigma_3 > \sigma_4 < \cdots$. In other words, $\sigma_i < \sigma_{i+1}$ for i even and $\sigma_i > \sigma_{i+1}$ for i odd. Moreover, the permutation σ is *reverse alternating* if $\sigma_1 < \sigma_2 > \sigma_3 < \sigma_4 > \cdots$. Let E_n denote the number of alternating permutations of $[n]$, and set $E_0 = 1$. These are known as the *Euler numbers*. The number of reverse alternating permutations of $[n]$ is also given by E_n.

By a result of André [3], we have

$$2E_{n+1} = \sum_{k=0}^{n} \binom{n}{k} E_k E_{n-k} \,,$$

and amazingly, the exponential generating function of the sequence of Euler numbers is given by

$$\sum_{n \geq 0} E_n \frac{x^n}{n!} = \sec x + \tan x \,.$$

Since

$$\sec x + \tan x = 1 + x + \frac{x^2}{2!} + 2\frac{x^3}{3!} + 5\frac{x^4}{4!} + 16\frac{x^5}{5!} + 61\frac{x^6}{6!} + \cdots,$$

the first few Euler numbers (sequence A000111 in [98]) are $E_0 = 1$, $E_1 = 1$, $E_2 = 1$, $E_3 = 2$, $E_4 = 5$, $E_5 = 16$, $E_6 = 61$.

4.4.2 The Main Bijection

It was shown by Hsu [51] that $\text{diam}(\Gamma_n) = n$. We have the following easy addition to this result.

Proposition 4.16. [38, Proposition 1] *There is a unique pair of diametrically opposite vertices in Γ_n, $n \geq 1$. They are*

$$(i) \;\; u = (01)^{\frac{n}{2}} \text{ and } v = (10)^{\frac{n}{2}} \qquad \text{if } n \text{ is even,}$$
$$(ii) \;\; u = (01)^{\frac{n-1}{2}} 0 \text{ and } v = (10)^{\frac{n-1}{2}} 1 \quad \text{if } n \text{ is odd.}$$

Since there is exactly one pair of diametrically opposite vertices in Γ_n, $n \geq 1$, we can define c_n to be the number of shortest paths between them. By direct inspection we see that $c_1 = 1$, $c_2 = 1$, $c_3 = 2$, $c_4 = 5$, $c_5 = 16$.

It is convenient to view the edges of a shortest path between vertices u and v to be directed from u to v. For a path

$$u = s_0 \rightarrow s_1 \rightarrow \cdots \rightarrow s_n = v,$$

each vertex s_{i+1} is obtained from s_i by flipping a 0 to a 1, or a 1 to a 0, with the proviso that no consecutive 1s appear in any s_i. In particular $c_3 = 2$ as there are two paths of length 3 from $u = 010$ to $v = 101$ in Γ_3 as shown in Table 4.1.

Step	b_1	b_2	b_3		Step	b_1	b_2	b_3
$v = s_3$	1	0	1		$v = s_3$	1	0	1
s_2	1	0	0		s_2	0	0	1
s_1	0	0	0		s_1	0	0	0
$u = s_0$	0	1	0		$u = s_0$	0	1	0

Table 4.1 Two different paths from $u = 010$ to $v = 101$ in Γ_3

Here we write u in the bottommost row. The ith step shows the string s_i after i edges on the path have been traversed. Note that in this representation the path proceeds from bottom up and the row indices are increasing as we go up.

By using this representation we construct a bijective proof that the sequence of the numbers of diametral paths in Fibonacci cubes is precisely the sequence of Euler numbers.

Theorem 4.17. [38, Theorem 1] *Let c_n be the number of diametral paths in Γ_n, $n \geq 1$. Then $c_n = E_n$, where E_n is the Euler number.*

Proof. We give a bijection between paths of length n from u to v in Γ_n and alternating permutations σ of $[n]$. The bijection is best communicated by an example. Suppose first that $n = 8$ and we are given the path from $u = 01010101$ to $v = 10101010$ whose steps are shown in Table 4.2.

Step	b_1	b_2	b_3	b_4	b_5	b_6	b_7	b_8
$v = s_8$	1	0	1	0	1	0	1	0
s_7	1	0	1	0	1	0	0	0
s_6	1	0	0	0	1	0	0	0
s_5	1	0	0	0	1	0	0	1
s_4	0	0	0	0	1	0	0	1
s_3	0	1	0	0	1	0	0	1
s_2	0	1	0	0	0	0	0	1
s_1	0	1	0	0	0	1	0	1
$u = s_0$	0	1	0	1	0	1	0	1

Table 4.2   A path from $u = (01)^4$ to $v = (10)^4$ in Γ_8

As the first step of the bijection, we mark the first appearance of 1 as we go up the table in every column with an odd index. In Table 4.3 these entries are circled.

Step	b_1	b_2	b_3	b_4	b_5	b_6	b_7	b_8
$v = s_8$	1	0	1	0	1	0	(1)	0
s_7	1	0	(1)	0	1	0	0	0
s_6	1	0	0	0	1	0	0	0
s_5	(1)	0	0	0	1	0	0	1
s_4	0	0	0	0	1	0	0	1
s_3	0	1	0	0	(1)	0	0	1
s_2	0	1	0	0	0	0	0	1
s_1	0	1	0	0	0	1	0	1
$u = s_0$	0	1	0	1	0	1	0	1

Table 4.3 First appearance of 1 as we go up in every column with an odd index is marked in the path from $u = (01)^4$ to $v = (10)^4$ in Γ_8

Next, we mark the first appearance of 0 as we go up the table in every column with an even index. Circling these entries gives Table 4.4.

Step	b_1	b_2	b_3	b_4	b_5	b_6	b_7	b_8
$v = s_8$	1	0	1	0	1	0	(1)	0
s_7	1	0	(1)	0	1	0	0	0
s_6	1	0	0	0	1	0	0	(0)
s_5	(1)	0	0	0	1	0	0	1
s_4	0	(0)	0	0	1	0	0	1
s_3	0	1	0	0	(1)	0	0	1
s_2	0	1	0	0	0	(0)	0	1
s_1	0	1	0	(0)	0	1	0	1
$u = s_0$	0	1	0	1	0	1	0	1

Table 4.4 First appearance of 0/1 as we go up in every column with an even/odd index is marked in the path from $u = (01)^4$ to $v = (10)^4$ in Γ_8

After this we record the corresponding step number in each column. For instance, by reading the indices of the corresponding rows, column 1 gives 5, column 2 gives 4, etc. The resulting alternating permutation is:

$$5 \quad 4 \quad 7 \quad 1 \quad 3 \quad 2 \quad 8 \quad 6$$

These steps are reversible. Suppose this time that $n = 7$ and we are given the alternating permutation 3 1 6 4 7 2 5. We construct Table 4.5 in which the odd numbered columns 1, 3, 5, 7 are assigned label 1 in the rows 3, 6, 7, 5, which are the entries in the odd positions of the given permutation. The even numbered columns 2, 4, 6 are assigned label 0 in the rows 1, 4, 2, which are the entries in the even indexed positions of the given permutation.

Now we fill in the odd indexed columns of this matrix by 0, up to the marked 1 in the column, followed by 0s all the way up; and we fill the even indexed columns by 1 up to the marked 0 in the column, followed by 1s all the way up. This results in the path of length $n = 7$ from u to v shown in Table 4.6 corresponding to the alternating permutation 3 1 6 4 7 2 5.

Considering now the general case, we see that going from u to v in n steps, every bit in u has to change exactly once. This means that the row indices of the marked entries in the matrix in Table 4.4 is a permutation σ of $[n]$. Now consider an element $t = \sigma_i$ with odd i with $1 < i < n$. This means that in step t of the path, that is in s_t, the entry in the ith column goes from 0 to 1. But all of the vertices that appear in the table as rows

Step	b_1	b_2	b_3	b_4	b_5	b_6	b_7
$v = s_7$					(1)		
s_6			(1)				
s_5							(1)
s_4				(0)			
s_3	(1)						
s_2						(0)	
s_1		(0)					
$u = s_0$							

Table 4.5 First appearance of 0/1 in every column with an even/odd index in the path from $u = (01)^3 0$ to $v = (10)^3 1$ in Γ_7 corresponding to the alternating permutation 3 1 6 4 7 2 5

Step	b_1	b_2	b_3	b_4	b_5	b_6	b_7
$v = s_7$	1	0	1	0	(1)	0	1
s_6	1	0	(1)	0	0	0	1
s_5	1	0	0	0	0	0	(1)
s_4	1	0	0	(0)	0	0	0
s_3	(1)	0	0	1	0	0	0
s_2	0	0	0	1	0	(0)	0
s_1	0	(0)	0	1	0	1	0
$u = s_0$	0	1	0	1	0	1	0

Table 4.6 The path from $u = (01)^3 0$ to $v = (10)^3 1$ in Γ_7 corresponding to the alternating permutation 3 1 6 4 7 2 5

are Fibonacci strings. This means that in s_{t-1} the entries in columns $i-1$ and $i+1$ which are adjacent to the entry at column i must already be 0. Therefore these entries were flipped from 1 to 0 in earlier steps. It follows that $\sigma_i > \sigma_{i+1}$ and $\sigma_i > \sigma_{i-1}$. The two extreme cases with $i = 1$ and $i = n$ are handled the same way. Therefore σ is an alternating permutation. The other direction is proved similarly.   □

4.5 Short Induced Paths and Cycles

It is known that counting cycles and paths in arbitrary graphs is a hard problem [40]. For a general bipartite graph with m vertices and girth g (length of a shortest cycle), a search algorithm to count short cycles in bipartite graphs is presented in [25]. Time complexity of the algorithm is $\mathcal{O}(m^2\Delta)$ to count g-cycles and $(g+2)$–cycles, and $\mathcal{O}(m^2\Delta^2)$ to count $(g+4)$-cycles, where Δ is the maximum degree of the graph in question.

We have already mentioned that Zagaglia Salvi proved that for $n \geq 7$, every edge of Γ_n belongs to cycles of every even length [123]. In this section we calculate the number of short induced paths and cycles of small length in Γ_n by using the fundamental decomposition. We follow the work of Eğecioğlu, E. Saygı and Z. Saygı that appeared in [37].

Let $p_k(n)$ denote the number of induced paths of length k in Γ_n. We will refer to such paths as induced k-paths. Clearly $p_1(n)$ is the number of edges of Γ_n. We have already seen that it is given by

$$p_1(n) = \tfrac{1}{5}\left(2(n+1)F_n + nF_{n+1}\right) \tag{4.6}$$

with the generating function

$$\sum_{n \geq 0} p_1(n)t^n = \frac{t}{(1-t-t^2)^2} . \tag{4.7}$$

4.5.1 *Enumerating Induced 2-Paths*

Since Γ_n is bipartite, every 2-path is induced. Therefore

$$p_2(n) = \sum_{v \in \Gamma_n} \binom{\deg_{\Gamma_n}(v)}{2} . \tag{4.8}$$

The following alternate expression for $p_2(n)$ is due to Eğecioğlu, E. Saygı, and Z. Saygı.

Proposition 4.18. [37, Proposition 1]

$$p_2(n) = \tfrac{1}{25}\left((n-1)(10n+9)F_n - 2nF_{n-1}\right) . \tag{4.9}$$

Proof. We will obtain $p_2(n)$ by making use of the fundamental decomposition of Γ_n. A 2-path is either completely in $0\Gamma_{n-1}$, or completely in $10\Gamma_{n-2}$, or uses one of the link edges between $00\Gamma_{n-2} \subset 0\Gamma_{n-1}$ and $10\Gamma_{n-2}$. The first two types are enumerated by $p_2(n-1)$ and $p_2(n-2)$, respectively. If one of the edges of the 2-path is a link edge, there are three cases to consider. These can be denoted schematically as in Fig. 4.7.

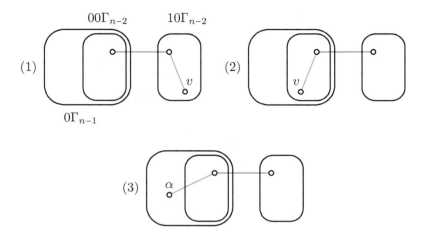

Fig. 4.7 The three possible cases for 2-paths which use link edges

Case 1: Such 2-paths are enumerated by

$$\sum_{v \in \Gamma_{n-2}} \deg_{\Gamma_n}(v) = 2p_1(n-2).$$

Case 2: This is similar to Case 1, and the number of such 2-paths is again $2p_1(n-2)$.

Case 3: Any vertex in $0\Gamma_{n-1} \setminus 00\Gamma_{n-2}$ is of the form 010α, where α is a Fibonacci string of length $n-3$. Therefore the number of 2-paths of this type is F_{n-1}.

As a consequence we have the recurrence relation

$$p_2(n) = p_2(n-1) + p_2(n-2) + 4p_1(n-2) + F_{n-1} \qquad (4.10)$$

for $n \geq 2$ with $p_2(0) = p_2(1) = 0$. We multiply (4.10) by t^n and sum for $n \geq 2$. Using the expression (4.7) for the generating function of the $p_1(n)$ and the generating function of the Fibonacci numbers themselves, we obtain

$$\sum_{n \geq 0} p_2(n) t^n = \frac{t^2(1 + 3t - t^2)}{(1 - t - t^2)^3}. \qquad (4.11)$$

The formula (4.9) can be obtained from this generating function by using Greene and Wilf theory and standard calculations. $\qquad \square$

The sequence $p_2(n)$ for $n \geq 1$ starts as

$$0, 1, 6, 17, 46, 108, 242, 515, 1062, 2131, 4188, 8088, \ldots$$

Proposition 4.18, in conjunction with (4.6) and the observation (4.8) yield the following expression for the second moment of the degrees in Γ_n.

Corollary 4.19. [37, Corollary 1]

$$\sum_{v \in V(\Gamma_n)} \deg_{\Gamma_n}(v)^2 = 2p_2(n) + 2p_1(n) = \frac{2}{25}\left((10n^2 + 14n + 1)F_n + 3nF_{n-1}\right).$$

The expression in Corollary 4.19 is also referred to as the first Zagreb index of Γ_n. This sequence starts as

$$0, 2, 6, 22, 54, 132, 292, 626, 1290, 2594, 5102, 9864, \ldots$$

4.5.2 *Enumerating Induced 3-Paths*

In the enumeration of the induced 3-paths in Γ_n we need to keep in mind that these are induced paths, and they cannot form a square in Γ_n.

By making use of the fundamental decomposition of Γ_n, we have the contribution of the induced 3-paths in $0\Gamma_{n-1}$ and the ones in $10\Gamma_{n-2}$ to $p_3(n)$, which are $p_3(n-1)$ and $p_3(n-2)$, respectively. All other induced 3-paths must include a single link edge. We consider the contribution arising from this last possibility, which can be denoted graphically as shown in Fig. 4.8.

It is shown in [37] that the total contribution of the six cases shown in Fig. 4.8 is

$$4p_1(n-2) + 2p_1(n-3) - 4p_1(n-4) + 6p_2(n-2) - 2F_{n-2}.$$

Therefore for $n \geq 2$,

$$\begin{aligned} p_3(n) = {}&p_3(n-1) + p_3(n-2) + 4p_1(n-2) + 2p_1(n-3) \\ &- 4p_1(n-4) + 6p_2(n-2) - 2F_{n-2}. \end{aligned}$$

It follows that the generating function of the $p_3(n)$ is given by

$$\frac{2t^3(1 + 4t + 5t^2 - 4t^3 + t^4)}{(1 - t - t^2)^4}.$$

First few values of $p_3(n)$ for $n \geq 2$ are

$$0, 2, 16, 70, 224, 640, 1648, 3994, 9200, 20414, 43920, 92160, \ldots$$

Finally, we have

Proposition 4.20. [37, Proposition 2] *The number of induced 3-paths in* Γ_n *is given by*

$$p_3(n) = \frac{2}{25}\left((n-2)(2n^2 + n - 4)F_n + n(2n^2 - 9n + 6)F_{n-2}\right).$$

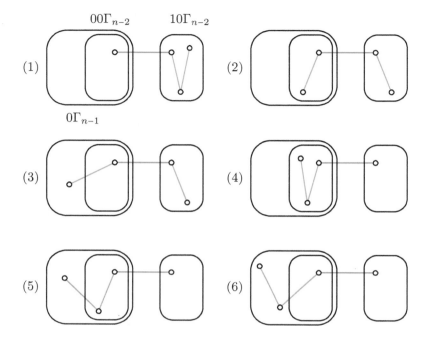

Fig. 4.8 The six possible cases for induced 3-paths that use link edges

Next we consider short induced cycles in Γ_n.

We denote by $c_k(n)$ the number of induced k-cycles in Γ_n. Since Γ_n is bipartite, this number is zero unless k is even. As special cases, we let $c_0(n)$ and $c_2(n)$ denote the order and the size of Γ_n. Then $c_0(n) = F_{n+2}$ and $c_2(n) = p_1(n)$.

The number of induced 4-cycles in Γ_n is a special case of counting the number of hypercubes Q_k in Γ_n for $k = 2$, see [58, 61, 92] and Corollary 5.4. We have

$$c_4(n) = \tfrac{1}{50}\left((n-2)(5n+1)F_n + 6nF_{n-2}\right)$$

with the generating function

$$\sum_{n\geq 0} c_4(n)t^n = \frac{t^3}{(1-t-t^2)^3}. \tag{4.12}$$

4.5.3 *Enumerating Induced 6-Cycles*

Using the fundamental decomposition of Γ_n, an induced 6-cycle is either completely contained in $0\Gamma_{n-1}$, completely contained in $10\Gamma_{n-2}$, or includes two link edges as shown in Fig. 4.9. The first two types are counted by $c_6(n-1)$ and $c_6(n-2)$, respectively. It remains to calculate the third type of induced 6-cycles to arrive at a recurrence relation for $c_6(n)$.

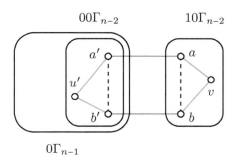

Fig. 4.9 An induced 6-cycle that uses link edges

In Fig. 4.9, let us call the rightmost vertex v, the leftmost vertex u', and refer to the two neighbors of v in Γ_{n-2} as a (top) and b (bottom). Then the neighbors of u' are a' and b', the mates of a and b, respectively. In the figure the vertical dotted lines indicate that the corresponding edge is not there. We make two observations:

(i) $u' \notin 0\Gamma_{n-1} \smallsetminus 00\Gamma_{n-2}$ since the vertices in the set difference have exactly one neighbor in $00\Gamma_{n-2}$.

(ii) u' is not the vertex v', the mate of v, for otherwise the 6-cycle would not be induced because of the existence of the link edge vv'.

Using these observations we deduce that u, a, v, b is a 4-cycle in Γ_{n-2}. Furthermore, a 4-cycle formed by four vertices u, a, v, b in Γ_{n-2} is responsible for a total of four induced 6-cycles in this way. This is because the pair a, b, a dotted diagonal, contributes two induced 6-cycles, one with using u' and v for the two extreme points, and the other by using u and v'. Similarly, the other dotted diagonal formed by u and v contribute two induced 6-cycles.

Therefore we have the recursion

$$c_6(n) = c_6(n-1) + c_6(n-2) + 4c_4(n-2) \tag{4.13}$$

for $n \geq 2$ with $c_6(0) = c_6(1) = 0$. We already have the generating function (4.12). Using the recurrence relation (4.13) in conjunction with this, followed by generating function manipulations and partial fractions expansion, we obtain the following.

Proposition 4.21. [37, Proposition 3] *For $n \geq 0$, let $c_6(n)$ denote the number of induced 6-cycles in the Fibonacci cube Γ_n. Then*

$$\sum_{n \geq 0} c_6(n)t^n = \frac{4t^5}{(1 - t - t^2)^4} \tag{4.14}$$

and $c_6(n)$ is explicitly given by

$$c_6(n) = \tfrac{1}{75}n(n - 2)\left((n - 7)F_{n+1} + 3(n + 1)F_{n-2}\right).$$

First few values of the sequence of numbers $c_6(n)$ for $n \geq 4$ are

$$0, 4, 16, 56, 160, 420, 1024, 2376, 5296, 11440, 24080, 49608, \ldots$$

It is easy to show by using induction on n and the fundamental decomposition of Γ_n that the 6-cycles in Γ_n are either induced, or have exactly one diagonal edge. This second type constitutes non-induced 6-cycles in Γ_n. These are pairs of 4-cycles in Γ_n sharing an edge. Let us denote by $s_6(n)$ this latter type of 6-cycles in Γ_n. Then

Proposition 4.22. [37, Proposition 4] *The generating function of $s_6(n)$ is given by*

$$\sum_{n \geq 0} s_6(n)t^n = \frac{2t^4(1 + 57 - t^2)}{(1 - t - t^2)^4} \tag{4.15}$$

with

$$s_6(n) = \tfrac{1}{50}\left((n - 2)(2n^2 - 9n - 3)F_{n+1} + (n + 1)(6n^2 - 17n + 6)F_{n-2}\right).$$

4.5.4   *Enumerating Induced 8-Cycles*

In the calculation of $c_8(n)$, we again make use of the fundamental decomposition of Γ_n. There are $c_8(n - 1)$ induced 8-cycles that are contributed by $0\Gamma_{n-1}$ and $c_8(n - 2)$ that are contributed by $10\Gamma_{n-2}$. The remaining induced 8-cycles must involve two of the link edges. The possible cases for this last family are shown in Fig. 4.10.

Case 1: Since the 8-cycle is induced, there are no additional edges than the ones shown in Fig. 4.10. Therefore $u_1' \neq v_1'$, $u_2' \neq v_2'$, $u_1' \neq v_2'$, $u_2' \neq v_1'$. This means that the vertices v_1, a, u_1, u_2, b, v_2 form an induced 6-cycle in

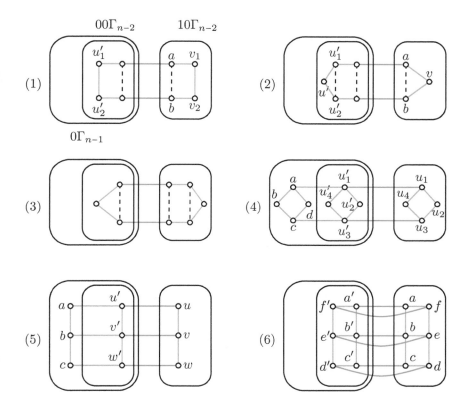

Fig. 4.10 The six possible cases for induced 8-cycles that use link edges

$10\Gamma_{n-2}$. Furthermore, given any induced 6-cycle in Γ_{n-2}, picking a polar opposite diagonal pair a, b in one of three ways, then picking which side of the 6-cycle is to be in $10\Gamma_{n-2}$ gives a total of six choices for each induced 6-cycle in Γ_{n-2}. Therefore the contribution of this case is $6c_6(n-2)$.

Case 2: The vertices v, a, u_1, u, u_2, b form an induced 6-cycle in $10\Gamma_{n-2}$. Furthermore, any vertex v of an induced 6-cycle and its neighbors a and b on the cycle can be used as the part in $10\Gamma_{n-1}$ of an induced 8-cycle with link edges aa' and bb'. Therefore induced 6-cycles in Γ_{n-2} contribute a total of $6c_6(n-2)$ induced 8-cycles to the count $c_8(n)$.

Case 3: The contribution of this case is identical to the one in Case 2.

Case 4: For any 4-cycle $abcd$ in $010\Gamma_{n-3}$, we know that there are corresponding 4-cycles in $00\Gamma_{n-2}$ and $10\Gamma_{n-2}$ uniquely determined by $abcd$. Then for any 2-path on $abcd$, we obtain two different induced 8-cycle in Γ_n. For instance, if we fix the 2-path abc, then the vertices $a, b, c, u_3', u_3, u_2, u_1, u_1'$ and $a, b, c, u_3', u_3, u_4, u_1, u_1'$ form two induced 8-cycles in Γ_n. Therefore the total contribution of this case is $8c_4(n - 3)$.

Case 5: We can use 2-paths in $010\Gamma_{n-3}$ in another way. Any 2-path abc in $010\Gamma_{n-3}$ which is not a part of a 4-cycle in $010\Gamma_{n-3}$, determines a unique 2-path $u'v'w'$ in $00\Gamma_{n-2}$ as shown in Fig. 4.10. The 2-path $u'v'w'$ in turn has its mate uvw in $100\Gamma_{n-3}$ to which it is connected by link edges. The eight vertices on the outside boundary of this subgraph forms an induced 8-cycle. Since abc is not on a 4-cycle, the contribution of this case is $p_2(n - 3) - 4c_4(n - 3)$.

Case 6:   Consider a non-induced 6-cycle formed by the vertices a, b, c, d, e, f in $10\Gamma_{n-2}$. Their mates a', b', c', d', e', f' form a non-induced 6-cycle in $00\Gamma_{n-2}$. In this situation, we obtain eight induced 8-cycles, namely $abcc'd'e'f'a'$, $fedd'c'b'a'f'$, $a'b'c'cdefa$, $f'e'd'dcbaf$, $abcdd'e'f'a'$, $a'b'c'd'defa$, $fedcc'b'a'f'$ and $f'e'd'c'cbaf$. Therefore the total contribution of this case is $8s_6(n - 2)$.

Adding up the contributions, we find that $c_8(n)$ satisfies the recurrence relation

$$c_8(n) = c_8(n - 1) + c_8(n - 2) + 18c_6(n - 2) +$$
$$+ 4c_4(n - 3) + p_2(n - 3) + 8s_6(n - 2)$$

for $n \geq 2$ with $c_8(3) = c_8(4) = 0$. Using the generating functions (4.14), (4.12), (4.11) and (4.15) in conjunction with this recurrence relation, we find the generating function for the number of induced 8-cycles in Γ_n as given below.

Proposition 4.23. [37, Proposition 5] *The generating function of $c_8(n)$ is given by*

$$\sum_{n \geq 0} c_8(n)t^n = \frac{t^5(1 + 22t + 143t^2 - 22t^3 + t^4)}{(1 - t - t^2)^5}. \tag{4.16}$$

A calculation with Mathematica using (4.16) gives a closed form expression for the number of induced 8-cycles in Γ_n as

$$c_8(n) = \tfrac{1}{250}\big((n - 2)(100n^2 - 400n - 21)F_{n+1} +$$
$$+ (70n^4 - 360n^3 + 195n^2 + 458n - 42)F_{n-2}\big).$$

First few values of the sequence of numbers $c_8(n)$ for $n \geq 4$ are

$$0, 1, 27, 273, 1198, 4371, 13551, 38297, 100578, 250278, 596316, \ldots$$

Chapter 5

Counting Substructures of Fibonacci Cubes

The motivation for studying hypercubes, maximal hypercubes, and disjoint hypercubes in Γ_n comes mainly from a related notion with applications in computer science, chemistry and graph theory. In the context of Fibonacci cubes, which are bipartite graphs, hypercubes play the role of cliques; for instance the cardinality of a maximal hypercube in Γ_n can be viewed as an analogue of the clique number, an important structural parameter in graph theory with applications in complexity. In this chapter, we therefore examine and count from different perspectives subgraphs of Fibonacci cubes isomorphic to hypercubes.

5.1 Cube Polynomial

The following result is well-known (see [46] for example).

Proposition 5.1. *In every induced subgraph H of Q_n isomorphic to Q_k there exists a unique vertex of minimal Hamming weight, the bottom vertex $b(H)$. There exists also a unique vertex of maximal Hamming weight, the top vertex $t(H)$. Furthermore $b = b(H)$ and $t = t(H)$ are at distance k and characterize H among the subgraphs of Q_n isomorphic to Q_k.*

If H is an induced subgraph of Γ_n, it is also an induced subgraph of Q_n. Thus Proposition 5.1 is still true for induced subgraphs of Fibonacci cubes. The *support* of an induced hypercube H, supp(H), is the set of k coordinates that vary in H. Therefore,

$$\text{supp}(H) = \{i \in [n] : t_i = 1, b_i = 0\}.$$

H is thus characterized by the couple (t, b) consisting of the top vertex and the bottom vertex of H.

For a graph G, let $c_k(G)$ $(k \geq 0)$ be the number of induced subgraphs of G isomorphic to Q_k. In particular $c_0(G) = n(G)$, $c_1(G) = m(G)$, and $c_2(G)$ is the number of induced 4-cycles. The *cube polynomial*, $C_G(x)$, of G, is the corresponding enumerator polynomial, that is, the generating function

$$C_G(x) = \sum_{k \geq 0} c_k(G) x^k . \tag{5.1}$$

This polynomial was introduced by Brešar, Klavžar, and Škrekovski in [14] where it was observed that it is multiplicative for the Cartesian product of graphs, that is,

$$C_{G \square H}(x) = C_G(x) C_H(x)$$

holds. Moreover, if G is a median graph (see Section 6.3.1 for the definition), then $C_G(-1) = 1$, and $C'_G(-1)$ (the derivative evaluated in -1) is the smallest k such that G isometrically embeds into Q_k.

By direct inspection of Fig. 3.6 we have $C_{\Gamma_6}(x) = 4x^3 + 22x^2 + 38x + 21$. See Table 5.1 for the coefficients of the first few polynomials.

$n \backslash k$	0	1	2	3	4	5	6
0	1	0	0	0	0	0	0
1	2	1	0	0	0	0	0
2	3	2	0	0	0	0	0
3	5	5	1	0	0	0	0
4	8	10	3	0	0	0	0
5	13	20	9	1	0	0	0
6	21	38	22	4	0	0	0
7	34	71	51	14	1	0	0

Table 5.1   The table of coefficients of the cube polynomials $C_{\Gamma_n}(x)$ by rows. The entry in row n, column k is the coefficient $c_k(\Gamma_n)$, the number of k-dimensional hypercubes in Γ_n

Similar to Fibonacci polynomials in Section 2.6, we can consider the generating function of the sequence $(C_{\Gamma_n}(x))_{n \geq 0}$. We have the following result due to Klavžar and Mollard.

Theorem 5.2. [61, Proposition 3.1] *The generating function of the sequence* $(C_{\Gamma_n}(x))_{n \geq 0}$ *is*

$$\sum_{n \geq 0} C_{\Gamma_n}(x) t^n = \frac{1 + (1+x)t}{1 - t - (1+x)t^2} . \tag{5.2}$$

Proof. Clearly, $C_{\Gamma_0}(x) = 1$ and $C_{\Gamma_1}(x) = x + 2$. Let $n \geq 2$ and consider the fundamental decomposition of Γ_n. Then $\mathcal{F}_n^{0\bullet}$, respectively $\mathcal{F}_n^{10\bullet}$, induces a subgraph of Γ_n isomorphic to Γ_{n-1}, respectively to Γ_{n-2}. Moreover, every vertex from $\mathcal{F}_n^{10\bullet}$ has exactly one neighbor in $\mathcal{F}_n^{0\bullet}$ and these edges form a matching. Hence for a subgraph H of Γ_n isomorphic to Q_k we have exactly one of the following exclusive possibilities: (i) H lies in the subgraph induced by $\mathcal{F}_n^{0\bullet}$ or (ii) H lies in the subgraph induced by $\mathcal{F}_n^{10\bullet}$ or (iii) $H = K \mathbin{\square} K_2$, where K is isomorphic to Q_{k-1} and the edges of $K \mathbin{\square} K_2$ corresponding to K_2 are edges between $\mathcal{F}_n^{0\bullet}$ and $\mathcal{F}_n^{10\bullet}$. It follows that for $n \geq 2$,

$$C_{\Gamma_n}(x) = C_{\Gamma_{n-1}}(x) + (1 + x)C_{\Gamma_{n-2}}(x). \tag{5.3}$$

Denoting by $f(x,t)$ the left hand side of (5.2), we obtain

$$f(x,t) - 1 - (x + 2)t = t(f(x,t) - 1) + (1 + x)t^2 f(x,t)$$

and the result follows. $\qquad\square$

Since Q_n can be represented as the Cartesian product of n copies of K_2, and since the cube polynomial is multiplicative for the Cartesian multiplication of graphs, we get:

$$C_{Q_n}(x) = (2 + x)^n = \sum_{m=0}^{n} \binom{n}{m}(1 + x)^m.$$

The parallel result for Fibonacci cubes reads as follows.

Theorem 5.3. [61, Theorem 3.2 and Corollary 3.3] *If $n \geq 0$, then $C_{\Gamma_n}(x)$ is of degree $\left\lfloor \frac{n+1}{2} \right\rfloor$. Moreover,*

$$C_{\Gamma_n}(x) = \sum_{m=0}^{\left\lfloor \frac{n+1}{2} \right\rfloor} \binom{n - m + 1}{m}(1 + x)^m,$$

and the number of induced subgraphs of Γ_n isomorphic to Q_k is

$$c_k(\Gamma_n) = \sum_{i=k}^{\left\lfloor \frac{n+1}{2} \right\rfloor} \binom{n - i + 1}{i}\binom{i}{k}.$$

Proof. Using Theorem 5.2 we have:

$$\sum_{n \geq 0} C_{\Gamma_n}(x)t^n = \frac{1 + (1+x)t}{1 - t - (1+x)t^2} = (1 + (1+x)t)\sum_{m \geq 0}(t + (1+x)t^2)^m$$

$$= \sum_{m \geq 0} t^m(1 + (1+x)t)^{m+1} = \sum_{m \geq 0}\sum_{i=0}^{m+1}\binom{m+1}{i}((1+x)t)^i t^m$$

$$= \sum_{m \geq 0}\sum_{i=0}^{m+1}\sum_{j=0}^{i}\binom{m+1}{i}\binom{i}{j}x^j t^{m+i}$$

$$= \sum_{m \geq 0}\sum_{n=m}^{2m+1}\sum_{j=0}^{n-m}\binom{m+1}{n-m}\binom{n-m}{j}x^j t^n$$

$$= \sum_{n \geq 0}\left(\sum_{m \geq 0}\sum_{j=0}^{n-m}\binom{m+1}{n-m}\binom{n-m}{j}x^j\right)t^n.$$

From here we obtain

$$C_{\Gamma_n}(x) = \sum_{m \geq 0}\sum_{j=0}^{n-m}\binom{m+1}{n-m}\binom{n-m}{j}x^j = \sum_{m \geq 0}\binom{m+1}{n-m}\sum_{j=0}^{n-m}\binom{n-m}{j}x^j$$

$$= \sum_{m \geq 0}\binom{m+1}{n-m}(1+x)^{n-m} = \sum_{m=0}^{n}\binom{m+1}{n-m}(1+x)^{n-m}$$

$$= \sum_{m=0}^{n}\binom{n-m+1}{m}(1+x)^m = \sum_{m=0}^{\lfloor \frac{n+1}{2} \rfloor}\binom{n-m+1}{m}(1+x)^m.$$

This proves the first formula, the second can be read from the first one. □

The expression for $c_k(\Gamma_n)$ from Theorem 5.3 can also be deduced by a combinatorial argument as follows. Let $i \geq k$. There exist $\binom{n-i+1}{i}$ Fibonacci strings u of Hamming weight i. Choose a set K of k coordinates among the i such that $u_i = 1$. A Q_k with top vertex u is induced by the 2^k vertices obtained by varying these k coordinates. Therefore u give rise to $\binom{i}{k}$ different induced k-cubes and the expression for $c_k(\Gamma_n)$ follows.

Let us recall that $c_0(\Gamma_n) = n(\Gamma_n) = F_{n+2}$ and

$$c_1(\Gamma_n) = m(\Gamma_n) = \sum_{i=1}^{n} F_i F_{n-i+1} = \sum_{i=0}^{n} F_{i+1}F_{n-i}.$$

Therefore the sequence $(c_1(\Gamma_n))_{n \geq 0}$ is the convolution of the sequence $(F_{n+1})_{n \geq 0}$ with $(F_n)_{n \geq 0}$ or, equivalently, an offset of the convolution of $(F_n)_{n \geq 0}$ with itself . This remark can be generalized. For any positive integer k it is not difficult to determine the generating function of the sequence $(c_k(\Gamma_n))_{n \geq 0}$ and from its expression to see that this sequence is an offset of k-fold convolution of the sequence $(F_n)_{n\geq 0}$ with itself. As a consequence we obtain:

Corollary 5.4. *If $n \geq 0$, then*

$$c_k(\Gamma_n) = \sum_{\substack{i_0,i_1,\dots,i_k \geq 0 \\ i_0+i_1+\dots+i_k=n-k+2}} F_{i_0} F_{i_1} \cdots F_{i_k}.$$

It is also possible to give a combinatorial interpretation of this formula. We already noted that we can associate, in a bijective way, to any subcube of Γ_n of dimension k its top vertex u and its support, a subset K of order k of the set of coordinates i such that $u_i = 1$. We can associate to the choice of the set K a decomposition of the string $0u$ in $k+1$ Fibonacci substrings beginning with a 0, whose lengths sum to $n - 2k + 1$, two consecutive substrings being separated by 01, where the 1's correspond to the coordinates in K. This construction can be reversed: first we choose the strings, this choice define K and then $0u$ by concatenation, separating them with k substrings 01. Since $|\mathcal{F}_i^{0\bullet}| = |\mathcal{F}_i^{\bullet 0}| = F_{i+1}$ and $F_0 = 0$ increasing the summation variables by 1, the formula follows.

5.1.1 *Roots, Unimodality and Divisibility of $C_{\Gamma_n}(x)$*

Some interesting properties of the cube polynomials of Fibonacci cubes are known. For example the roots of $C_{\Gamma_n}(x)$ are explicitly calculated in [61]. Let's observe an arbitrary row in the Pascal triangle (Fig 1.2). The binomial coefficients are first increasing and then decreasing. We say that the sequence of coefficients of the polynomial $(1 + x)^n$ is *unimodal*. More generally, a sequence $a_0, \dots, a_m$ of real numbers is *unimodal* if for some $j \in \{0, 1, \dots, m\}$ we have

$$a_0 \leq a_1 \leq \cdots \leq a_j \geq a_{j+1} \geq \cdots \geq a_m.$$

This is also the case for the coefficients of $C_{\Gamma_6}(x) = 4x^3 + 22x^2 + 38x + 21$. In the rest of this section we are going to demonstrate that for any n, the sequence of coefficients in $C_{\Gamma_n}(x)$ is unimodal.

For all these results the starting point is the following Binet-like formula (cf. Section 1.9) for $C_{\Gamma_n}(x)$, where by abuse of notation, $\sqrt{y}$ stands for $i\sqrt{|y|}$ for $y < 0$. The formula is proved by standard methods for second order linear recursion applied to (5.3) or by induction.

Theorem 5.5. [61, Theorem 6.2] *Let $x \neq -5/4$. Then*

$$C_{\Gamma_n}(x) = \frac{1}{\sqrt{5+4x}} \left[\left(\frac{1 + \sqrt{5+4x}}{2} \right)^{n+2} - \left(\frac{1 - \sqrt{5+4x}}{2} \right)^{n+2} \right] \qquad (n \geq 0).$$

When $x = -5/4$ we obtain by continuity (or with the standard method when the characteristic polynomial has repeated roots) that

$$C_{\Gamma_n}(-5/4) = \frac{n+2}{2^{n+1}} \neq 0.$$

Therefore Theorem 5.5 covers all possible roots of $C_{\Gamma_n}(x)$.

In order to establish unimodality of coefficients of Fibonacci cube polynomials, we next explicitly determine its zeros.

Proposition 5.6. [61, Proposition 6.4] *The zeros of $C_{\Gamma_n}(x)$, $n \geq 1$, are*

$$-\frac{\tan^2\left(\frac{r\pi}{n+2}\right) + 5}{4}, \quad 1 \leq r \leq \left\lfloor \frac{n+1}{2} \right\rfloor.$$

In particular, all the zeros are simple and are negative reals.

Proof. By Theorem 5.5, zeros of $C_{\Gamma_n}(x)$ are determined by solving

$$\left(1 + \sqrt{5 + 4x}\right)^{n+2} = \left(1 - \sqrt{5 + 4x}\right)^{n+2}.$$

If $x \in \mathbb{R}$ is a zero then $5 + 4x < 0$ must hold. Writing $\sqrt{5 + 4x} = iy$ we need to solve $(1 + iy)^{n+2} = (1 - iy)^{n+2}$. Setting $z = 1 + iy = |z|(\cos\phi + i\sin\phi)$ this reduces to $\sin(n+2)\phi = 0$ so that $y = \tan\phi = \tan(\frac{k\pi}{n+2})$, which gives the zeros. Note that these zeros are all different because $\tan^2(x)$ is strictly increasing on $0 \leq x < \pi/2$.

The degree of $C_{\Gamma_n}(x)$ is $\left\lfloor \frac{n+1}{2} \right\rfloor$ thus we conclude that all zeros are distinct negative reals. $\qquad\square$

A sequence $s_0, s_1, \ldots, s_m$ of positive reals is said to be *logarithmically concave* (or *log-concave* for short) if $s_{i-1}s_{i+1} \leq s_i^2$ for all $0 < i < m$. It is easy to see that a positive log-concave sequence is unimodal. Various additional methods are known for showing the unimodality or log-concavity of a sequence [100]. For our purposes it is important that by a result of Newton, if $s_0, s_1, \ldots, s_m$ is a sequence of coefficients of a polynomial with negative real zeros, then the sequence is is log-concave and therefore also unimodal (see [100, Theorem 2] and the note after the theorem therein).

A consequence of Proposition 5.6 is thus that the sequence of coefficients of $C_{\Gamma_n}(x)$ is unimodal.

Theorem 5.5 and Proposition 5.6 lead to numerous divisibility consequences, for example:

Corollary 5.7. *If $n, k \geq 0$, then $C_{\Gamma_n}(x)$ divides $C_{\Gamma_{k(n+2)+n}}(x)$.*

Proof. Set

$$f(x) = \frac{1 + \sqrt{5 + 4x}}{2} \quad \text{and} \quad g(x) = \frac{1 - \sqrt{5 + 4x}}{2}.$$

Suppose $C_{\Gamma_n}(x_0) = 0$. Then by Theorem 5.5, $f^{n+2}(x_0) = g^{n+2}(x_0)$. It follows that

$$f^{(k+1)(n+2)}(x_0) = g^{(k+1)(n+2)}(x_0),$$

which in turn implies that $C_{\Gamma_{k(n+2)+n}}(x_0) = 0$. Since the zeros of $C_{\Gamma_n}(x)$ are simple, divisibility follows. □

5.2 Maximal Hypercubes in Fibonacci Cubes

A *maximal hypercube* of a graph G is an induced subgraph H isomorphic to a hypercube such that H is not contained in a larger induced hypercube of G. For a given interconnection topology it is important to characterize maximal hypercubes, for example from the point of view of embeddings.

Let $h_k(G)$ be the number of maximal hypercubes of dimension k of G and $H_G(x)$ the corresponding enumerator polynomial, that is,

$$H_G(x) = \sum_{k \geq 0} h_k(G) x^k.$$

As an example, by direct inspection of Fig. 3.6 we have $H_{\Gamma_6}(x) = 4x^3 + x^2$.

Let H be an induced subgraph of Q_n isomorphic to some Q_k. We have already introduced the top vertex t, the bottom vertex b, and the support of H. For $i \notin \text{supp}(H)$, we will denote by $H \bar{\mp} \delta_i$ the subgraph induced by $V(H) \cup \{x + \delta_i : x \in V(H)\}$. Note that $H \bar{\mp} \delta_i$ is isomorphic to Q_{k+1}.

A Fibonacci string can be viewed as blocks of 0s separated by isolated 1s, or as a single 0s possibly separated by isolated 1s. The first point of view gives the decomposition of Fibonacci strings we already met in Proposition 4.3. The second gives the following decomposition.

Proposition 5.8. *Any vertex of Hamming weight w from Γ_n can be uniquely decomposed as $1^{k_0} 0 1^{k_1} \ldots 0 1^{k_i} \ldots 0 1^{k_q}$, where $q = n - w$, $\sum_{i=0}^{q} k_i = w$, and $k_0, \ldots, k_q \leq 1$.*

Using the decomposition of Fibonacci strings as blocks of 0s separated by isolated 1s it is possible to characterize the bottom and top vertices of maximal hypercubes in Γ_n.

Lemma 5.9. *If H is a maximal hypercube of dimension k in Γ_n, then $b(H) = 0^n$ and $t(H) = 0^{l_0} 10^{l_1} \ldots 10^{l_i} \ldots 10^{l_k}$, where $\sum_{i=0}^{k} l_i = n - k$, $l_0, l_k \in \mathcal{B}$, and $l_i \in \{1, 2\}$ for $i \in [k-1]$. Furthermore, any such vertex $t(H)$ is the top vertex of a unique maximal hypercube.*

Proof. Let H be a maximal hypercube in Γ_n. Assume there exists an integer j such that $b(H)_j = 1$. Then $H \widetilde{+} \delta_j$ must be an induced subgraph of Γ_n, which contradicts the maximality of H.

Consider now $t(H) = 0^{l_0} 10^{l_1} \ldots 10^{l_i} \ldots 10^{l_k}$.

Assume that $l_0 \geq 2$. Then for any vertex x of H we have $x_0 = x_1 = 0$, thus $x + \delta_0 \in V(\Gamma_n)$. Therefore H is contained in an induced Q_{k+1} of Γ_n, which again contradicts the maximality of H. The case $l_k \geq 2$ is similar by symmetry.

Assume now $l_i \geq 3$, for some $i \in [k-1]$. Let $j = i + \sum_{p=0}^{i-1} l_p$. We thus have $t(H)_j = 1$ and $t(H)_{j+1} = t(H)_{j+2} = t(H)_{j+3} = 0$. Then for any vertex x of H we have $x_{j+1} = x_{j+2} = x_{j+3} = 0$, thus $x + \delta_{j+2} \in V(\Gamma_n)$ and H is not maximal, a contradiction.

Conversely, consider a vertex $z = 0^{l_0} 10^{l_1} \ldots 10^{l_i} \ldots 10^{l_k}$, where $\sum_{i=0}^{k} l_i = n - k$, $l_0, l_k \in \mathcal{B}$, and $l_i \in \{1, 2\}$ for $i \in [k-1]$. Then the couple $(t(H) = z, b(H) = 0^n)$ defines a unique hypercube H in Q_n isomorphic to Q_k. Clearly all vertices of H are Fibonacci strings. Notice that for any $i \notin \operatorname{supp}(H)$ $z + \delta_i$ is not a Fibonacci string thus H is maximal. $\qquad\square$

The next step is to count binary strings of this kind, that is, top vertices of maximal hypercubes. This will be done by a remarkable bijective argument due to Mollard.

Theorem 5.10. [73, Theorem 2.10] *If $0 \leq k \leq n$, and $h_k(\Gamma_n)$ is the number of maximal hypercubes of dimension k in Γ_n, then*

$$h_k(\Gamma_n) = \binom{k+1}{n - 2k + 1}.$$

Proof. This is clearly true for $k = 0$ so assume $k \geq 1$. Since maximal hypercubes of Γ_n are characterized by their top vertices, let us consider the set T of strings which can be written as $0^{l_0} 10^{l_1} \ldots 10^{l_i} \ldots 10^{l_k}$ where $\sum_{i=0}^{k} l_i = n - k$, $l_0, l_k \in \mathcal{B}$, and $l_i \in \{1, 2\}$ for $i \in [k-1]$. Let $l_i' = l_i - 1$ for $i \in [k-1]$, $l_0' = l_0$, and $l_k' = l_k$. We have thus a one to one mapping between T and the set of strings $D = \{0^{l_0'} 10^{l_1'} \ldots 10^{l_i'} \ldots 10^{l_k'}\}$, where $\sum_{i=0}^{k} l_i' = n - 2k + 1$ with $l_i' \leq 1$ for $i \in \{0, \ldots, k\}$. This set is in bijection with the set $E = \{1^{l_0'} 01^{l_1'} \ldots 01^{l_i'} \ldots 01^{l_k'}\}$. By Proposition 5.8, E is the set of Fibonacci strings of length $n - k + 1$ and Hamming weight $n - 2k + 1$ and we obtain the value of $h_k(\Gamma_n)$. □

Note that $h_k(\Gamma_n) \neq 0$ if and only if $\lceil \frac{n}{3} \rceil \leq k \leq \lfloor \frac{n+1}{2} \rfloor$. As a corollary it is easy to determine the generating function of $H_{\Gamma_n}(x)$.

Corollary 5.11. *[73, Corollary 2.11] Let*

$$H_{\Gamma_n}(x) = \sum_{k \geq 0} h_k(\Gamma_n) x^k$$

denote the enumerator polynomial of the maximal hypercubes of dimension k in Γ_n. Then

$$H_{\Gamma_n}(x) = x\left(H_{\Gamma_{n-2}}(x) + H_{\Gamma_{n-3}}(x)\right) \tag{5.4}$$

for $n \geq 3$ with $H_{\Gamma_0}(x) = 1$, $H_{\Gamma_1}(x) = x$ and $H_{\Gamma_2}(x) = 2x$. The generating function of the sequence $(H_{\Gamma_n}(x))_{n \geq 0}$ is

$$\sum_{n \geq 0} H_{\Gamma_n}(x) t^n = \frac{1 + xt(1+t)}{1 - xt^2(1+t)}. \tag{5.5}$$

Proof. By Theorem 5.10 and Pascal identity we obtain

$$h_k(\Gamma_n) = h_{k-1}(\Gamma_{n-2}) + h_{k-1}(\Gamma_{n-3})$$

for $n \geq 3$ and $k \geq 1$. Note that $h_0(\Gamma_n) = 0$ for $n \neq 0$. The recurrence relation for $H_{\Gamma_n}(x)$ follows. Denoting the left hand side of (5.5) by $f(x,t)$, we deduce from (5.4) the identity

$$f(x,t) - 1 - xt - 2xt^2 = x\left(t^2(f(x,t) - 1) + t^3 f(x,t)\right)$$

and (5.5) follows. □

5.3 Disjoint Hypercubes in Γ_n

In this section we study the maximum number of disjoint subgraphs isomorphic to Q_k of the Fibonacci cube Γ_n. This problem appears naturally in the context of parallel or distributed systems where different tasks occur in parallel on each Q_k without conflict.

Denote the maximum number of disjoint subgraphs isomorphic to Q_k of Γ_n by $q_k(n)$. Note that $q_0(n)$ is the number of vertices of Γ_n. To be able to determine $q_k(n)$, some preparation is needed.

If s is a string of length m, then it will be convenient to denote by $s\Gamma_{n-m}$ the subgraph of Γ_n induced by $\mathcal{F}_n^{s\bullet}$. By the fundamental decomposition, Γ_n, $n \geq 3$, can be partitioned into two subgraphs in the following way. The first subgraph is obtained by adding the canonical perfect matching between $00\Gamma_{n-2}$ and $10\Gamma_{n-2}$. We will denote it by $00\Gamma_{n-2} \equiv 10\Gamma_{n-2}$. The second subgraph is $010\Gamma_{n-3}$. Note that between these two subgraphs, there is the canonical matching between $000\Gamma_{n-3}$ and $010\Gamma_{n-3}$, but in the construction below we shall not need these edges. We use the notation $\dot{\cup}$ to denote the above partition, that is,

$$\Gamma_n = (00\Gamma_{n-2} \equiv 10\Gamma_{n-2}) \,\dot{\cup}\, 010\Gamma_{n-3}.$$

Let q, r be defined by $n = 3q + r$, $q \in \mathbb{N}$, $r \in \{0, 1, 2\}$. We can repeat this process for $010\Gamma_{n-3}$ and more generally for $(010)^i\Gamma_{n-3i}$, $i < q$, and obtain the following partition:

$$\Gamma_n = \overset{\cdot}{\underset{i=1}{\overset{q}{\bigcup}}}\left((010)^{i-1}00\Gamma_{n+1-3i} \equiv (010)^{i-1}10\Gamma_{n+1-3i}\right)\dot{\cup}(010)^q\Gamma_r. \qquad (5.6)$$

We first derive $q_1(n)$, that is, the number of edges in a largest matching of Γ_n.

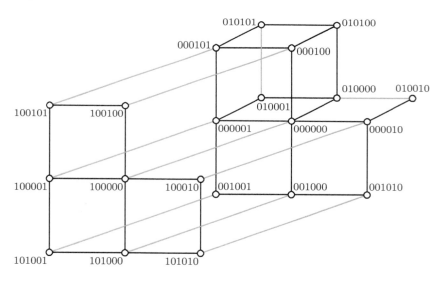

Fig. 5.1 A maximum matching in Γ_6

We have already observed in Section 4.3 that $n(\Gamma_n)$ is even if and only if $n \equiv 1 \pmod 3$. By direct inspection we find a perfect matching in Γ_1 and in Γ_4, and a matching in Γ_2, Γ_3, Γ_5, and in Γ_6 missing only one vertex. In Fig. 5.1 this is illustrated for Γ_6. This is true in general as demonstrated by Gravier, Mollard, Špacapan, and Zemljič.

Lemma 5.12. [43, Lemma 2.1] *For $n \geq 1$, the cardinality of a maximum matching in Γ_n is*

$$q_1(n) = \frac{n(\Gamma_n) - \gamma}{2} = \left\lfloor \tfrac{1}{2}F_{n+2} \right\rfloor ,$$

where $\gamma = 0$ if $n \equiv 1 \, (\mathrm{mod} \, 3)$, and $\gamma = 1$ otherwise.

Proof. By (5.6) each $\left((010)^{i-1}00\Gamma_{n+1-3i} \equiv (010)^{i-1}10\Gamma_{n+1-3i} \right)$ has a perfect matching, and therefore we only need to consider Γ_r. If $r \in \{0, 2\}$, then Γ_r has a maximum matching that misses one vertex. Otherwise $\Gamma_r = \Gamma_1$ has a perfect matching. From this we get the lower bound. The upper bound follows from the parity of $n(\Gamma_n)$. $\qquad\square$

From $F_{n+2} = 2F_n + F_{n-1}$ and $q_0(n) = n(\Gamma_n) = F_{n+2}$, the cardinality of a maximum matching satisfies the recursion

$$q_1(n) = q_0(n-2) + q_1(n-3). \tag{5.7}$$

By similar construction (5.7) can be generalized.

Theorem 5.13. [43, Theorem 2.2] *If $n \geq 3$ and $k \geq 1$, then*

$$q_k(n) = q_{k-1}(n-2) + q_k(n-3). \tag{5.8}$$

Proof. Since the case $k = 1$ is already done, assume $k \geq 2$. Since for $n \leq 2$ $q_k(n) = 0$, (5.8) is equivalent to

$$q_k(n) = \sum_{i=1}^{\lfloor n/3 \rfloor} q_{k-1}(n+1-3i).$$

The lower bound follows directly from (5.6). We construct a family of disjoint k-hypercubes by taking the maximum number of disjoint $(k-1)$-cubes in $00\Gamma_{n-2}$ and connecting each of them with the corresponding $(k-1)$-cube in $10\Gamma_{n-2}$. By doing so, we get $q_{k-1}(n-2)$ k-cubes in $00\Gamma_{n-2} \equiv 10\Gamma_{n-2}$. Then we add the maximum number of k-cubes in $010\Gamma_{n-3} \cong \Gamma_{n-3}$, which is additional $q_k(n-3)$ k-cubes.

To prove the upper bound consider the partition of Γ_n described in (5.6). Let $\mathcal{U}$ be a family of disjoint k-cubes in Γ_n. We claim that

$$\left| \cup \mathcal{U} \cap V\left((010)^{i-1}00\Gamma_{n+1-3i} \equiv (010)^{i-1}10\Gamma_{n+1-3i} \right) \right| \leq 2^k q_{k-1}(n+1-3i). \tag{5.9}$$

To prove this, note that for every k-cube $Q_k \in \mathcal{U}$ we have

$$Q_k \cap \left((010)^{i-1}00\Gamma_{n+1-3i} \equiv (010)^{i-1}10\Gamma_{n+1-3i} \right) \in \{\varnothing, Q_{k-1}, Q_k\},$$

for every $i \leq \lfloor n/3 \rfloor$. Therefore, every k-cube in $\mathcal{U}$ intersects $(010)^{i-1}00\Gamma_{n+1-3i}$ in some number of disjoint $(k-1)$-cubes (every k-cube contained in $(010)^{i-1}00\Gamma_{n+1-3i}$ is regarded as a disjoint union of two $(k-1)$-cubes). This number is at most $q_{k-1}(n+1-3i)$ and hence (5.9) follows. Thus

$$|\cup \mathcal{U} \cap V(\Gamma_n)| \le 2^k \sum_{i=1}^{\lfloor n/3 \rfloor} q_{k-1}(n+1-3i),$$

which completes the proof. □

From Theorem 5.13 it is possible to determine the value of $q_k(n)$ and the generating function of the sequence $(q_k(n))_{n\ge 0}$.

Corollary 5.14. [43, Corollary 2.4] *If $n \ge 0$ and $k \ge 1$, then*

$$q_k(n) = \sum_{i=k-1}^{\lfloor \frac{n+k-2}{3} \rfloor} \binom{i}{k-1} F_{n+k-3i-1}.$$

Corollary 5.15. [43, Corollary 2.5] *If $k \ge 0$, then the generating function of the sequence $(q_k(n))_{n\ge 0}$ is*

$$\sum_{n\ge 0} q_k(n)t^n = \frac{t^{2k-1}}{(1-t^3)^k(1-t-t^2)}. \tag{5.10}$$

A vertex is *covered* by a set of subgraphs if it belongs to at least one of them. The particular case of matchings suggests a conjecture that, for any k, asymptotically all vertices of Γ_n are covered by a maximum set of disjoint subgraphs isomorphic to Q_k. More formally

$$\lim_{n\to\infty} \frac{p_k(n)}{n(\Gamma_n)} = 0, \tag{5.11}$$

where $p_k(n)$ stand for the number of non-covered vertices.

This is true. Indeed let $p_k(n)$ be the number of non-covered vertices. It was first proved by E. Saygı and Eğecioğlu in [91] that $p_k(n)$ is a polynomial of degree at most $k-1$ by a deep study of the generating function of the $q_k(n)$. Later a shorter proof of the same property was obtained by Mollard in [74] proving that for $k \ge 2$, $p_k(n)$ satisfies the recursive relation

$$p_k(n+3) = p_k(n) + 2p_{k-1}(n+1).$$

Since the number of non-covered vertices is polynomial in n for any k and

$$n(\Gamma_n) = F_{n+2} \sim \frac{1}{\sqrt{5}}\varphi^{n+2}$$

by the Binet formula, we obtain the limit (5.11).

5.4   *q*-Cube Enumerator Polynomial

In this section we consider a q-analogue of the cube polynomial of Fibonacci cubes as studied by E. Saygı and Eğecioğlu in [92]. These bivariate polynomials satisfy a recurrence relation similar to the standard one, and at the same time they refine the count of the number of hypercubes of a given dimension in Fibonacci cubes Γ_n. This is done by keeping track of the distances of the hypercubes to the all 0 vertex, that is, the vertex 0^n. The q-cube polynomial $C_{\Gamma_n}(x, q)$ is a refinement of the standard cube polynomial $C_{\Gamma_n}(x)$ studied in Section 5.1. For $q = 1$ they specialize to the standard cube polynomials; in other words $C_{\Gamma_n}(x, 1) = C_{\Gamma_n}(x)$.

5.4.1   *q-Analogues of Fibonacci Numbers*

Consider the q-analogue of the Fibonacci numbers defined by

$$F_n(q) = F_{n-1}(q) + q F_{n-2}(q) \tag{5.12}$$

for $n \geq 2$ with $F_0(q) = 0$ and $F_1(q) = 1$. This q-analogue is simpler than the standard one defined by

$$F_n(q) = F_{n-1}(q) + q^{n-2} F_{n-2}(q)$$

due to Schur, which was studied by Carlitz, Cigler, and others [17, 18, 22]. These are also different from the Fibonacci polynomials considered in Section 2.6.

In this section we use the polynomials $F_n(q)$ as defined by (5.12). The first few $F_n(q)$ are computed as:

$$1, \ 1 + q, \ 1 + 2q, \ 1 + 3q + q^2, \ 1 + 4q + 3q^2, \ 1 + 5q + 6q^2 + q^3, \ \ldots,$$

and their generating function is given by

$$\sum_{n \geq 0} F_n(q) t^n = \frac{t}{1 - t - qt^2}. \tag{5.13}$$

5.4.2   *q-Cube Polynomial*

Let $c_k(\Gamma_n)$ denote the number of k-dimensional hypercubes in the Fibonacci cube Γ_n. As defined in (5.1), the cube polynomial, or the cube enumerator polynomial $C_{\Gamma_n}(x)$ of Γ_n is

$$C_{\Gamma_n}(x) = \sum_{k \geq 0} c_k(\Gamma_n) x^k.$$

Evidently the constant terms are the number of Q_0s, i.e., the number of vertices of Γ_n. Therefore $C_{\Gamma_n}(0) = F_{n+2}$.

It can be observed that the numbers in Table 5.1 satisfy the recursion

$$c_k(\Gamma_n) = c_k(\Gamma_{n-1}) + c_k(\Gamma_{n-2}) + c_{k-1}(\Gamma_{n-2}), \qquad (5.14)$$

which is a consequence of the identity (5.3). The first column entries ($k = 0$) of the table are $F_0, F_1, F_2, \ldots$ and the diagonal entries are $1, 1, 0, 0, \ldots$. Given these, all other entries can be filled row by row by using the recursion (5.14).

The polynomial $C_{\Gamma_n}(x, q)$ is defined as the sum of terms of the form $q^d x^k$, one for each hypercube subgraph of Γ_n. The exponent k is the dimension of the hypercube under consideration, and the exponent d is its distance to the all 0 vertex in Γ_n. By convention, we take $C_0(x, q) = 1$. Recall that the distance between two subgraphs of a graph is the smallest distance between pairs of vertices taken one from each.

It is useful to think of $C_{\Gamma_n}(x, q)$ as a polynomial in x whose coefficients are polynomials in q. We can then write

$$C_{\Gamma_n}(x, q) = \sum_{k \geq 0} c_{n,k}(q) x^k .$$

First few $C_{\Gamma_n}(x, q)$ are as follows:

$$C_{\Gamma_0}(x, q) = 1,$$
$$C_{\Gamma_1}(x, q) = 1 + q + x,$$
$$C_{\Gamma_2}(x, q) = 1 + 2q + 2x,$$
$$C_{\Gamma_3}(x, q) = 1 + 3q + q^2 + (3 + 2q)x + x^2,$$
$$C_{\Gamma_4}(x, q) = 1 + 4q + 3q^2 + (4 + 6q)x + 3x^2 .$$

5.4.3   *Example Calculations*

We illustrate the structure of $C_{\Gamma_2}(x, q)$ and $C_{\Gamma_3}(x, q)$ in detail.

Calculation of $C_{\Gamma_2}(x, q)$.
There are three vertices and two edges in Γ_2. The 0-dimensional hypercubes are the vertices of the graph. There is a single vertex having distance 0 to the vertex 00 (i.e., 00 itself) and there are two vertices having distance 1. Therefore the coefficient of x^0 in $C_{\Gamma_2}(x, q)$ is $1 + 2q$. Similarly, 1-dimensional hypercubes are the edges of the graph and there are a total of two of those, each having distance 0 to the vertex 00. Therefore the coefficient of x^1 is 2. This gives $C_{\Gamma_2}(x, q) = 1 + 2q + 2x$.

Calculation of $C_{\Gamma_3}(x, q)$.
To construct $C_{\Gamma_3}(x, q)$ we consider all hypercubes in Γ_3 of dimension $k < 3$

and their distances to the 000. For $k = 0$ we know that there are five vertices in the graph giving 0-dimensional hypercubes. The vertex 000 has distance 0, the vertices 010, 100 and 001 each have distance 1 and the vertex 101 has distance 2 to 000. So the coefficient of x^0 is $1 + 3q + q^2$.

Now consider $k = 1$, that is, 1-dimensional hypercubes in the graph. We know that they are the edges of the graph and from Fig. 5.2 we see that there are three with distance 0 and two with distance 1 to the vertex 000. So the coefficient of x^1 in $C_{\Gamma_3}(x, q)$ is $3 + 2q$.

Finally consider $k = 2$. There is only one 2-dimensional hypercube in Γ_3 and this hypercube contains the vertex 000. So the contribution from 2-dimensional subcubes is x^2. Therefore

$$C_{\Gamma_3}(x, q) = (1 + 3q + q^2) + (3 + 2q)x + x^2 .$$

A graphical presentation of these hypercubes in Γ_3 and their contribution to $C_{\Gamma_3}(x, q)$ is presented in Fig. 5.2.

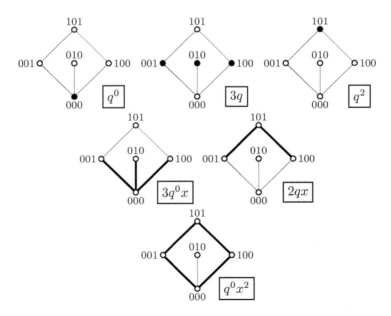

Fig. 5.2 The elements of the calculation of the q-cube polynomial $C_{\Gamma_3}(x, q) = (1 + 3q + q^2) + (3 + 2q)x + x^2$

5.4.4 The Main Recursion

The following recursion allows for the calculation of the polynomials $C_{\Gamma_n}(x, q)$.

Lemma 5.16. [92, Lemma 1] *If $n \geq 2$, then*

$$C_{\Gamma_n}(x, q) = C_{\Gamma_{n-1}}(x, q) + (q + x)C_{\Gamma_{n-2}}(x, q) \tag{5.15}$$

with $C_{\Gamma_0}(x, q) = 1$ and $C_{\Gamma_1}(x, q) = 1 + q + x$.

Proof. We have $C_{\Gamma_2}(x, q) = 1 + 2q + 2x = C_{\Gamma_1}(x, q) + (q + x)C_{\Gamma_0}(x, q)$. We make use of the fundamental decomposition of Γ_n and use induction on n. There are three kinds of hypercubes in Γ_n.

Case 1: A k-dimensional hypercube in Γ_{n-1} remains a k-dimensional hypercube in Γ_n and the distances of these cubes to the all 0 vertex remain unchanged. By induction, these are enumerated by $C_{\Gamma_{n-1}}(x, q)$.

Case 2: Any k-dimensional hypercube in Γ_{n-2} is again a k-dimensional hypercube in Γ_n, and the distances of these cubes in Γ_n to the all 0 vertex go up by 1 due to the matching edges identifying the vertices in Γ_{n-2} to its copy Γ'_{n-2} in Γ_n. This increase in the distance to the all 0 vertex by 1 means multiplication by q, and the contribution of these hypercubes is $qC_{\Gamma_{n-2}}(x, q)$.

Case 3: A k-dimensional hypercube in Γ_{n-2} has an isomorphic copy in Γ'_{n-2} and all the corresponding vertices of these k-dimensional hypercubes are connected by the matching edges. Therefore these two k-dimensional hypercubes together with the edges connecting them gives a $(k+1)$-dimensional hypercube in Γ_n. The distances of these cubes to the all 0 vertex remain unchanged. The contribution of these hypercubes is $xC_{\Gamma_{n-2}}(x, q)$, since multiplication by x has the effect of increasing the dimension by 1. Adding up these three contributions we obtain (5.15). $\square$

Proposition 5.17. [92, Proposition 1] *The generating function of the q-cube polynomial $C_{\Gamma_n}(x, q)$ is*

$$\sum_{n \geq 0} C_{\Gamma_n}(x, q)t^n = \frac{1 + (q + x)t}{1 - t - (q + x)t^2}. \tag{5.16}$$

Proof. Let S denote the left hand side of (5.16). Then $C_{\Gamma_0}(x, q) = 1$, $C_{\Gamma_1}(x, q) = 1 + q + x$, and by a routine calculation using (5.15), S satisfies

$$S - 1 - (1 + q + x)t = t(S - 1) + (q + x)t^2 S,$$

which gives the desired result. $\square$

We can solve the recursion in (5.15) directly to find $C_{\Gamma_n}(x,q)$.

Theorem 5.18. [92, Theorem 1] *For any non-negative integer n, the q-cube polynomial $C_{\Gamma_n}(x,q)$ has degree $\left\lfloor \frac{n+1}{2} \right\rfloor$ in x and is given explicitly as*

$$C_{\Gamma_n}(x,q) = \frac{1}{2^{n+1}} \sum_{i=0}^{\left\lfloor \frac{n+1}{2} \right\rfloor} \binom{n+2}{2i+1} (1 + 4(q+x))^i . \tag{5.17}$$

Proof. The characteristic equation of the recursion in (5.15) is

$$r^2 - r - (q+x) = 0.$$

This equation gives an explicit expression in the form

$$C_{\Gamma_n}(x,q) = \frac{(1+\theta)^{n+2} - (1-\theta)^{n+2}}{2^{n+2}\theta},$$

where $\theta = \sqrt{1 + 4(q+x)}$. Using binomial expansions for $(1 \pm \theta)^{n+2}$ followed by some algebraic manipulation, we obtain the expresion in (5.17). ☐

A few of the coefficient polynomials $c_{n,k}(q)$ of the q-cube polynomial $C_{\Gamma_n}(x,q)$ are given in Table 5.2.

$n \backslash k$	0	1	2	3	4
0	1	0	0	0	0
1	$1+q$	1	0	0	0
2	$1+2q$	2	0	0	0
3	$1+3q+q^2$	$3+2q$	1	0	0
4	$1+4q+3q^2$	$4+6q$	3	0	0
5	$1+5q+6q^2+q^3$	$5+12q+3q^2$	$6+3q$	1	0
6	$1+6q+10q^2+4q^3$	$6+20q+12q^2$	$10+12q$	4	0
7	$1+7q+15q^2+10q^3+q^4$	$7+30q+30q^2+4q^3$	$15+30q+6q^2$	$10+4q$	1

Table 5.2 The table of coefficients of the q-cube polynomials $C_{\Gamma_n}(x,q)$ by rows. The entry in row n and column k is the coefficient polynomial $c_{n,k}(q)$

5.4.5 Convolutions

The main result relating the $c_{n,k}(q)$ and the q-analogue of the Fibonacci numbers is a generalization of Corollary 5.4.

Proposition 5.19. [92, Proposition 2] *The coefficient polynomials $c_{n,k}(q)$ of the q-cube enumerator $C_{\Gamma_n}(x,q)$ are given by*

$$c_{n,k}(q) = \sum_{\substack{i_0,i_1,\ldots,i_k \geq 0 \\ i_0+i_1+\cdots+i_k = n-k+2}} F_{i_0}(q) F_{i_1}(q) \cdots F_{i_k}(q) .$$

Proof. Using (5.13), the $(k+1)$-fold convolutions of the $F_n(q)$ have the generating function

$$\frac{t^{k+1}}{(1-t-qt^2)^{k+1}} . \qquad (5.18)$$

Setting

$$g_0(t,q) = \frac{t^{-1}}{(1-t-qt^2)} - \frac{1}{t} \quad \text{and} \quad g_k(t,q) = \frac{t^{2k-1}}{(1-t-qt^2)^{k+1}} \quad (k \geq 1)$$

and calculating directly, we find

$$\sum_{k\geq 0} g_k(t,q)x^k = -\frac{1}{t} + \frac{1}{t(1-t-qt^2)} \sum_{k\geq 0} \left(\frac{xt^2}{1-t-qt^2} \right)^k$$

$$= \frac{1+(q+x)t}{1-t-(q+x)t^2} .$$

By Proposition 5.17, this is the generating function of the $C_{\Gamma_n}(x,q)$. Therefore the $g_k(t,q)$ are the generating functions of the columns of Table 5.2. This proves the proposition by equating the coefficients of $t^n x^k$ in the two expressions. $\qquad \square$

We have the following explicit expression for $c_{n,k}(q)$.

Proposition 5.20. [92, Proposition 1] *The coefficient polynomials $c_{n,k}(q)$ of the q-cube enumerator $C_{\Gamma_n}(x,q)$ of Γ_n are given by*

$$c_{n,k}(q) = \sum_{i=0}^{\lfloor \frac{n+1}{2} \rfloor} \binom{n-i+1-k}{i+k}\binom{i+k}{k}q^i .$$

The above proposition can be proved directly from the recurrence in (5.12), by using induction on k, and verifying a binomial identity.

5.4.6   *Divisibility Properties of $C_{\Gamma_n}(x,q)$*

In this section we present divisibility properties of the q-cube polynomials of the Fibonacci cubes. We start with some examples.

The polynomial $C_{\Gamma_1}(x,q) = 1 + q + x$ divides $C_{\Gamma_4}(x,q)$, $C_{\Gamma_7}(x,q)$, and $C_{\Gamma_{10}}(x,q)$ since

$$C_{\Gamma_4}(x,q) = C_{\Gamma_1}(x,q)(1+3q+3x),$$

$$C_{\Gamma_7}(x,q) = C_{\Gamma_1}(x,q)\left(1+6q+9q^2+q^3+(6+18q+3q^2)x+(9+3q)x^2+x^3\right),$$

$$C_{\Gamma_{10}}(x,q) = C_{\Gamma_1}(x,q)\left(1+9q+27q^2+29q^3+6q^4+(9+54q+87q^2+24q^3)x\right.$$

$$\left. +(27+87q+36q^2)x^2+(29+24q)x^3+6x^4\right).$$

Similarly, $C_{\Gamma_2}(x,q) = 1 + 2q + 2x$ divides $C_{\Gamma_6}(x,q)$ and $C_{\Gamma_{10}}(x,q)$ since

$$C_{\Gamma_6}(x,q) = C_{\Gamma_2}(x,q)\left(1 + 4q + 2q^2 + (4+4q)x + 2x^2\right),$$
$$C_{\Gamma_{10}}(x,q) = C_{\Gamma_2}(x,q)\left(1 + 8q + 20q^2 + 16q^3 + 3q^4 + (8 + 40q + 48q^2 + 12q^3)x\right.$$
$$\left. + (20 + 48q + 18q^2)x^2 + (16 + 12q)x^3 + 3x^4\right).$$

Next, $C_{\Gamma_3}(x,q) = 1 + 3q + q^2 + (3+2q)x + x^2$ divides $C_{\Gamma_8}(x,q)$ and $C_{\Gamma_{13}}(x,q)$ since

$$C_{\Gamma_8}(x,q) = C_{\Gamma_3}(x,q)(1 + 5q + 5q^2 + (5 + 10q)x + 5x^2),$$
$$C_{\Gamma_{13}}(x,q) = C_{\Gamma_3}(x,q)(1 + 10q + 35q^2 + 50q^3 + 25q^4 + q^5$$
$$+ (10 + 70q + 150q^2 + 100q^3 + 5q^4)x + (35 + 150q + 150q^2 + 10q^3)x^2$$
$$+ (50 + 100q + 10q^2)x^3 + (25 + 5q)x^4 + x^5).$$

The above examples hint at certain divisibility properties for the q-cube polynomials of the Fibonacci cubes. Also, the coefficients of the polynomials x^k on the right hand side seem to be polynomials in q with non-negative integral coefficients. These observations are proved in the following theorem.

Theorem 5.21. [92, Theorem 2] *For any $m \geq 0$, $C_{\Gamma_m}(x,q)$ divides $C_{\Gamma_{(m+2)n+m}}(x,q)$ as a polynomial in x for $n \geq 0$. Furthermore, the coefficients of powers of x in the quotient are polynomials in q with non-negative integral coefficients.*

The constant term of the quotient can be written as

$$\frac{C_{\Gamma_{(m+2)n+m}}(0,q)}{C_{\Gamma_m}(0,q)} = \frac{F_{(m+2)n+m+2}(q)}{F_{m+2}(q)}.$$

The integrality of the quotient implies that in particular $F_m(q) \mid F_{mn}(q)$ for $m, n \geq 1$. If we take $q = 1$, this reduces to the well-known divisibility result [105] of Fibonacci numbers $F_m \mid F_{mn}$ for $m, n \geq 1$.

Letting $q = 1$, we obtain from Theorem 5.21 that for any $m \geq 0$, $C_{\Gamma_m}(x) \mid C_{\Gamma_{(m+2)n+m}}(x)$ for $n \geq 0$ which was given in Corollary 5.7. Theorem 5.21 shows that the quotient polynomials have only non-negative integer coefficients.

Evidently, the quotients of the q-cube polynomials carry interesting combinatorial information as the coefficients polynomials are all integral and have non-negative coefficients.

5.5　Boundary Enumerator Polynomial

The material we present here can be viewed as the generalization of the sequence of degrees presented in Section 3.6.

We consider the number of edges in the boundary of hypercubes in Γ_n. For a graph G and a subset $X \subseteq V(G)$, there are two standard ways to define the boundary of X in G: *the vertex-boundary* or *the edge-boundary*. The vertex-boundary ∂X of X is the set of vertices that are not in X but adjacent to some vertex in X. In other words

$$\partial X = \{v \in V(G) \setminus X : v \text{ is adjacent to some } u \in X\}.$$

The edge-boundary $\partial_e X$ of X is the set of edges in $E(G)$ which connect vertices in X with vertices in $V(G) \setminus X$, that is,

$$\partial_e X = \{uv \in E(G) : u \in X, v \in V(G) \setminus X\}.$$

We use the term *boundary* for edge-boundary.

Note that in the case we are considering for $G = \Gamma_n$, $H = Q_k$ for some non-negative integer k and X as the vertex set of H, by the structure of $\Gamma_n \subseteq Q_n$ and $H = Q_k$, a vertex $v \in \partial X$ is adjacent to the vertex $u \in X$ by a unique edge $uv \in E(\Gamma_n)$. This means $|\partial X| = |\partial_e X|$. This is not true for arbitrary G and X, since a vertex in the vertex-boundary of X can be joined to more than one vertex in X.

Let $\mathbb{D}_{n,k}(d)$ be the polynomial that enumerates the boundary of the hypercubes Q_k in Γ_n. The degree of any monomial in $\mathbb{D}_{n,k}(d)$ shows the number of edges in the boundary of the corresponding Q_k and the coefficient of that monomial is the number of such hypercubes.

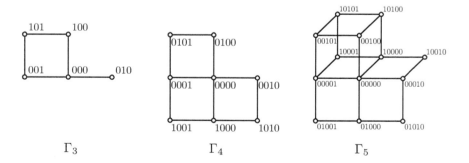

Fig. 5.3　Fibonacci cubes Γ_3, Γ_4 and Γ_5

As an example, in Γ_5 there are only 0, 1, 2 and 3-dimensional hypercubes as we can see in Fig. 5.3. So need to consider only $\mathbb{D}_{5,k}(d)$ for $k \in \{0, 1, 2, 3\}$.

Again from Fig. 5.3, Γ_5 has 13 vertices, three of them have degree 2; seven of them have degree 3; two of them have degree 4; and one of them has degree 5. Similarly, there is only one 3-dimensional cube with four edges in its boundary. Hence,

$$\mathbb{D}_{5,0}(d) = 3d^2 + 7d^3 + 2d^4 + d^5 ,$$
$$\mathbb{D}_{5,3}(d) = d^4 .$$

Similarly, by considering the edges and squares in Γ_5 by inspection, we obtain

$$\mathbb{D}_{5,1}(d) = 4d^3 + 7d^4 + 4d^5 + 3d^6 + 2d^7 ,$$
$$\mathbb{D}_{5,2}(d) = d^4 + 3d^5 + 2d^6 + 2d^7 + d^8 .$$

Let $\mathbb{C}_{n,k}(d)$ denote the boundary enumerator polynomial of the hypercubes Q_k in Γ_n that are obtained during the connection of Γ_{n-1} and Γ_{n-2}. In other words, these hypercubes involve link edges. The polynomials $\mathbb{C}_{n,k}$ arise in the recursive computation of $\mathbb{D}_{n,k}$ in which we are actually interested.

Table 5.3 is a list of the boundary enumerator polynomials $\mathbb{D}_{n,k}$ and $\mathbb{C}_{n,k}$ for small values of n and k.

n \ k	$\mathbb{D}_{n,0}$	$\mathbb{C}_{n,1}$	$\mathbb{D}_{n,1}$	$\mathbb{C}_{n,2}$	$\mathbb{D}_{n,2}$
0	1	0	0	0	0
1	$2d$	1	1	0	0
2	$2d + d^2$	d	$2d$	0	0
3	$d + 3d^2 + d^3$	$d^2 + d^3$	$3d^2 + 2d^3$	d	d
4	$5d^2 + 2d^3 + d^4$	$d^2 + d^3 + d^5$	$2d^2 + 4d^3 + 2d^4 + 2d^5$	$d^3 + d^4$	$2d^3 + d^4$

Table 5.3   The boundary enumerator polynomials $\mathbb{D}_{n,k}$ and $\mathbb{C}_{n,k}$ for small values of n and k

5.5.1   *An Example*

Now, for $k \in \mathcal{B}$ we present a counting method to find $\mathbb{D}_{5,k}(d)$ by using the fundamental decomposition of Fibonacci cubes recursively. This idea can be generalized to obtain a recursion for $\mathbb{D}_{n,k}(d)$ for any non-negative integer n and k as given in Theorem 5.22.

Consider $k = 0$. From the fundamental decomposition we know that

$$\Gamma_5 = 0\Gamma_4 + 10\Gamma_3 = (00\Gamma_3 + 010\Gamma_2) + 10\Gamma_3 . \tag{5.19}$$

Let v be any vertex in Γ_5. Then we have two cases:

(i) Assume that $v \in 10\Gamma_3$. If we consider all $v \in \Gamma_3$, then the boundary enumerator becomes $\mathbb{D}_{3,0}(d)$. The degrees of these vertices increase by 1 in Γ_5. Therefore all of these vertices contribute $d\,\mathbb{D}_{3,0}(d)$ to $\mathbb{D}_{5,0}(d)$.

(ii) Assume that $v \in 0\Gamma_4$. Then there are two subcases:

  (a) Assume that $v \in 010\Gamma_2$. If we consider all $v \in \Gamma_2$, then the boundary enumerator becomes $\mathbb{D}_{2,0}(d)$. Similarly we see that degrees of these vertices again increase by 1 in $0\Gamma_4$ and Γ_5. Therefore these vertices contribute $d\,\mathbb{D}_{2,0}(d)$ to $\mathbb{D}_{4,0}(d)$ and $\mathbb{D}_{5,0}(d)$.

  (b) Assume that $v \in 0\Gamma_4 \smallsetminus 010\Gamma_2$. If we consider all such vertices in Γ_4 then we have $\mathbb{D}_{4,0}(d) - d\,\mathbb{D}_{2,0}(d)$ from the previous subcase. Also the degrees of these vertices again increase by 1 in Γ_5. Therefore, such vertices contribute $d\,(\mathbb{D}_{4,0}(d) - d\,\mathbb{D}_{2,0}(d))$ to $\mathbb{D}_{5,0}(d)$.

Therefore, in total we have

$$\mathbb{D}_{5,0}(d) = d\,\mathbb{D}_{3,0}(d) + d\,\mathbb{D}_{2,0}(d) + d\,(\mathbb{D}_{4,0}(d) - d\,\mathbb{D}_{2,0}(d))$$
$$= d\,(\mathbb{D}_{4,0}(d) + \mathbb{D}_{3,0}(d) + (1-d)\,\mathbb{D}_{2,0}(d))\,.$$

Consider $k = 1$. In this case we will use the decomposition of Γ_5 given in (5.19) again. Let e be any edge in Γ_5. This time we have three cases:

(i) Assume that $e \in 10\Gamma_3$. If we consider all $e \in \Gamma_3$ then the boundary enumerator becomes $\mathbb{D}_{3,1}(d)$. The degrees of vertices of these edges increase by 1 in Γ_5, that is, the boundary of the edges increase by 2. Therefore all of these edges contribute $d^2\,\mathbb{D}_{3,1}(d)$ to $\mathbb{D}_{5,1}(d)$.

(ii) Assume that $e = v_1 v_2 \in \Gamma_5$ with $v_1 \in 10\Gamma_3$ and $v_2 \in 0\Gamma_4$ (in particular $v_2 \in 00\Gamma_3$). These edges are not in Γ_m for $m < 5$ and they first occur when we connect Γ_4 and Γ_3 to obtain Γ_5. We denote the contribution of these edges to $\mathbb{D}_{5,1}(d)$ by $\mathbb{C}_{5,1}(d)$. We will consider this case later in detail.

(iii) Assume that $e \in 0\Gamma_4$. Since $0\Gamma_4 = 00\Gamma_3 + 010\Gamma_2$ we have three subcases:

  (a) Assume that $e \in 010\Gamma_2$. Considering all $e \in \Gamma_2$ we have $\mathbb{D}_{2,1}(d)$ and we see that the boundary of these edges increases by 2 in Γ_5. Therefore all of these edges contribute $d^2\,\mathbb{D}_{2,1}(d)$ to $\mathbb{D}_{5,1}(d)$.

  (b) Assume that $e = v_1 v_2 \in 0\Gamma_4$ with $v_1 \in 010\Gamma_2$ and $v_2 \in 00\Gamma_3$. These edges are not in Γ_m for $m < 4$ and they first occur when we connect Γ_3 and Γ_2 to obtain Γ_4. Then as we need to consider $e \in \Gamma_5$ we see that the degree of v_2 increases by 1 when we connect $0\Gamma_4$ and $10\Gamma_3$ to obtain Γ_5. Then as in the above Case 2, the contribution of these edges to $\mathbb{D}_{5,1}(d)$ becomes $d\,\mathbb{C}_{4,1}(d)$.

(c) Assume that $e \in 00\Gamma_3$. Then one can observe that these edges are the ones in $0\Gamma_4$ that are not in $010\Gamma_2$ and that are not occur as connection edges between $00\Gamma_3$ and $010\Gamma_2$. Also note that the boundary of these edges increases by 2 during the connection of $0\Gamma_4$ and $10\Gamma_3$ to obtain Γ_5. Therefore, the contribution of these edges to $\mathbb{D}_{5,1}(d)$ becomes $d^2\big(\mathbb{D}_{4,1}(d) - d^2\,\mathbb{D}_{2,1}(d) - \mathbb{C}_{4,1}(d)\big)$.

Therefore, in total we have

$$\begin{aligned}
\mathbb{D}_{5,1}(d) &= d^2\,\mathbb{D}_{3,1}(d) + \mathbb{C}_{5,1}(d) + d^2\,\mathbb{D}_{2,1}(d) + d\,\mathbb{C}_{4,1}(d) \\
&\quad + d^2\big(\mathbb{D}_{4,1}(d) - d^2\,\mathbb{D}_{2,1}(d) - \mathbb{C}_{4,1}(d)\big) \\
&= d^2\big(\mathbb{D}_{4,1}(d) + \mathbb{D}_{3,1}(d) + (1 - d^2)\,\mathbb{D}_{2,1}(d)\big) \\
&\quad + \mathbb{C}_{5,1}(d) + (d - d^2)\,\mathbb{C}_{4,1}(d).
\end{aligned}$$

Now let us consider $\mathbb{C}_{5,1}(d)$ in detail. This number enumerates the boundary of the edges e that first occur during the connection of $0\Gamma_4$ and $10\Gamma_3$ to obtain Γ_5. From the fundamental decomposition we have

$$\begin{aligned}
\Gamma_5 = 0\Gamma_4 + 10\Gamma_3 &= (00\Gamma_3 + 010\Gamma_2) + 10\Gamma_3 \\
&= \big((000\Gamma_2 + 0010\Gamma_1) + 010\Gamma_2\big) + (100\Gamma_2 + 1010\Gamma_1).
\end{aligned}$$

Assume that $e = v_1 v_2$ with $v_1 \in 0\Gamma_4$ and $v_2 \in 10\Gamma_3$. We have the two different cases.

(i) Assume $v_2 \in 1010\Gamma_1$. Then $v_1 \in 0010\Gamma_1$ and the degrees of all such vertices in Γ_1 are $\mathbb{D}_{1,0}(d)$ and therefore they becomes $d\,\mathbb{D}_{1,0}(d)$ in both $10\Gamma_3$ and $0\Gamma_4$. So, the boundary of all such edges becomes $d^2\,\mathbb{D}_{1,0}(d^2)$ in Γ_5.

(ii) Assume $v_2 \in 100\Gamma_2$. Then $v_1 \in 000\Gamma_2$ and the degrees of all such vertices in $00\Gamma_3$ are $\mathbb{D}_{3,0}(d) - d\,\mathbb{D}_{1,0}(d)$ as $00\Gamma_3 = 000\Gamma_2 + 0010\Gamma_1$. But note that the degree of v_1 becomes $d\,(\mathbb{D}_{3,0}(d) - d\,\mathbb{D}_{1,0}(d))$ in $0\Gamma_4$. So, the boundary of all such edges becomes $d\,\big(\mathbb{D}_{3,0}(d^2) - d^2\,\mathbb{D}_{1,0}(d^2)\big)$ in Γ_5.

If we sum up we have

$$\begin{aligned}
\mathbb{C}_{5,1}(d) &= d^2\,\mathbb{D}_{1,0}(d^2) + d\,\big(\mathbb{D}_{3,0}(d^2) - d^2\,\mathbb{D}_{1,0}(d^2)\big) \\
&= d\,\mathbb{D}_{3,0}(d^2) + \big(d^2 - d^3\big)\,\mathbb{D}_{1,0}(d^2).
\end{aligned}$$

By the same argument we have $\mathbb{C}_{4,1}(d) = d\,\mathbb{D}_{2,0}(d^2) + (d^2 - d^3)\,\mathbb{D}_{0,0}(d^2)$.

Along similar lines, two recursions relating $\mathbb{D}_{n,k}$ and $\mathbb{C}_{n,k}$ can be constructed. The rather technical proof of the following result is due to E. Saygı and Eğecioğlu and appears in [94].

Theorem 5.22. [94, Theorem 1] *Let n, k be non-negative integers and let $\mathbb{D}_{n,k}(d)$ be the boundary enumerator polynomial of the k-dimensional hypercubes in Γ_n and $\mathbb{C}_{n,k}(d)$ be the boundary enumerator polynomial of the k-dimensional hypercubes in Γ_n that are obtained during the connection of Γ_{n-1} and Γ_{n-2}. Then for $n \geq 3$ and $k \geq 0$ we have*

$$\mathbb{D}_{n,k}(d) = d^{2^k}\left(\mathbb{D}_{n-1,k}(d) + \mathbb{D}_{n-2,k}(d) + \left(1 - d^{2^k}\right)\mathbb{D}_{n-3,k}(d)\right) + \mathbb{C}_{n,k}(d)$$
$$+ \left(d^{2^{k-1}} - d^{2^k}\right)\mathbb{C}_{n-1,k}(d)\,,$$

and for $n \geq 4$ and $k \geq 1$,

$$\mathbb{C}_{n,k}(d) = d^{2^k}\left(1 - d^{2^{k-1}}\right)\mathbb{D}_{n-4,k-1}(d^2) + d^{2^{k-2}}\left(1 - d^{2^{k-2}}\right)\mathbb{C}_{n-2,k-1}(d^2)$$
$$+ d^{2^{k-1}}\mathbb{D}_{n-2,k-1}(d^2)\,,$$

where the initial conditions are given in Table 5.3 and $\mathbb{D}_{m,k}(d) = \mathbb{C}_{m,k}(d) = 0$ for $m < 2k - 1$.

Let $f_{n,m}$ denote the number of vertices of Γ_n having degree m. In [65, Section 6], the generating function $f(x,y) = \sum_{n,m \geq 0} f_{n,m} x^n y^m$ is obtained. From the denominator of $f(x,y)$ we know that $f_{n,m}$ satisfies the recursion

$$f_{n,m} = f_{n-1,m-1} + f_{n-2,m-1} + f_{n-3,m-1} - f_{n-3,m-2} \qquad (5.20)$$

for all large enough n and m. Note that (5.20) corresponds to the $k = 0$ case, that is, it can be written in the form

$$\mathbb{D}_{n,0}(d) = d\left(\mathbb{D}_{n-1,0}(d) + \mathbb{D}_{n-2,0}(d) + \mathbb{D}_{n-3,0}(d)\right) - d^2\,D_{n-3,0}(d)\,.$$

5.5.2   *Derivation of the Generating Function*

Using Theorem 5.22 one can obtain the generating functions for $\mathbb{D}_{n,k}(d)$ and $\mathbb{C}_{n,k}(d)$.

Theorem 5.23. *Let $D_k(d,t) = \displaystyle\sum_{n \geq 0} \mathbb{D}_{n,k}(d)t^n$ and $C_k(d,t) = \displaystyle\sum_{n \geq 0} \mathbb{C}_{n,k}(d)t^n$*

be the generating functions of $\mathbb{D}_{n,k}(d)$ and $\mathbb{C}_{n,k}(d)$. Then we have

$$D_0(d,t) = \frac{1 + dt + (d - d^2)t^2}{1 - dt - dt^2 - (d - d^2)t^3},$$

$$C_k(d,t) = \frac{d^{(k-1)2^{k-2}} t^{2k-1} \left(1 + \left(d^{2^{k-1}} - d^{2^k}\right)t\right) \left(f(d^{2^k}, t)\right)^{k-1}}{\left(g(d^{2^k}, t)\right)^k},$$

$$D_k(d,t) = \frac{d^{(k-1)2^{k-2}} t^{2k-1} \left(1 + \left(d^{2^{k-1}} - d^{2^k}\right)t\right)^2 \left(f(d^{2^k}, t)\right)^{k-1}}{\left(g(d^{2^k}, t)\right)^{k+1}},$$

where

$$f(d,t) = 1 + \left(d^3 - d^4\right)\left(t + t^2\right) - d^4 \left(1 - 2d + 2d^3 - d^4\right) t^3 \quad \text{and}$$
$$g(d,t) = 1 - d\left(t + t^2 + t^3\right) + d^2 t^3.$$

Proof. For $k = 0$ and $n \geq 3$, using Theorem 5.22, we have

$$\mathbb{D}_{n,0}(d) = d\left(\mathbb{D}_{n-1,0}(d) + \mathbb{D}_{n-2,0}(d) + (1 - d)\,\mathbb{D}_{n-3,0}(d)\right).$$

Using the initial conditions given in Table 5.3 we get

$$D_0(d,t) - (2d + d^2)t^2 - 2dt - 1$$
$$= dt\,(D_0(d,t) - 2dt - 1) + dt^2\,(D_0(d,t) - 1) + d(1 - d)t^3 D_0(d,t),$$

which gives the desired result for $D_0(d,t)$. Similarly, using Theorem 5.22 for $k = 1$ and $n \geq 4$ we have

$$\mathbb{C}_{n,1}(d) = d^2\,(1 - d)\,\mathbb{D}_{n-4,0}(d^2) + d\mathbb{D}_{n-2,0}(d^2),$$

which gives

$$C_1(d,t) - (d^2 + d^3)t^3 - dt^2 - t = d^2\,(1 - d)\,t^4 D_0(d^2, t)$$
$$+ dt^2(D_0(d^2, t) - 2d^2 t - 1). \qquad (5.21)$$

For $k = 1$ and $n \geq 3$ we have

$$\mathbb{D}_{n,1}(d) = d^2\left(\mathbb{D}_{n-1,1}(d) + \mathbb{D}_{n-2,1}(d) + \left(1 - d^2\right)\mathbb{D}_{n-3,1}(d)\right) +$$
$$\mathbb{C}_{n,1}(d) + \left(d - d^2\right)\mathbb{C}_{n-1,1}(d),$$

and this gives

$$D_1(d,t) - 2dt^2 - t = d^2 t\,(D_1(d,t) - t) + d^2 t^2 D_1(d,t)$$
$$+ d^2\,(1 - d^2)t^3 D_1(d,t) + \left(C_1(d,t) - dt^2 - t\right)$$
$$+ \left(d - d^2\right)t\,(C_1(d,t) - t). \qquad (5.22)$$

For $k = 2$ and $n \geq 4$ we have

$$\mathbb{C}_{n,2}(d) = d^4 \left(1 - d^2\right) \mathbb{D}_{n-4,1}(d^2)$$
$$+ (1 - d)\, \mathbb{C}_{n-2,1}(d^2) + d^2 \mathbb{D}_{n-2,1}(d^2),$$

which gives

$$C_2(d,t) - dt^3 = d^4 \left(1 - d^2\right) t^4 D_1(d^2,t) + d\left(1 - d\right) t^2 \left(C_1(d^2,t) - t\right)$$
$$+ d^2 t^2 \left(D_1(d^2,t) - t\right). \tag{5.23}$$

Furthermore, for $k \geq 3$ and $n \geq 4$ we have

$$\mathbb{C}_{n,k}(d) = d^{2^k} \left(1 - d^{2^{k-1}}\right) \mathbb{D}_{n-4,k-1}(d^2) + d^{2^{k-2}} \left(1 - d^{2^{k-2}}\right) \mathbb{C}_{n-2,k-1}(d^2)$$
$$+ d^{2^{k-1}} \mathbb{D}_{n-2,k-1}(d^2),$$

which gives

$$C_k(d,t) = \left(d^{2^k} \left(1 - d^{2^{k-1}}\right) t^4 + d^{2^{k-1}} t^2\right) D_{k-1}(d^2,t)$$
$$+ d^{2^{k-2}} \left(1 - d^{2^{k-2}}\right) t^2 C_{k-1}(d^2,t). \tag{5.24}$$

On the other hand, for $k \geq 2$ and $n \geq 3$ we have

$$\mathbb{D}_{n,k}(d) = d^{2^k} \left(\mathbb{D}_{n-1,k}(d) + \mathbb{D}_{n-2,k}(d) + \left(1 - d^{2^k}\right) \mathbb{D}_{n-3,k}(d)\right)$$
$$+ \mathbb{C}_{n,k}(d) + \left(d^{2^{k-1}} - d^{2^k}\right) \mathbb{C}_{n-1,k}(d),$$

and from this we obtain

$$D_k(d,t) = d^{2^k} \left(t D_k(d,t) + t^2 D_k(d,t) + \left(1 - d^{2^k}\right) t^3 D_k(d,t)\right)$$
$$+ C_k(d,t) + \left(d^{2^{k-1}} - d^{2^k}\right) t C_k(d,t)$$
$$= \frac{1 + \left(d^{2^{k-1}} - d^{2^k}\right) t}{1 - d^{2^k}(t + t^2 + t^3) + d^{2^{k+1}} t^3} C_k(d,t). \tag{5.25}$$

Finally, using $D_0(d,t)$, (5.21), (5.22), (5.23), (5.24), and (5.25), we complete the proof. $\qquad\square$

The generating functions for the first two values of k are given as

$$D_0(d) = \frac{1 + dt + \left(d - d^2\right) t^2}{1 - d(t + t^2) - \left(d - d^2\right) t^3}$$
$$= 1 + 2dt + \left(d^2 + 2d\right) t^2 + \left(d^3 + 3d^2 + d\right) t^3 + \cdots$$

$$D_1(d) = \frac{t\left(1 + \left(d - d^2\right) t\right)^2}{\left(1 - d^2(t + t^2) - (d^2 - d^4) t^3\right)^2}$$
$$= t + 2dt^2 + \left(2d^3 + 3d^2\right) t^3 + 2\left(d^5 + d^4 + 2d^3 + d^2\right) t^4 + \cdots$$

5.5.3 *Some Specializations*

Note that $D_0(d,t)$ in Theorem 5.23 is the generating function $f(x,y)$ given in [65, Section 6]. In the notation of this section, d plays the role of y and t plays the role of x.

Consider next the cube polynomial $C_{\Gamma_n}(x)$ of Γ_n studied in Section 5.1 and its q-analogue $C_{\Gamma_n}(x,q)$ studied in Section 5.4. $C_{\Gamma_n}(x,q)$ is a refinement of the cube polynomial $C_{\Gamma_n}(x)$ with $C_{\Gamma_n}(x,1) = C_{\Gamma_n}(x)$.

The material presented in this section provides a similar refinement of $C_{\Gamma_n}(x)$. Writing

$$C_{\Gamma_n}(x) = \sum_{k\geq0} a_{n,k}x^k \quad \text{and} \quad C_{\Gamma_n}(x,q) = \sum_{k\geq0} b_{n,k}(q)x^k,$$

we obtain

$$a_{n,k} = b_{n,k}(1) = \mathbb{D}_{n,k}(1).$$

Taking $d=1$ in Theorem 5.23, $f(1,t)=1$ and $g(1,t)=1-t-t^2$ so that

$$D_0(1,t) = \frac{1+t}{1-t-t^2}$$

and

$$D_k(1,t) = \frac{t^{2k-1}}{(1-t-t^2)^{k+1}}$$

for $k>0$. The first one of these is the generating function of the sequence of the number of vertices $(F_{n+2})_{n\geq0}$, and the second one is the generating function of the $(k+1)$-fold convolution of Fibonacci numbers enumerating the number of k-dimensional hypercubes in Γ_n.

Chapter 6

Characterizations and Recognition

In this chapter, we first present a simple characterization of Fibonacci cubes as the simplex graphs of complements of paths. In Section 6.2, we present an extremely interesting connection between Fibonacci cubes and mathematical chemistry, yielding another characterization of Fibonacci cubes; they are precisely the resonance graphs of fibonaccenes. In the final section of the chapter we demonstrate that Fibonacci cubes can be recognized in linear time. The sophisticated metric structure of the Fibonacci cubes is very helpful for this purpose. Along the way, we prove that Fibonacci cubes are median graphs and give a characterization of Fibonacci cubes among median graphs.

6.1 Fibonacci Cubes as Simplex Graphs

Simplex graphs were introduced in 1989 by Bandelt and van de Vel as follows [10]. Let G be a graph. The vertex set of the *simplex graph* $\mathcal{K}(G)$ of G is the set of all cliques of G, that is, for each clique K of G there is a vertex u_K in $\mathcal{K}(G)$. In particular, $\varnothing$, each vertex, and each edge of G yields a vertex of $\mathcal{K}(G)$. Two vertices of $\mathcal{K}(G)$ are adjacent whenever the corresponding cliques of G differ by exactly one vertex. For instance, there is an edge between $u_\varnothing$ and u_x for each $x \in V(G)$, and there is an edge between u_x and u_{xy} for each edge $xy \in E(G)$.

The two extreme examples of simplex graphs are the simplex graphs of complete graphs and their complements. We have:

$$\mathcal{K}(K_n) \cong Q_n \quad \text{and} \quad \mathcal{K}(\overline{K_n}) \cong K_{1,n} .$$

We now have the following characterization of Fibonacci cubes.

Proposition 6.1. *If $n \geq 1$, then $\mathcal{K}(\overline{P_n}) \cong \Gamma_n$.*

Proof. Let $V(P_n) = V(\overline{P_n}) = [n]$ and $E(P_n) = \{i(i+1) : i \in [n-1]\}$. Then $\{i_1, \ldots, i_k\}$ induces a clique of $\overline{P_n}$ if and only if $|i_j - i_{j'}| \geq 2$ holds for each $j, j' \in [k]$. To each clique $K = \overline{P_n}[\{i_1, \ldots, i_k\}]$ we assign the binary string $f(K) = b_1 \ldots b_n \in \mathcal{B}_n$, where $b_i = 1$ if and only if $i \in \{i_1, \ldots, i_k\}$. In particular, $f(\varnothing) = 0^n$. Since for such a K we have $|i_j - i_{j'}| \geq 2$ for each $j, j' \in [k]$, we infer that $f(K)$ is a Fibonacci string, that is,

$$f : V(\overline{P_n}) \to V(\Gamma_n).$$

The mapping $f : V(\overline{P_n}) \to V(\Gamma_n)$ is clearly injective, and is also equally clear that it is surjective. Moreover, by the definition of $E(\overline{P_n})$ and $E(\Gamma_n)$, we infer that $KK' \in E(\overline{P_n})$ if and only if $f(K)f(K') \in E(\Gamma_n)$. Hence f is a graph isomorphism. $\square$

Fig. 6.1 shows the simplex graph $\mathcal{K}(\overline{P_6})$, where the notation for the vertices is simplified so that the vertex $\overline{P_6}[\{i_1, \ldots, i_k\}]$ is abbreviated as $i_1 \ldots i_k$. The figure can be seen as a new, exotic way of looking at Γ_6.

Proposition 6.1 can also be interpreted as follows. Since a clique in $\overline{P_6}$ corresponds to an independent set in P_n, we can naturally associate a vertex x of Γ_n to the independent set of P_n which contains the vertices i of P_n (recall that $V(P_n) = [n]$) such that $x_i = 1$. Two vertices in Γ_n are then adjacent if and only if the symmetric difference of the corresponding independent sets has cardinality 1. That is, we can consider Γ_n as the Hasse diagram of the independent sets of P_n ordered by inclusion. Codara and D'Antona have applied this perspective and studied the Hasse diagrams of the independent sets of powers of paths ordered by inclusion [23]. Here, by the kth power of P_n we mean the graph with the same vertex set as P_n, two vertices being adjacent if they are at distance at most k in P_n.

We point out here that Fibonacci cubes also appear in the theory of oriented matroids as the so called tope graphs of certain complexes of oriented matroids. The technical details would take us too far afield, but we direct the interested reader to the paper of Bandelt, Chepoi and Knauer [9, p. 225].

6.2 Fibonacci Cubes as Resonance Graphs

In this section we connect Fibonacci cubes with mathematical chemistry. In the main theorem we prove that Fibonacci cubes are exactly the so-called resonance graphs of fibonaccenes. Resonance graphs of chemical graphs play an important role in theoretical (organic) chemistry and fibonaccenes are an appealing family of benzenoid systems. To be able to state and understand the main theorem, some preparation is needed.

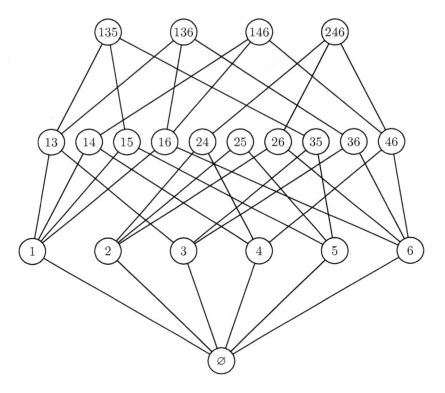

Fig. 6.1 Γ_6 as $\mathcal{K}(\overline{P_6})$

A *hexagonal chain* G with $h \geq 1$ hexagons is a graph defined as follows. If $h = 1$, then G is the cycle on six vertices. If $h > 1$, then G is constructed from a hexagonal chain H with $h-1$ hexagons by attaching the hth hexagon along an edge e of the $(h-1)^{\text{st}}$ hexagon, where the end vertices of e are of degree 2 in the hexagonal chain H. In Fig. 6.2 a hexagonal chain with four hexagons is drawn. The edge e over which the last hexagon has been attached is also marked.

A hexagon of a hexagonal chain is *inner* if it is adjacent to two other hexagons. Note that each inner hexagon of a hexagonal chain contains exactly two vertices of degree 2. A hexagonal chain is a *fibonaccene*, if in every inner hexagon, its degree 2 vertices are adjacent. Intuitively this means that a hexagonal chain is a fibonaccene if no three consecutive hexagons are aligned in the same direction. For instance, the hexagonal chain from Fig. 6.2 is not a fibonaccene because in the first (from the left) inner hexagon

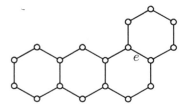

Fig. 6.2 A hexagonal chain composed of four hexagons

the two degree 2 vertices are not adjacent (that is, the first three hexagons are aligned in the same direction), while in Fig. 6.3 a fibonaccene is shown. Fibonaccenes are also known as *zigzag hexagonal chains*.

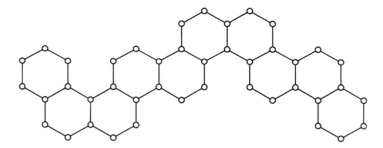

Fig. 6.3 A hexagonal chain which is a fibonaccene

The last concept needed is the one of the resonance graph. It can be defined much more generally but this is not needed here for our purposes. We only add that the concept was introduced independently several times in mathematics as well as in theoretical chemistry, thus demonstrating it is a natural and important concept. In chemistry, the motivation for its introduction was the fact that perfect matchings (alias Kekuléan structures in chemistry) can be used to represent the distribution of double bonds in benzenoids, and experiments have shown that the more perfect matchings a benzenoid has, the more stable it is.

Let H be a hexagonal chain. The *resonance graph* $R(H)$ of H has the perfect matchings of H as vertices, two perfect matchings being adjacent in $R(H)$ if their symmetric difference forms the edge set of a hexagon of H. In other words, perfect matchings M_1 and M_2 are adjacent if there exists a hexagon h of H with consecutive edges $e_1, \ldots, e_6$, such that $M_1 \cap E(h) = \{e_1, e_3, e_5\}$, and $M_2 = (M_1 \cup \{e_2, e_4, e_6\}) \setminus \{e_1, e_3, e_5\}$. Intuitively, M_2 is obtained from M_1 by rotating three edges of M_1 that are on some hexagon of H.

We now have the following beautiful description of Fibonacci cubes due to Klavžar and Žigert Pleteršek.

Theorem 6.2. [68, Theorem 1] *If H is a fibonaccene with $n \geq 1$ hexagons, then*

$$R(H) \cong \Gamma_n.$$

Proof. We first show that H contains F_{n+2} perfect matchings. If $n = 1$, then $H \cong C_6$ and it contains $F_3 = 2$ perfect matchings. Similarly, if H contains two hexagons, we easily see that H contains $F_4 = 3$ perfect matchings. Suppose now that H contains $n \geq 3$ hexagons and let h be its arbitrary non-inner hexagon. Consider the hexagonal chain $H \setminus h$ obtained from H after deletion of h (but keeping the edge with which h is attached to the rest of H). Let $e_1, \ldots, e_6$ be the consecutive edges of h, where e_4 is the edge shared by h and $H \setminus h$. Then e_1 is the edge opposite to e_4 on h. Let M be a perfect matching of H and distinguish the following two cases.

Case 1: If $e_1 \in M$, then necessarily also $e_3 \in M$ and $e_5 \in M$. Moreover, in the hexagon h' attached to h, the edge f whose end vertices are of degree 2 is also forced to lie in M. Then $M \setminus \{e_1, e_3, e_5, f\}$ is a perfect matching of $(H \setminus h) \setminus h'$. Conversely, any matching of $(H \setminus h) \setminus h'$ can be completed in a unique way to a matching of H containing e_1. By induction it follows that the number of the perfect matchings in H which contain e_1 is F_n.

Case 2: Suppose next that $e_1 \notin M$. Then necessarily $e_2 \in M$ and $e_6 \in M$. But then by an argument parallel to the above we see that there are exactly F_{n+1} perfect matchings in H which do not contain e_1. Hence H contains $F_n + F_{n+1} = F_{n+2}$ perfect matchings.

We next establish an explicit bijection between the perfect matchings of H and $V(\Gamma_n)$. For this purpose let M be an arbitrary perfect matching of H and let $h_1, \ldots, h_n$ be the consecutive hexagons of H. If e is the edge of h_1 opposite to the common edge of h_1 and h_2, then set

$$b_1(M) = \begin{cases} 1 & \text{if } e \in M, \\ 0 & \text{otherwise}. \end{cases}$$

Consider now h_i, $i \geq 2$. An edge of h_i that has exactly one end-vertex on h_{i-1} is called a *link from h_i to h_{i-1}*. Clearly, there are exactly two links from h_i to h_{i-1}. Set:

$$b_i(M) = \begin{cases} 1 & \text{if } M \text{ contains both links from } h_i \text{ to } h_{i-1}, \\ 0 & \text{otherwise}. \end{cases}$$

We have thus defined an assignment

$$M \mapsto b_1(M) \dots b_n(M) \qquad\qquad (6.1)$$

which assigns to each perfect matching M of H a binary string $b_1(M) \dots b_n(M) \in \mathcal{B}_n$. Actually, $b_1(M) \dots b_n(M) \in \mathcal{F}_n$, that is, $b_1(M) \dots b_n(M)$ is a Fibonacci string. Indeed, we see directly that the string $b_1(M) \dots b_n(M)$ cannot start by two 1s neither end by two 1s. Moreover, if $b_i(M)b_{i+1}(M) = 11$, where $2 \le i < n-1$, then we would have two consecutive pairs of link edges in M, but since H does not contains three hexagons in the same direction, two of these edges would share a vertex. This is not possible since M is a matching.

We have thus proved that the assignment (6.1) maps perfect matchings of H to Fibonacci strings of length n. Since different perfect matchings are mapped into different strings, and since we have proved above that there are F_{n+2} perfect matchings in H, the assignment is a bijection.

It remains to prove that matchings M and M' are adjacent in $R(H)$ if and only if $b_1(M) \dots b_n(M)$ and $b_1(M') \dots b_n(M')$ are adjacent in Γ_n, that is, if and only if they differ in precisely one position. Suppose first that M and M' are adjacent in $R(H)$. This means that there exists a hexagon h_i such that the restriction of $M \cup M'$ to h_i is the whole edge set of H_i. If $i = 1$, then exactly one of M and M' contains the edge opposite to the common edge of h_1 and h_2, and if $i \ge 2$, then exactly one of M and M' contains the two link edges from h_i to h_{i-1}. Hence in any case, $b_i(M) \ne b_i(M')$, while $b_j(M) = b_j(M')$ for any $j \ne i$. Conversely, suppose that $b_1(M) \dots b_n(M)$ and $b_1(M') \dots b_n(M')$ differ in precisely one position i. If $i = 1$, then neither M nor M' contains the two link edges from h_2 to h_1. This means that the symmetric difference of M and M' is the edge set of h_1. Since M and M' coincide on all the other hexagons, they are adjacent in $R(H)$. Suppose next $2 \le i \le n-1$. Then neither M nor M' contains the two link edges from h_{i+1} to h_i, as well as the two link edges from h_{i-1} to h_i. Hence the symmetric difference of M and M' is the edge set of h_i. Since the case $i = n$ is treated analogously as the case $i = 1$, the proof is complete. □

Theorem 6.2 and its proof are illustrated in Fig. 6.4. The figure shows all eight perfect matching of the fibonaccene H with four hexagons. Each of these perfect matchings is a vertex of $R(H)$. The binary strings that provide a bijection between the vertices of Γ_4 and the perfect matchings are also displayed. Finally, the bold edges are the edges of $R(H)$. Note that each edge represents a rotation of three edges on some hexagon of H.

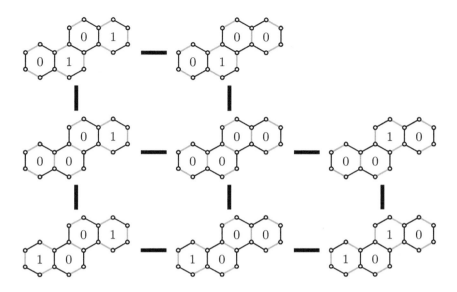

Fig. 6.4 The resonance graph of the fibonaccene with four hexagons. The perfect matchings are indicated in green

Theorem 6.2 has been extended in several different directions. In Section 9.8 we will describe a particularly interesting extension to daisy cubes.

6.3 Recognition of Fibonacci Cubes in Linear Time

In this section, we will derive a linear recognition algorithm for Fibonacci cubes. It will take some preparation to do this. Fortunately, the preparatory concepts and results are interesting in themselves. We will first prove that Fibonacci cubes are median graphs. Then we will characterize Fibonacci cubes among median graphs. Before arriving at a characterization of Fibonacci cubes which enables their fast recognition, we will also prove that Γ_n contains exactly two convex subgraphs isomorphic to Γ_{n-1}. Along the way, the Hosoya triangle will naturally join the game.

6.3.1 *Fibonacci Cubes are Median Graphs*

Let u, v, and w be different vertices of a connected graph G. A *median* of the triple u, v, w is a vertex x that simultaneously lies on a shortest u, v-path, a shortest u, w-path, and a shortest v, w-path, that is, if the following equalities hold:

$$d_G(u,v) = d_G(u,x) + d_G(x,v),$$
$$d_G(u,w) = d_G(u,x) + d_G(x,w),$$
$$d_G(v,w) = d_G(v,x) + d_G(x,w).$$

The graph G is a *median graph* if every triple of its vertices has a unique median.

As an example take a tree T and an arbitrary triple of its vertices u, v, w. Let P be the unique u, v-path in T and let Q be the unique w, u-path. Then the first vertex of Q that lies on P is a median of u, v, w. Note that it is possible that one of u, v, and w itself is the median of u, v, w. Moreover, this median is unique, hence trees are median graphs.

We next show that hypercubes are also median graphs. For this sake let $u = u_1 \ldots u_n$, $v = v_1 \ldots v_n$, and $w = w_1 \ldots w_n$ be three different vertices of Q_n. Suppose that $x = x_1 \ldots x_n$ is a median of u, v, w and consider the bits u_i, v_i, and w_i. By the pigeonhole principle, two of these bits must be equal. Assume without loss of generality that $u_i = v_i$. Then in order for x to lie on a u, v-shortest path, we must have $x_i = u_i = v_i$. As this must hold for each coordinate $i \in [n]$, we see that a potential median x of u, v, w is uniquely determined. We say that x is obtained from u, v, w by the *majority rule*. On the other hand, since for every pair of vertices $u, v \in V(Q_n)$, $d_{Q_n}(u,v)$ is equal to the Hamming distance $H(u,v)$, the vertex x obtained by the majority rule from u, v, w is a median of u, v, w. So each triple of vertices from Q_n has a unique median and we are done.

From the perspective of this book, the most important thing is that Fibonacci cubes are median graphs. This was showed by Klavžar in a more general context of the so-called extended Fibonacci cubes.

Theorem 6.3. [58, Theorem 1] Γ_n *is a median graph for* $n \geq 0$.

Proof. By Lemma 4.1, $d_{\Gamma_n}(u,v) = H(u,v)$ for any $u, v \in V(\Gamma_n)$. To show that Γ_n, is a median graph, we now proceed as we did above for hypercubes, the only difference being that in addition we need to prove that the vertex x obtained from a triple u, v, w of vertices of Γ_n by the majority rule lies in Γ_n. Suppose not, that is, there exists $i \in [n-1]$ such that $x_i = x_{i+1} = 1$. By the majority rule this means that at least two of u_i, v_i, w_i are equal to 1 and at least two of $u_{i+1}, v_{i+1}, w_{i+1}$ are equal to 1. But then (by the pigeonhole principle) for at least one of u, v, w the ith and the $(i+1)^{\text{st}}$ coordinates are both 1, a contradiction with the fact that each of u, v, and w is a Fibonacci string. $\qquad\square$

As an example, consider the triple $10101, 01000, 10010$ of vertices of Γ_5. The vertex obtained from the triple by the majority rule is 10000, hence this is the median of the triple. See Fig. 6.5 where the vertices of the triple are black and their median is red.

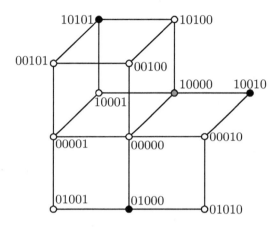

Fig. 6.5 The median of the vertices $10101, 01000, 10010$ in Γ_5

Another way to derive Theorem 6.3 is to use [10, Proposition 2.2] which asserts that the simplex graph of an arbitrary graph is a median graph. Theorem 6.3 then follows from Proposition 6.1.

Let us add that in [69], Klavžar, Žigert Pleteršek, and Brinkmann extended Theorem 6.3 by proving that the resonance graphs of to so-called catacondensed even ring systems are median.

6.3.2 *Characterization Among Median Graphs*

For a connected graph G and an edge $ab \in E(G)$, set

$$W_{ab} = \{w \in V(G) : d(a, w) < d(b, w)\},$$
$$W_{ba} = \{w \in V(G) : d(w, b) < d(w, a)\},$$
$$U_{ab} = \{w \in W_{ab} : w \text{ has a neighbor in } W_{ba}\},$$
$$U_{ba} = \{w \in W_{ba} : w \text{ has a neighbor in } W_{ab}\},$$
$$F_{ab} = \{e = uv \in E(G) : u \in U_{ab}, v \in U_{ba}\}.$$

Note that if G is bipartite, then $V(G) = W_{ab} \cup W_{ba}$. For an example see Fig. 6.6, where for an edge ab of the drawn bipartite graph, the sets W_{ab},

W_{ba}, U_{ab}, and U_{ba} are encircled, while the edges from the set F_{ab} are in green.

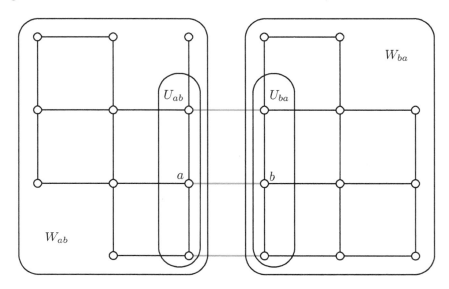

Fig. 6.6   Sets W_{ab}, W_{ba}, U_{ab}, U_{ba}, and F_{ab} in a bipartite graph

The celebrated Djoković-Winkler relation Θ is defined on the edge set of a connected graph G in the following way. Edges xy and uv are in the relation Θ if

$$d(x,u) + d(y,v) \neq d(x,v) + d(y,u).$$

The relation Θ is clearly reflexive and symmetric, but in general it is not transitive. Winkler [121] proved that among bipartite graphs, Θ is transitive precisely for partial cubes. In particular, by Proposition 4.2, Θ is transitive on Fibonacci cubes.

Just as Q_n, the Fibonacci cube Γ_n contains n Θ-classes $E_1, \ldots, E_n$, where E_i, $i \in [n]$, consists of the edges that differ in the ith coordinate. See Fig. 6.7 where the Θ-classes E_1, E_2, E_3, E_4, and E_5 of Γ_5 are shown with respective colors black, blue, yellow, red, green.

Let G be a median graph (or a partial cube for that matter), and let $ab \in E(G)$. Then the induced subgraph $G[W_{ab}]$ is *peripheral* if $U_{ab} = W_{ab}$. Further, the τ-*graph*, G^τ, of G has the Θ-classes of G as vertices, two classes F and F' being adjacent if there exists edges $f \in F$ and $f' \in F'$ which induce

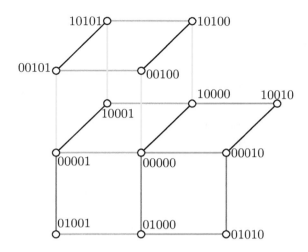

Fig. 6.7 The Θ-classes of Γ_5

a convex P_3. With these two concepts we can now state the result of this subsection due to Vesel.

Theorem 6.4. [107, Theorem 8] *Let G be a median graph. Then $G \cong \Gamma_n$ (for some n) if and only if every Θ-class is peripheral and $G^\tau \cong P_n$.*

Instead of the technical proof of Theorem 6.4, let us give the intuition behind it. Consider an arbitrary Θ-class E_i of Γ_n. Then the edges of E_i differ in the ith coordinate. If uv is an arbitrary edge from E_i, where $u_i = 1$ (and $v_i = 0$), then each vertex from W_{uv} has the ith coordinate equal to 1 and so has a neighbor in W_{vu}. Hence $W_{uv} = U_{uv}$ and so E_i is peripheral. To see why $G^\tau \cong P_n$ must hold, proceed by induction. Considering Γ_n and its fundamental decomposition, we may assume without loss of generality that the nth Θ-class of Γ_n (which is added to the $n-1$ Θ-classes of Γ_{n-1}) is E_n. After that we infer that an edge from E_n can only be in a convex P_3 with an edge from E_{n-1} which prolongs the path $\Gamma_{n-1}^\tau \cong P_{n-1}$ to P_n.

6.3.3 *Recognition Algorithm*

In order to be able to formulate and prove a theorem that allows us to quickly recognize Fibonacci cubes, we need some more preparation. We first recall *Mulder's convex expansion theorem*, the seminal characterization of median graphs due to Mulder [79]. The formulation here is given in the form suitable for our purposes.

Theorem 6.5. *Let ab be an edge of a connected, bipartite graph G. Then G is a median graph if and only if the following three conditions are satisfied:*

>   *(i) F_{ab} is a matching defining an isomorphism between $G[U_{ab}]$ and $G[U_{ba}]$.*
>
>   *(ii) $G[U_{ab}]$ is convex in $G[W_{ab}]$, and $G[U_{ba}]$ is convex in $G[W_{ba}]$.*
>
>   *(iii) $G[W_{ab}]$ and $G[W_{ba}]$ are median graphs.*

Now let us take a closer look to the Θ-classes of Γ_n.

Proposition 6.6. *Let $n \geq 1$, and let E_i, $i \in [n]$, be the Θ-classes of Γ_n, where E_i contains the edges that differ in the ith coordinate. Then,*

$$|E_i| = F_i F_{n-i+1}\,.$$

Proof. Consider first E_1. If $e \in E_1$, then $e = uv$, where $u = 00u'$ and $v = 10u'$ with $u' \in \mathcal{F}_{n-2}$. Hence $|E_1| = |\mathcal{F}_{n-2}| = F_n = F_1 F_n$ and the result holds for E_1. Analogously we see that the result holds for E_n. Assume in the rest that $i \in \{2, \ldots, n-1\}$ and consider an arbitrary edge $e \in E_i$. Then $e = uv$, where $u = u'000u''$ and $v = u'010u''$ with $u' \in \mathcal{F}_{i-2}$ and $u'' \in \mathcal{F}_{n-i-1}$. Hence

$$|E_i| = |\mathcal{F}_{i-2}| \cdot |\mathcal{F}_{n-i-1}| = F_i F_{n-i+1}$$

and we are done. $\square$

Proposition 6.6 was independently and at the same time found by Taranenko and Vesel [104, Proposition 1] and by Klavžar and Peterin [66, Theorem 4.1]. Since the Θ-classes of a partial cube G partition $E(G)$, Proposition 6.6 yields another proof of Proposition 3.3.

The *Hosoya triangle* is defined by setting

$$H(n, i) = F_i F_{n-i+1}, \ i \in [n]\,,$$

where n denotes the row, and i the position in the nth row of the entry $H(n, i)$. The first several rows of the Hosoya triangle are shown in Table 6.1.

In view of Proposition 6.6, the nth row of the Hosoya triangle thus corresponds to the orders of the Θ-classes of Γ_n. To prove our next theorem, we need the following fact about these orders.

Lemma 6.7. *If $n \geq 2$, then Γ_n contains exactly two Θ-classes of order F_n.*

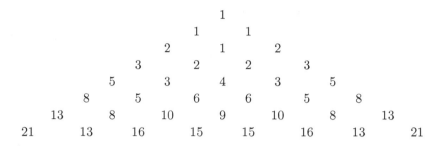

Table 6.1 The first few rows of the Hosoya triangle

Proof. By Proposition 6.6 it suffices to show that $F_i F_{n-i+1} < F_n$ holds for $i \in \{2, \ldots, n-1\}$. By checking Table 6.1 we see that the assertion holds for the first few values of n (where there is nothing to observe $n = 2$). We proceed by induction and estimate as follows:

$$F_i F_{n-i+1} = F_i(F_{n-i} + F_{n-i-1}) = F_i F_{n-i} + F_i F_{n-i-1} < F_{n-1} + F_{n-2} = F_n$$

and we are done. $\square$

We have come to the last auxiliary result, which reads as follows.

Theorem 6.8. [104, Lemma 2] *If $n \geq 2$, then Γ_n contains exactly two convex subgraphs isomorphic to Γ_{n-1}.*

Proof. It follows from the fundamental decomposition of Γ_n that $\Gamma_n[0\mathcal{F}_{n-1}]$ is a convex subgraph of Γ_n isomorphic to Γ_{n-1}. The same holds for the induced subgraph $\Gamma_n[\mathcal{F}_{n-1}0]$. It remains to prove that there are no other convex subgraphs of Γ_n isomorphic to Γ_{n-1}.

Suppose that H is an arbitrary convex subgraph of Γ_n isomorphic to Γ_{n-1}. As H is convex in Γ_n and is isomorphic to Γ_{n-1}, we see that H contains $n-1$ Θ-classes. Applying the Convexity Lemma due to Imrich and Klavžar from [55, Lemma 2.6] it follows that no edge from the edge boundary $\partial_e H = \partial_e V(H)$ is in relation Θ to an edge in H. As Γ_n contains n Θ-classes, it follows that all the edges of $\partial_e H$ must lie in the same Θ-class, denote it by F. So $\partial_e H \subseteq F$. We claim that $\partial_e H = F$. Suppose on the contrary that $xy \in F \setminus \partial_e H$. As Γ_n is bipartite, we may without loss of generality assume that $d(x, H) < d(y, H)$. Let P be a shortest path between x and H. Then yxP is also a shortest path. Since $xy \in F$ and the last edge of this path is also in F, we have a contradiction because no two edges of a shortest path are in relation Θ. This contradiction proves that $\partial_e H = F$.

By Theorem 6.4, each Θ-class of Γ_n is peripheral, therefore the class F must be peripheral. As $n(\Gamma_n) = F_{n+2}$ and $n(H) = F_{n+1}$, it follows that $|F| = F_n$. By Lemma 6.7, F can only be one of the Θ-classes E_1 and E_n of Γ_n, which in turn implies that H is one of the two convex subgraphs described in the first paragraph of the proof. $\square$

The two convex subgraphs of Γ_5 isomorphic to Γ_4 are shown in Fig. 6.8.

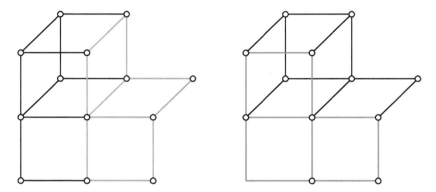

Fig. 6.8   The two convex subgraphs of Γ_5 isomorphic to Γ_4

A characterization of Fibonacci cubes by Taranenko and Vesel which is the key tool for their recognition algorithm is as follows.

Theorem 6.9. [104, Theorem 5] *Let ab be an edge of a connected, bipartite graph G with $\deg_G(a) = n$ and $\deg_G(b) = n - 1$. Then $G \cong \Gamma_n$ if and only if the following conditions are satisfied:*

  (i) $G[U_{ab}]$ is convex in $G[W_{ab}]$.
  (ii) F_{ab} is a matching defining an isomorphism between $G[U_{ab}]$ and $G[U_{ba}]$.
  (iii) $G[W_{ab}]$ is isomorphic to Γ_{n-1}, and $G[W_{ba}]$ is isomorphic to Γ_{n-2}.
  (iv) $W_{ba} = U_{ba}$.

Proof. Suppose first that $G \cong \Gamma_n$. Then we know that the only vertex of degree n in Γ_n is 0^n and the only vertices of degree $n - 1$ are 10^{n-1} and $0^{n-1}1$. Hence $a = 0^n$ and we may assume without loss of generality that $b = 10^{n-1}$. By Theorem 6.3 Γ_n is a median graph. Consider its Θ-class E_1. Then conditions *(i)* and *(ii)* hold by Theorem 6.5, *(iii)* holds by the fundamental decomposition, while *(iv)* holds because E_1 is peripheral.

Conversely, suppose that the conditions *(i)-(iv)* hold, and let ab be an edge of a connected, bipartite graph G with $\deg_G(a) = n$ and $\deg_G(b) = n - 1$. Since $G[W_{ba}] = G[U_{ba}]$ is isomorphic to Γ_{n-2}, and F_{ab} is a matching defining an isomorphism between $G[U_{ab}]$ and $G[U_{ba}]$, we infer that $G[U_{ab}]$ is isomorphic to Γ_{n-2}. As $G[U_{ab}]$ is convex in $G[W_{ab}] \cong \Gamma_{n-1}$, Theorem 6.8 uniquely (up to two symmetric options) determines the position of $G[U_{ab}] \cong \Gamma_{n-2}$ in $G[W_{ab}] \cong \Gamma_{n-1}$. But then the fundamental decomposition yields that $G \cong \Gamma_n$. $\square$

To recognize Fibonacci cubes, first check whether a given input graph G is connected, bipartite, and of order F_{n+2}. If not, then G is rejected. After this preprocessing, proceed by checking whether all the conditions of Theorem 6.9 are fulfilled. By a careful implementation this can be done in $\mathcal{O}(m \log n)$ time, where $m = m(G)$ and $n = n(G)$. This complexity comes from the fact that the condition *(iii)* of Theorem 6.9 forces that the total number of edges processed during the checking is $\mathcal{O}(m \log n)$.

Vesel [108] further elaborated the above approach by avoiding checking that $G[W_{ba}]$ is isomorphic to Γ_{n-2}. Instead, it suffices that the three additional conditions given as *(v)-(vii)* below hold.

Theorem 6.10. [108, Theorem 2] *Let ab be an edge of a connected, bipartite graph G with $\deg_G(a) = n$ and $\deg_G(b) = n - 1$, $n \geq 3$. Then $G \cong \Gamma_n$ if and only if the following conditions are satisfied:*

(i) *$G[U_{ab}]$ is convex in $G[W_{ab}]$.*
(ii) *F_{ab} is a matching defining an isomorphism between $G[U_{ab}]$ and $G[U_{ba}]$.*
(iii) *$G[W_{ab}]$ is isomorphic to Γ_{n-1}.*
(iv) *$W_{ba} = U_{ba}$.*
(v) *G contains exactly one vertex $c \in N_G(a) \setminus (U_{ab} \cup U_{ba})$ such that $\deg_G(c) = n - 2$.*
(vi) *$|W_{ca}| = F_{n-1}$.*
(vii) *$|U_{ab}| = F_n$.*

The proof of Theorem 6.10 proceeds along similar lines as the proof of Theorem 6.9. Instead of giving the technical details, let us look at the example in Fig. 6.9, which illustrates the conditions of the theorem on Γ_5. The vertex a is the unique vertex of degree 5. Among the two vertices of degree 4, one is selected without loss of generality as the vertex b. The vertices from the set W_{ab} are blue, the vertices from the set $W_{ba} = U_{ba}$ are red. The vertex c is the unique vertex of degree 3 in $N_G(a) \smallsetminus (U_{ab} \cup U_{ba})$. Note that $|W_{ca}| = 3 = F_4$ and $|U_{ab}| = |U_{ba}| = 5 = F_5$.

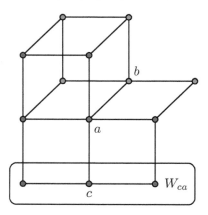

Fig. 6.9   The conditions of Theorem 6.10 illustrated on Γ_5

A careful checking whether conditions of Theorem 6.10 are fulfilled, culminates in the following result.

Theorem 6.11. [108, Theorem 3] *Given graph G, it can be checked in $\mathcal{O}(m(G))$ time whether G is a Fibonacci cube.*

Chapter 7

Invariants of Fibonacci Cubes

The interesting structure of Fibonacci cubes has attracted researchers to investigate various graph invariants on them. In this chapter, we report a number of results obtained in this direction. To start with, we describe what is known about the domination number and the total domination number of Fibonacci cubes; it turns out that both invariants are intrinsically difficult to pin down. In the subsequent section we present two formulas for the Wiener index of Γ_n, where the one giving a closed formula is derived using the Greene and Wilf theory we presented in Chapter 3. In Section 7.3 we first determine the irregularity of Γ_n. We then generalize the approach to consider the irregularity polynomial, determine it for Γ_n, and give the corresponding generating function. After that we give a bijective proof of the formula for the irregularity of Γ_n. In the last section we present a closed formula for the Mostar index of Γ_n and point out a connection to its Wiener index.

7.1 Domination-Type Invariants

The area of graph theory that perhaps offers the greatest variety of applications is domination theory, cf. [48]. It is therefore not surprising that domination invariants have also been studied on Fibonacci cubes. Here we will concentrate on the two most important ones, the domination number and the total domination number.

The problem of determining the domination number of Fibonacci cubes turns out to be a very difficult problem. In Table 7.1 all known exact values are listed.

The first few values from Table 7.1 can be obtained by looking at all the options, in other words by brute force. To obtain more values, Ilić and

n	1	2	3	4	5	6	7	8	9	10	11
$\gamma(\Gamma_n)$	1	1	2	3	4	5	8	12	17	25	39

Table 7.1   Known domination numbers of Fibonacci cubes

Milošević [54] came up with the idea of using integer linear programming. This is done as follows.

Suppose that each vertex $v \in V(\Gamma_n)$ is associated with a binary variable x_v which indicates whether the vertex v is included ($x_v = 1$) or not included ($x_v = 0$) in a dominating set. Then

$$\gamma(\Gamma_n) = \min \sum_{v \in V(\Gamma_n)} x_v$$

subject to

$$\sum_{w \in N_{\Gamma_n}[v]} x_w \geq 1, \text{ for all } v \in V(\Gamma_n), \quad x_w \in \mathcal{B}.$$

Applying this integer linear program and using standard packages to solve it, Ilić and Milošević [54] determined $\gamma(\Gamma_n)$ for $n \leq 10$, while the last known value $\Gamma(\Gamma_{11}) = 39$ was added later by Azarija, Klavžar, Rho, and Sim in [8].

In general, however, only bounds on $\gamma(\Gamma_n)$ are known. We first present a lower bound, for which the following concept is useful. For a graph G and a dominating set D of G, the *over-domination* of G with respect to D is defined as

$$\mathrm{OD}_G(D) = \left(\sum_{u \in D} (\deg_G(u) + 1) \right) - n(G).$$

The over-domination thus counts the redundancy in domination. For instance, if $v \notin D$ is dominated by two vertices from D, then v contributes 1 to $\mathrm{OD}_G(D)$. Note also that $\mathrm{OD}_G(D) = 0$ means that each vertex of G is dominated by exactly one vertex from D, in which case D forms a so-called *efficient dominating set* of G. Such sets in generalized Fibonacci cubes will be treated in Section 9.3.

We are now ready for the following theorem due to Pike and Zou.

Theorem 7.1. [86, Theorem 3.2] *If $n \geq 9$, then*

$$\gamma(\Gamma_n) \geq \left\lceil \frac{F_{n+2} - 2}{n - 2} \right\rceil.$$

Proof. Let D be a minimum dominating set of Γ_n. Let K denote the set of vertices u from D with $|u|_1 = 1$ and $\deg_G(u) = n - 2$ and let $k = |K|$. Then $0 \le k \le n - 2$. Let further $L = \{1010^{n-3}, 10^{n-2}1, 0^{n-3}101\}$ and let $\ell = |D \cap L|$. Note that each vertex from L is of degree $n - 2$. Finally set $S = \{0^n, 0^{n-1}1, 10^{n-1}\}$.

Suppose that $S \subseteq D$. Now 0^n dominates $n + 1$ vertices; each of the vertices $0^{n-1}1$ and 10^{n-1} dominates n vertices; each vertex from $K \cup L$ dominates $n - 1$ vertices; and every additional vertex from D is of degree at most $n - 3$. Therefore we have the following estimate:

$$(n+1) + 2n + (k+\ell)(n-1) + (|D| - 3 - k - l)(n-2) - \mathrm{OD}_{\gamma_n}(D) \ge n(\Gamma_n). \quad (7.1)$$

Since $|D| = \gamma(\Gamma_n)$ and $n(\Gamma_n) = F_{n+2}$, this inequality can be rewritten as

$$\gamma(\Gamma_n)(n-2) \ge F_{n+2} - k - \ell - 7 + \mathrm{OD}_{\gamma_n}(D).$$

Let us now estimate $\mathrm{OD}_{\gamma_n}(D)$. The edge between 0^n and $0^{n-1}1$, and the edge between 0^n and 10^{n-1}, each contributes 2 to $\mathrm{OD}_{\gamma_n}(D)$. Since $10^{n-2}1$ is a common neighbor of $0^{n-1}1$ and 10^{n-1}, we get an additional contribution of 1. Similarly we infer that because each vertex from K is adjacent to 0^n, a vertex from K yields additional contribution to the over-domination of at least 2, that is, 1 at the vertex and 1 at 0^n. Moreover, each vertex from L causes an addition of at least 3 to the over-domination. This summarizes into

$$\mathrm{OD}_{\gamma_n}(D) \ge 5 + 2k + 3\ell.$$

When we substitute this estimate into (7.1), we get

$$\gamma(\Gamma_n)(n-2) \ge F_{n+2} + k + 2\ell - 2 \ge F_{n+2} - 2,$$

hence the assertion of the theorem follows when $S \subseteq D$.

The remaining cases to be considered are $D \cap S = \{0^n, 0^{n-1}1\}$ (or symmetrically $D \cap S = \{0^n, 10^{n-1}\}$), $D \cap S = \{0^{n-1}1, 10^{n-1}\}$, $D \cap S = \{0^n\}$, $D \cap S = \{0^{n-1}1\}$ (or symmetrically $D \cap S = \{10^{n-1}\}$), and $D \cap S = \varnothing$. Each of these can be treated along similar lines as the case $D \cap S = S$ above, which we have worked through in detail. $\quad\square$

Using integer linear programming, the following bounds were computed in [8] and by E. Saygı in [90], respectively:

$$54 \le \gamma(\Gamma_{12}) \le 61 \quad \text{and} \quad 78 \le \gamma(\Gamma_{13}) \le 93.$$

Using these two upper bounds, it was proved in [90, Theorem 2.5] that if $n \ge 12$, then $\gamma(\Gamma_n) \le 21F_{n-8} - (2F_{n-10} + 8F_{n-12})$. In [33], Eğecioğlu, E. Saygı, and Z. Saygı improved the bounds for Γ_{12} to

$$55 \le \gamma(\Gamma_{12}) \le 60,$$

which can in turn be used to derive the following upper bound.

Theorem 7.2. *If* $n \geq 12$, *then*

$$\gamma(\Gamma_n) \leq 20F_{n-8} - 7F_{n-12}.$$

Proof. It follows from the fundamental decomposition of Γ_n that $\gamma(\Gamma_n) \leq \gamma(\Gamma_{n-1}) + \gamma(\Gamma_{n-2})$. Indeed, a dominating set of Γ_n can be simply formed as the union of a minimum dominating set of Γ_{n-1} and a minimum dominating set of Γ_{n-2}. As stated before the theorem, $\gamma(\Gamma_{12}) \leq 60$ and $\gamma(\Gamma_{13}) \leq 93$. Define the sequence $(a_n)_{n \geq 12}$, with $a_{12} = 60$, $a_{13} = 93$, and $a_n = a_{n-1} + a_{n-2}$ for $n \geq 14$. Then one can check by a simple induction argument that $a_n = 20F_{n-8} - 7F_{n-12}$ holds for any $n \geq 12$. Since $\gamma(\Gamma_n) \leq a_n$, the argument is complete.   □

It is clear from the above proof that an improvement of known specific upper bounds will lead to an improved general upper bound.

The proof of Theorem 7.2 simulates the proof of a similar result derived for the *total domination number* of Fibonacci cubes. The total domination number is probably the second most important invariant being studied in the field of graph domination. The only difference between the domination number and the total domination number is that in the case of the total domination, each vertex of a graph must have a neighbor in a total dominating set. This in particular means that the total domination number is not defined for graphs containing isolated vertices.

The total domination number of Fibonacci cubes is known up to Γ_{12}. These values are listed in Table 7.2.

n	1	2	3	4	5	6	7	8	9	10	11	12
$\gamma_t(\Gamma_n)$	2	2	2	3	5	7	10	13	20	30	44	65

Table 7.2   Known total domination numbers of Fibonacci cubes

The values from Table 7.2 were computed in [8]. The integer linear programming approach was again used, where the only difference with the program for the domination number is that now the constraints are

$$\sum_{w \in N_{\Gamma_n}(v)} x_w \geq 1, \text{ for all } v \in V(\Gamma_n), \quad x_w \in \mathcal{B}.$$

Results analogous to Theorems 7.1 and 7.2 for the total domination number read as follows.

Theorem 7.3. [8, Theorem 2.2] *If $n \geq 9$, then*

$$\gamma_t(\Gamma_n) \geq \left\lceil \frac{F_{n+2} - 11}{n - 3} \right\rceil - 1.$$

Theorem 7.4. [90, Theorem 2.5] *If $n \geq 16$, then*

$$\gamma(\Gamma_n) \leq 21F_{n-8} - (2F_{n-10} + 8F_{n-12}).$$

We conclude the section with the remark that in addition to domination and total domination, other domination-type invariants for Fibonacci cubes have also been investigated. In [20] the 2-packing number of Fibonacci cubes was considered. Next to domination and 2-packing, the paper [54] investigated the independent domination number of Fibonacci cubes. The paper [8] added to this list the connected domination number, the paired domination number, and the signed domination number of Fibonacci cubes.

7.2 Wiener Index

The Wiener index is one of the most studied invariants in mathematical chemistry, and has been also extensively investigated in mathematics either as the Wiener index or, equivalently, as the average distance of a graph.

The *Wiener index* of a connected graph G is the sum of distances over all unordered pairs of vertices of G that is

$$W(G) = \sum_{\{u,v\} \subset V(G)} d(u,v).$$

From Proposition 4.2 we know that Fibonacci cubes are partial cubes. Hence the following result due to Klavžar, Gutman, and Mohar on the Wiener index of partial cubes will be very useful to us. To understand it, let us recall that for a connected graph G and an edge $ab \in E(G)$, the set W_{ab} consists of the vertices which are closer a than to b.

Theorem 7.5. [60, Proposition 3.1] *Let G be a partial cube and let $E_1, \ldots, E_k$ be the Θ-classes of G. If $a_i b_i \in E_i$, $i \in [k]$, then*

$$W(G) = \sum_{i=1}^{k} n(G[W_{a_i b_i}]) \, n(G[W_{b_i a_i}]).$$

Using Theorem 7.5, we now prove the following result due to Klavžar and Mollard.

Theorem 7.6. [62, Theorem 3.1] *If $n \geq 0$, then*

$$W(\Gamma_n) = \sum_{i=1}^{n} F_i \, F_{i+1} \, F_{n-i+1} \, F_{n-i+2}.$$

Proof. $W(\Gamma_0) = 0$, hence the result holds for $n = 0$. For the rest of the argument let $n \geq 1$ and let $E_1, \ldots, E_n$ be the Θ-classes of Γ_n, where E_i contains the edges that differ in the ith coordinate (see Proposition 6.6, where we have determined the cardinalities of the Θ-classes of Γ_n.) Let $a_i b_i \in E_i$, where the ith coordinate of a_i is 0 (and hence the ith coordinate of b_i is 1). Then $\Gamma_n[W_{a_i b_i}]$ consists of the vertices of Γ_n whose i^{th} coordinate is 0 and $\Gamma_n[W_{b_i a_i}]$ consists of the vertices of Γ_n whose i^{th} coordinate is 1. If $c = c_1 \ldots c_n \in W_{b_i a_i}$, then $c_i = 1$ which implies that $c_{i-1} = 0$ and $c_{i+1} = 0$. It follows that for $2 \leq i \leq n-1$, $|W_{b_i a_i}| = F_i F_{n-i+1}$. Furthermore, $|W_{b_1 a_1}| = |W_{b_n a_n}| = F_n$. Similarly, $|W_{a_i b_i}| = F_{i+1} F_{n-i+2}$ for $2 \leq i \leq n-1$, and $|W_{a_1 b_1}| = |W_{a_n b_n}| = F_{n+1}$. Therefore by Theorem 7.5,

$$W(\Gamma_n) = \sum_{i=2}^{n-1} (F_i F_{n-i+1} F_{i+1} F_{n-i+2}) + 2 F_n F_{n+1}$$

$$= \sum_{i=1}^{n} F_i F_{n-i+1} F_{i+1} F_{n-i+2},$$

which is the content of the theorem.   □

In order to obtain a closed formula for $W(\Gamma_n)$ we apply the Greene and Wilf theory presented in Section 3.5. The values of $\sum_{i=0}^{n-1} F_i F_{n-i+1} F_{i+1} F_{n-i+2}$ for $n \in \{0, 1, \ldots, 5\}$ are 0, 0, 2, 10, 39, 136, respectively. Hence the values of the linear combination

$$a F_n^2 + b F_{n+1}^2 + c F_n F_{n+1} + d n F_n^2 + e n F_{n+1}^2 + f n F_n F_{n+1}$$

must be

$$\begin{pmatrix} 0 & 1 & 0 & 0 & 0 & 0 \\ 1 & 1 & 1 & 1 & 1 & 1 \\ 1 & 4 & 2 & 2 & 8 & 4 \\ 4 & 9 & 6 & 12 & 27 & 18 \\ 9 & 25 & 15 & 36 & 100 & 60 \\ 25 & 64 & 40 & 125 & 320 & 200 \end{pmatrix} \begin{pmatrix} a \\ b \\ c \\ d \\ e \\ f \end{pmatrix} = \begin{pmatrix} 0 \\ 0 \\ 2 \\ 10 \\ 39 \\ 136 \end{pmatrix},$$

whose solution is found to be $a = \frac{4}{25}$, $b = 0$, $c = -\frac{23}{25}$, $d = \frac{4}{25}$, $e = \frac{6}{25}$, and $f = \frac{9}{25}$. Hence we have

$$\sum_{i=0}^{n-1} F_i F_{n-i+1} F_{i+1} F_{n-i+2} = \frac{4}{25} F_n^2 + \frac{4}{25} n F_n^2 - \frac{23}{25} F_n F_{n+1}$$

$$+ \frac{9}{25} n F_n F_{n+1} + \frac{6}{25} n F_{n+1}^2.$$

Since

$$W(\Gamma_n) = \sum_{i=1}^{n} F_i F_{n-i+1} F_{i+1} F_{n-i+2} = F_n F_{n+1} + \sum_{i=0}^{n-1} F_i F_{n-i+1} F_{i+1} F_{n-i+2} \,,$$

we have derived the following result.

Theorem 7.7. [62, Theorem 3.2] *If $n \geq 0$, then*

$$W(\Gamma_n) = \tfrac{1}{25}\left(4(n+1)F_n^2 + (9n+2)F_n F_{n+1} + 6n F_{n+1}^2\right).$$

We will consider the asymptotic behavior of $W(\Gamma_n)$ in Chapter 10.

7.3 Irregularity

As we first discussed in Section 3.6, Fibonacci cubes have a considerable variety of vertex degrees. It is therefore interesting to consider the extent of their "degree of irregularity." To quantify this, define the *imbalance* $\mathrm{imb}_G(e)$ of an edge $e = uv \in E(G)$ by

$$\mathrm{imb}_G(e) = |\deg_G(u) - \deg_G(v)|\,.$$

The imbalance of an edge is thus a local measure of non-regularity. To measure graph's global non-regularity, different approaches have been proposed. One of the most natural such measures is the *irregularity* $\mathrm{irr}(G)$ of G introduced by Michael Albertson [1] as follows:

$$\mathrm{irr}(G) = \sum_{uv \in E(G)} |\deg_G(u) - \deg_G(v)| = \sum_{e \in E(G)} \mathrm{imb}_G(e)\,.$$

As it turns out, the irregularity of the Fibonacci cubes is very interesting, as the following result which was first proved by Alizadeh, Deutsch and Klavžar demonstrates. This was followed by two alternative proofs which will be presented in the following subsections.

Theorem 7.8. [2, Theorem 4.1] *If $n \geq 2$, then*

$$\mathrm{irr}(\Gamma_n) = \frac{2}{5}\left((n-1)F_n + 2nF_{n-1}\right) = 2m(\Gamma_{n-1})\,.$$

Proof. The second equality is a consequence of Proposition 3.2.

From Section 3.3 recall the fundamental decomposition $\mathcal{F}_n = \mathcal{F}_n^{0\bullet} + \mathcal{F}_n^{10\bullet}$ of Γ_n. By further splitting the set $\mathcal{F}_n^{0\bullet}$ into $\mathcal{F}_n^{00\bullet}$ and $\mathcal{F}_n^{010\bullet}$, the fundamental decomposition is transformed into

$$\mathcal{F}_n = \mathcal{F}_n^{00\bullet} + \mathcal{F}_n^{010\bullet} + \mathcal{F}_n^{10\bullet}\,.$$

In addition, the subgraphs induced by $\mathcal{F}_n^{00\bullet}$, $\mathcal{F}_n^{010\bullet}$, and $\mathcal{F}_n^{10\bullet}$ are isomorphic to Γ_{n-2}, Γ_{n-3}, and Γ_{n-2}, respectively.

The definition of the irregularity of a graph G extends naturally to its subgraphs as follows. If H is a subgraph of G, then $\mathrm{irr}_G(E(H))$ is

$$\sum_{uv \in E(H)} |\deg_G(u) - \deg_G(v)|,$$

that is, $\mathrm{irr}_G(E(H))$ is the contribution of the edges from H to $\mathrm{irr}(G)$.

The proof now proceeds by induction on n. By a direct computation we see that $\mathrm{irr}(\Gamma_2) = 2$, $\mathrm{irr}(\Gamma_3) = 4$, $\mathrm{irr}(\Gamma_4) = 10$, and $\mathrm{irr}(\Gamma_5) = 20$, hence the stated formula holds for $n \le 5$. Assume now that $n \ge 6$. Using the above notation we have the following facts:

(i) $\mathrm{irr}_{\Gamma_n}(E(\Gamma_n[\mathcal{F}_n^{10\bullet}])) = \mathrm{irr}(\Gamma_{n-2})$,

(ii) $\mathrm{irr}_{\Gamma_n}(E(\Gamma_n[\mathcal{F}_n^{010\bullet}])) = \mathrm{irr}(\Gamma_{n-3})$,

(iii) $\mathrm{irr}_{\Gamma_n}(E(\Gamma_n[\mathcal{F}_n^{00\bullet}])) = \mathrm{irr}(\Gamma_{n-2}) + F_{n-2}$,

(iv) the contribution of the edges between $\mathcal{F}_n^{00\bullet}$ and $\mathcal{F}_n^{10\bullet}$ to $\mathrm{irr}(\Gamma_n)$ is $F_{n-2} + F_{n-3}$,

(v) the contribution of the edges between $\mathcal{F}_n^{00\bullet}$ and $\mathcal{F}_n^{010\bullet}$ to $\mathrm{irr}(\Gamma_n)$ is $2F_{n-2} + F_{n-3}$.

The first fact follows because each vertex from $\Gamma_n[\mathcal{F}_n^{10\bullet}]$ has exactly one neighbor not in the subgraph. The second fact follows by a parallel argument. The arguments for the other three facts are a little more involved, but are not difficult. For instance, consider the edges uv between $\mathcal{F}_n^{00\bullet}$ and $\mathcal{F}_n^{010\bullet}$. Then $u = 000u_4 \ldots u_n$ and $v = 010u_4 \ldots u_n$. Among such edges, the edges where $u = 0000u_5 \ldots u_n$ contribute $2F_{n-2}$ and the edges where $u = 00010u_6 \ldots u_n$ contribute F_{n-3}.

All edges of Γ_n are accounted for in the five cases above as there are no edges between $\mathcal{F}_n^{10\bullet}$ and $\mathcal{F}_n^{010\bullet}$. It follows that

$$\mathrm{irr}(\Gamma_n) = 2\mathrm{irr}(\Gamma_{n-2}) + \mathrm{irr}(\Gamma_{n-3}) + 4F_{n-2} + 2F_{n-3}$$
$$= 2\mathrm{irr}(\Gamma_{n-2}) + \mathrm{irr}(\Gamma_{n-3}) + 2F_n .$$

Using the induction assumption we get

$$\mathrm{irr}(\Gamma_n) = \frac{4}{5}\Big((n-3)F_{n-2} + 2(n-2)F_{n-3}\Big)$$
$$+ \frac{2}{5}\Big((n-4)F_{n-3} + 2(n-3)F_{n-4}\Big) + 2F_n$$
$$= \frac{2}{5}\Big((n-1)F_n + 2nF_{n-1}\Big),$$

where the last equality follows by a lengthy but straightforward computation using the definition of the Fibonacci numbers. $\square$

7.3.1 *Irregularity Polynomial*

The method described above leading to the proof of Theorem 7.8 can be extended to a more general context as presented in this subsection. In this way not only the theorem can be proved, but additional results can be deduced and extended to Lucas cubes.

Eğecioğlu, E. Saygı, and Z. Saygı introduced in [35] the *irregularity polynomial* of a graph G as

$$I_G(x) = \sum_{uv \in E(G)} x^{|\deg_G(u) - \deg_G(v)|},$$

which carries the irregularity information of the graph in more detail. Namely, it enumerates the number of edges in $E(G)$ having a fixed imbalance, that is, the coefficient of x^r in $I_G(x)$ is the number of edges $e \in E(G)$ with $\mathrm{imb}_G(e) = r$. In particular, the constant term of $I_G(x)$ is the number of edges e with $\mathrm{imb}_G(e) = 0$. Hence, if G is regular, then $I_G(x) = m(G)$, while in general $m(G) = I_G(1)$. From our point of view it is most important that

$$\mathrm{irr}(G) = \frac{d}{dx} I_G(x) \bigg|_{x=1} = I_G'(1).$$

To simplify the notation, in the rest of the section let $I_n(x) = I_{\Gamma_n}(x)$ denote the irregularity polynomial of Γ_n.

Theorem 7.9. [35, Theorem 1] *For $n \geq 4$,*

$$I_n(x) = 2I_{n-1}(x) + I_{n-2}(x) - 2I_{n-3}(x) - I_{n-4}(x)$$

with $I_0(x) = 0$, $I_1(x) = 1$, $I_2(x) = 2x$ and $I_3(x) = x^2 + 2x + 2$.

Proof. The values of $I_n(x)$ for $n \leq 4$ can be easily obtained directly. Assume that $n \geq 4$. Using the fundamental decomposition of Γ_n, the proof now mimics the proof of Theorem 7.8 by establishing the following facts.

(i) The edges from $E(\Gamma_n[\mathcal{F}_n^{10\bullet}])$ contribute $I_{n-2}(x)$ to $I_n(x)$.

(ii) The edges from $E(\Gamma_n[\mathcal{F}_n^{010\bullet}])$ contribute $I_{n-3}(x)$ to $I_n(x)$.

(iii) The edges from $E(\Gamma_n[\mathcal{F}_n^{00\bullet}])$ contribute $I_{n-1}(x) - I_{n-3}(x) - (F_{n-2}x + F_{n-3})$ to $I_n(x)$.

(iv) The edges between $\mathcal{F}_n^{00\bullet}$ and $\mathcal{F}_n^{10\bullet}$ contribute $F_{n-1}x + F_{n-2}$ to $I_n(x)$.

(v) The edges between $\mathcal{F}_n^{00\bullet}$ and $\mathcal{F}_n^{010\bullet}$ contribute $x(F_{n-2}x + F_{n-3}) = F_{n-2}x^2 + F_{n-3}x$ to $I_n(x)$.

Summing up the above contributions we obtain

$$I_n(x) = I_{n-1}(x) + I_{n-2}(x) + F_{n-2}x^2 + 2F_{n-3}x + F_{n-4}\,.$$

To eliminate the terms which involve Fibonacci numbers, write

$$I_{n+1}(x) = I_n(x) + I_{n-1}(x) + F_{n-1}x^2 + 2F_{n-2}x + F_{n-3}$$

and

$$I_{n+2}(x) = I_{n+1}(x) + I_n(x) + F_n x^2 + 2F_{n-1}x + F_{n-2}\,.$$

By adding the first two of the above three equations and using the recursion of Fibonacci numbers we obtain

$$I_{n+1}(x) = 2I_{n-1}(x) + I_{n-2}(x) + F_n x^2 + 2F_{n-1}x + F_{n-2}\,.$$

The last two equations then give

$$F_n x^2 + 2F_{n-1}x + F_{n-2} = I_{n+2}(x) - I_{n+1}(x) - I_n(x)$$
$$= I_{n+1}(x) - 2I_{n-1}(x) - I_{n-2}(x)\,,$$

which gives the claimed result.   □

Consider next the generating function $I(x,t)$ of the sequence $(I_n(x))_{n\geq 0}$, that is,

$$I(x,t) = \sum_{n\geq 0} I_n(x)t^n = t + 2xt^2 + (x^2 + 2x + 2)t^3 + \cdots$$

Using Theorem 7.9, we obtain a closed form for $I(x,t)$.

Corollary 7.10. [35, Corollary 1] *The generating function of the sequence $(I_n(x))_{n\geq 0}$ of the irregularity polynomials $I_n(x)$ of Γ_n is given by*

$$I(x,t) = \sum_{n\geq 0} I_n(x)t^n = \frac{t\big(1 + (x-1)t\big)^2}{(1 - t - t^2)^2}\,.$$

Proof. Multiplying the identity of Theorem 7.9 by t^n and summing for all $n \geq 4$ we get

$$\sum_{n\geq 4} I_n(x)t^n = \sum_{n\geq 4} \big(2I_{n-1}(x) + I_{n-2}(x) - 2I_{n-3}(x) - I_{n-4}(x)\big)t^n\,,$$

which in turn implies that

$$I(x,t) - \sum_{n=0}^{3} I_n(x)t^n = 2t\left(I(x,t) - \sum_{n=1}^{3} I_{n-1}(x)t^{n-1}\right)$$
$$+ t^2\left(I(x,t) - \sum_{n=2}^{3} I_{n-2}(x)t^{n-2}\right)$$
$$- 2t^3\big(I(x,t) - I_0(x)\big) - t^4 I(x,t)\,.$$

Using the polynomials $I_n(x)$, $0 \leq n \leq 3$, and some length but straightforward calculations, the result follows.   □

From Corollary 7.10 we next deduce a closed form for the polynomials $I_n(x)$ themselves.

Corollary 7.11. [35, Corollary 2] *If* $n \geq 2$ *and* $E_n = m(\Gamma_n)$, *then*

$$I_n(x) = E_n + 2E_{n-1}(x-1) + E_{n-2}(x-1)^2$$
$$= (E_n - 2E_{n-1} + E_{n-2}) + (2E_{n-1} - 2E_{n-2})x + E_{n-2}x^2 .$$

Proof. Recall from Section 3.5 that

$$\sum_{n \geq 0} E_n t^n = \frac{t}{(1 - t - t^2)^2} .$$

Combining this generating function with the one from Corollary 7.10 gives

$$I(x,t) = \sum_{n \geq 0} I_n(x)t^n = \frac{t}{(1-t-t^2)^2}\left(1 + (x-1)t\right)^2$$
$$= \left(\sum_{n \geq 0} E_n t^n\right)\left(1 + 2(x-1)t + (x-1)^2 t^2\right) ,$$

from which we can read the result. $\qquad \square$

Since $\mathrm{irr}(G) = I'_G(1)$, Theorem 7.8 follows from the first expression of Corollary 7.11. This is the first of the two announced alternative proofs of Theorem 7.8.

The second expression of Corollary 7.11 provides formulas for the number of edges $uv \in E(\Gamma_n)$ for which $|\deg_{\Gamma_n}(u) - \deg_{\Gamma_n}(v)| = r$. Denoting this number by $\delta_r(\Gamma_n)$ for $n \geq 2$, we clearly have

$$\delta_r(\Gamma_n) = 0, \quad r \geq 2 ,$$

as $I_n(x)$ is a quadratic polynomial. For $r \in \{0, 1, 2\}$, the following formulas hold:

$$\delta_0(\Gamma_n) = E_n - 2E_{n-1} + E_{n-2} = \tfrac{1}{5}(nL_{n-3} + 2F_n)$$
$$\delta_1(\Gamma_n) = 2E_{n-1} - 2E_{n-2} = \tfrac{2}{5}(nL_{n-2} + F_n)$$
$$\delta_2(\Gamma_n) = E_{n-2} = \tfrac{1}{5}(nL_{n-1} - 2F_n) ,$$

where Proposition 3.2 is used together with (1.10). These in turn give the higher moments of $|\deg_{\Gamma_n}(u) - \deg_{\Gamma_n}(v)|$ over $uv \in E(\Gamma_n)$ as

$$\sum_{uv \in E(\Gamma_n)} |\deg_{\Gamma_n}(u) - \deg_{\Gamma_n}(v)|^m = \delta_1(\Gamma_n) + 2^m \delta_2(\Gamma_n)$$

$$= 2m(\Gamma_{n-1}) + (2^m - 2)m(\Gamma_{n-2}) .$$

7.3.2   *A Bijection for* irr(Γ_n)

In this subsection, we will present yet another proof of Theorem 7.8 giving a direct explanation of the simple relation irr(Γ_n) $= 2m(\Gamma_{n-1})$. It is due to Mollard [76] and is bijective in its nature. The proof constructs a one-to-one correspondence between the edges of Γ_{n-1} and certain pairs of edges that in turn reflect the contributions to the irregularity of Γ_n.

Let G be an induced subgraph of the n-cube Q_n. Let $e = xy \in E(G)$, where $x_i = 1$ and $y_i = 0$, so that $x_j = y_j$ for all $j \in [n] \setminus \{i\}$. Recall from the beginning of Chapter 3 that we can write $x = y + \delta_i$ as well as $y = x + \delta_i$. Now, we say that an edge $e' = y(y + \delta_j)$ of G is an *imbalanced edge for e* if $x + \delta_j \notin V(G)$. Note that in this case the edge between x and $x + \delta_j$ is not in $E(G)$.

Let us illustrate the above key definition in Fig. 7.1, where Γ_3 is drawn in blue as a subgraph of Q_3. Consider the edge $e \in E(\Gamma_3)$ between vertices $y = 000$ and $x = 010$. Selecting $j = 1$, the edge e' between $y = 000$ and $y + \delta_1 = 100$ is an imbalanced edge for e because $x + \delta_1 = 110$ does not lie in $V(\Gamma_3)$.

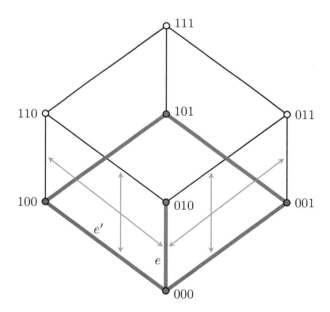

Fig. 7.1   Imbalanced edges in Γ_3

The key insight now is that if e' is an imbalanced edge for $e = xy$, then e' contributes 1 to the degree of y in G, while the edge between x and $x + \delta_j$ does not contribute to the degree of x in G. That is, the pair (e, e') contributes 1 to the imbalance of G. See Fig. 7.1 again, where the edge connected to e' by a double red arrow does not contribute to $\deg_{\Gamma_3}(010)$, while e' contributes 1 to $\deg_{\Gamma_3}(000)$. We also point out that the roles of the edges e and e' can be reversed. That is, starting with the edge e' and selecting $j = 2$ we infer that the edge e is an imbalanced edge for e', so that the pair (e', e) also contributes 1 to the imbalance of G. In the figure this is indicated by the leftmost arrow. There are exactly two more such pairs as indicated in the figure. In Fig. 7.1 we have found four imbalanced pairs of edges which is equal to irr(Γ_3). We claim that this holds in general, that is, there are $2E(\Gamma_{n-1})$ such pairs of edges. Let $e = xy \in E(\Gamma_n)$, where $x_i = 1$ and $y_i = 0$. Let $e' = y(y + \delta_j)$ be an imbalanced edge for e. Then we easily infer that either $j = i + 1$ or $j = i - 1$. Note that if $i = 1$ or $i = n$, then clearly only one case is possible. We say that e' a *right imbalanced edge* for e if $j = i + 1$, otherwise e' a *left imbalanced edge* for e. Let

$$R_{\Gamma_n} = \{(e, e') : e \in E(\Gamma_n),\ e' \text{ is a right imbalanced edge for } e\}$$

and

$$L_{\Gamma_n} = \{(e, e') : e \in E(\Gamma_n),\ e' \text{ is a left imbalanced edge for } e\}.$$

We now claim that $|R_{\Gamma_n}| = m(\Gamma_{n-1}) = |L_{\Gamma_n}|$. Let

$$\alpha : R_{\Gamma_n} \to E(\Gamma_{n-1})$$

be defined as follows. If $(e, e') \in R_{\Gamma_n}$, where $e = xy$ with $x_i = 1$, $y_i = 0$, and $i \in [1, n-1]$, then set

$$\alpha((e, e')) = (x_1 \ldots x_{i-1} 1 x_{i+2} \ldots x_n)(x_1 \ldots x_{i-1} 0 x_{i+2} \ldots x_n).$$

It is not difficult to prove that α is one-to-one, hence $|R_{\Gamma_n}| = m(\Gamma_{n-1})$. Similarly it can be shown that $|L_{\Gamma_n}| = m(\Gamma_{n-1})$. Technical details can be found in [76].

7.4   Mostar Index

Let G be a graph. For an edge $uv \in E(G)$, let $n_u(G)$ denote the number of vertices in $V(G)$ that are closer to u than to v; and let $n_v(G)$ denote the number of vertices in $V(G)$ that are closer to v than to u. When G is clear from the context, we may write $n_u = n_u(G)$ and $n_v = n_v(G)$. The *Mostar index* of G which was introduced in the context of the study of the properties of chemical graphs in [27]. It is defined by

$$\text{Mo}(G) = \sum_{uv \in E(G)} |n_u(G) - n_v(G)|.$$

7.4.1   *Mostar Index of Fibonacci Cubes*

The Mostar index of Fibonacci cubes was determined by Eğecioğlu, E. Saygı, and Z. Saygı as presented in this subsection. For the main result, a couple of lemmas are needed.

Lemma 7.12. [36, Lemma 1] *For $n \geq 2$, assume that $uv \in E(\Gamma_n)$ with $u_k = 0$ and $v_k = 1$ for some $k \in [n]$. Then $n_u(\Gamma_n) = F_{k+1}F_{n-k+2}$ and $n_v(\Gamma_n) = F_k F_{n-k+1}$.*

Proof. The result is clear for $n = 2$. Assume that $n \geq 3$, $1 < k < n$, and let $\alpha \in V(\Gamma_n)$ have string representation $b_1 b_2 \ldots b_n$. Since $uv \in E(\Gamma_n)$, u and v must be of the form $a_1 \ldots a_{k-1} 0 a_{k+1} \ldots a_n$ and $a_1 \ldots a_{k-1} 1 a_{k+1} \ldots a_n$, respectively. Since $v \in V(\Gamma_n)$ we must have $a_{k-1} = a_{k+1} = 0$. From these representations we observe that the difference between $d(\alpha, u)$ and $d(\alpha, v)$ depends on the value of b_k only. If $b_k = 0$ we have $d(\alpha, u) = d(\alpha, v) - 1$ and if $b_k = 1$ we have $d(\alpha, u) = d(\alpha, v) + 1$. Therefore, the vertices whose k^{th} coordinate is 0 are closer to u than to v; and the vertices whose k^{th} coordinate is 1 are closer to v than to u. This means $n_u(\Gamma_n)$ is equal to the number of vertices in Γ_n whose k^{th} coordinate is 0. These vertices have string representation of the form $\beta_1 0 \beta_2$ where β_1 is a Fibonacci string of length $k - 1$ and β_2 is a Fibonacci string of length $n - k$. Consequently $n_u(\Gamma_n) = F_{k+1}F_{n-k+2}$. Similarly $n_u(\Gamma_n)$ is number of Fibonacci strings of the form $\beta_3 010 \beta_4$, and this is given by $F_k F_{n-k+1}$.

For the case $k = 1$ we have $u \in V(0\Gamma_{n-1})$ and $v \in V(10\Gamma_{n-2})$. Therefore $n_u(\Gamma_n) = |V(0\Gamma_{n-1})| = F_{n+1}$ and $n_v(\Gamma_n) = |V(10\Gamma_{n-2})| = F_n$. Similarly, for $k = n$ we have $u \in V(\Gamma_{n-1}0)$ and $v \in V(\Gamma_{n-2}01)$. This gives again $n_u(\Gamma_n) = F_{n+1}$ and $n_v(\Gamma_n) = F_n$ for $k = n$. As $F_1 = F_2 = 1$, these are also of the form claimed. $\square$

To calculate $\text{Mo}(\Gamma_n)$, we only need to find the number of edges uv in Γ_n for which $u_k = 0$ and $v_k = 1$ for a fixed $k \in [n]$ and add up these contributions over k.

Lemma 7.13. [36, Lemma 2] *For $n \geq 2$, assume that $uv \in E(\Gamma_n)$ with $u_k = 0$ and $v_k = 1$ for some $k \in [n]$. Then the number of such edges in Γ_n is equal to $F_k F_{n-k+1}$.*

Proof. As in the proof of Lemma 7.12, the result is clear for $n = 2$. Assume that $n \geq 3$. For $1 < k < n$ we know that u and v are of the form $a_1 \ldots a_{k-2}000a_{k+2} \ldots a_n$ and $a_1 \ldots a_{k-2}010a_{k+2} \ldots a_n$. Then the number edges uv in Γ_n satisfying $u_k = 0$ and $v_k = 1$ is equal to the number of vertices of the form $a_1 \ldots a_{k-2}000a_{k+2} \ldots a_n$, which gives the desired result.

For the boundary cases $k = 1$ and $k = n$ we need to find the number of vertices of the form $00a_3 \ldots a_n$ and $a_1 \ldots a_{n-2}00$, respectively. Clearly, this number is equal to $|V(00\Gamma_{n-2})| = F_n$ and $F_1 = 1$. This completes the proof. $\qquad \square$

Using Lemma 7.12 and Lemma 7.13 the following main result is obtained.

Theorem 7.14. [36, Theorem 1] *If* $n \geq 2$, *then*

$$\mathrm{Mo}(\Gamma_n) = \sum_{k=1}^{n} F_k F_{n-k+1} \left(F_{k+1} F_{n-k+2} - F_k F_{n-k+1} \right). \qquad (7.2)$$

Proof. Let $uv \in E(\Gamma_n)$ with $u_k = 0$ and $v_k = 1$ for some fixed $k \in [n]$. Then from Lemma 7.12 we know that

$$|n_u - n_v| = F_{k+1} F_{n-k+2} - F_k F_{n-k+1}$$

and therefore using Lemma 7.13 we have

$$\mathrm{Mo}(\Gamma_n) = \sum_{uv \in E(\Gamma_n)} |n_u - n_v|$$

$$= \sum_{k=1}^{n} F_k F_{n-k+1} \left(F_{k+1} F_{n-k+2} - F_k F_{n-k+1} \right).$$

$\qquad \square$

Note that $F_{k+1} F_{n-k+2} - F_k F_{n-k+1} = F_k F_{n-k} + F_{k-1} F_{n-k+2}$, so that we can equivalently write

$$\mathrm{Mo}(\Gamma_n) = \sum_{k=1}^{n} F_k F_{n-k+1} \left(F_k F_{n-k} + F_{k-1} F_{n-k+2} \right),$$

in which there are no cancellations on the right.

7.4.2 *A Closed Formula for* $\mathrm{Mo}(\Gamma_n)$

A closed form formula for $\mathrm{Mo}(\Gamma_n)$ can be obtained by using the theory of generating functions. By the fundamental decomposition of Γ_n, the set of edges $E(\Gamma_n)$ consists of three distinct types:

(i) The edges in $0\Gamma_{n-1}$, which we denote by $E(0\Gamma_{n-1})$.

(ii) The link edges between $10\Gamma_{n-2}$ and $00\Gamma_{n-2} \subset 0\Gamma_{n-1}$, which we denote by C_n.

(iii) The edges in $10\Gamma_{n-2}$, which we denote by $E(10\Gamma_{n-2})$.

We keep track of the contribution of each part of this decomposition by setting for $n \geq 2$,

$$M_n(x, y, z) = \sum_{uv \in E(0\Gamma_{n-1})} |n_u - n_v|x + \sum_{uv \in C_n} |n_u - n_v|y$$
$$+ \sum_{uv \in E(10\Gamma_{n-2})} |n_u - n_v|z. \qquad (7.3)$$

Clearly, $\mathrm{Mo}(\Gamma_n) = M_n(1, 1, 1)$. By direct inspection we observe that

$$M_2 = x + y$$
$$M_3 = 4x + 2y + z$$
$$M_4 = 16x + 6y + 6z$$
$$M_5 = 54x + 15y + 23z$$

which gives

$$\mathrm{Mo}(\Gamma_2) = M_2(1, 1, 1) = 2$$
$$\mathrm{Mo}(\Gamma_3) = M_3(1, 1, 1) = 7$$
$$\mathrm{Mo}(\Gamma_4) = M_4(1, 1, 1) = 28$$
$$\mathrm{Mo}(\Gamma_5) = M_5(1, 1, 1) = 92,$$

consistent with the values that are calculated using Theorem 7.14.

Proposition 7.15. [36, Proposition 1] *If $n \geq 2$, then*

$$M_n(x, y, z) = M_{n-1}(x + z, 0, x) + M_{n-2}(2x + z, x + z, x + z)$$
$$+ F_{n-1}(F_n + F_{n-2})x + F_nF_{n-1}y,$$

where $M_0(x, y, z) = M_1(x, y, z) = 0$.

Proof. By the definition (7.3), there are three cases to consider.

Case 1: $uv \in C_n$, where $u \in V(0\Gamma_{n-1})$ and $v \in V(10\Gamma_{n-2})$.

We know that $d(u, v) = 1$ and the string representations of u and v must be of the form $00b_3 \ldots b_n$ and $10b_3 \ldots b_n$, respectively. Then using Lemma 7.12 with $k = 1$ we have $|n_u - n_v| = F_{n+1} - F_n = F_{n-1}$ for each edge uv in C_n. As $|C_n| = F_n$ all of these edges contribute $F_nF_{n-1}y$ to $M_n(x, y, z)$.

Case 2: $uv \in E(10\Gamma_{n-2})$.

Let the string representations of u and v be $10u_3 \ldots u_n$ and $10v_3 \ldots v_n$, respectively. Using the fundamental decomposition of Γ_n there exist vertices of the form $u' = 0u_3 \ldots u_n$ and $v' = 0v_3 \ldots v_n$ in $V(\Gamma_{n-1})$; $u'' = u_3 \ldots u_n$ and $v'' = v_3 \ldots v_n$ in $V(\Gamma_{n-2})$. Then n_u counts the number of vertices 0α in $V(0\Gamma_{n-1})$ and $10\beta \in V(10\Gamma_{n-2})$ satisfying $d(0\alpha, u) < d(0\alpha, v)$ and $d(10\beta, u) < d(10\beta, v)$. For any $0\alpha \in V(0\Gamma_{n-1})$ we know that $d(0\alpha, u) = d(\alpha, u')+1$ and $d(0\alpha, v) = d(\alpha, 0v')+1$. Therefore, for a fixed $0\alpha \in V(0\Gamma_{n-1})$, $d(\alpha, u') < d(\alpha, v')$ if and only if $d(0\alpha, u) < d(0\alpha, v)$. Similarly, for any $10\beta \in V(10\Gamma_{n-2})$ we have $d(10\beta, u) = d(\beta, u'')$ and $d(\beta, v) = d(\beta, v'')$. Then we can write

$$\sum_{uv \in E(10\Gamma_{n-2})} \left| n_u(\Gamma_n) - n_v(\Gamma_n) \right| = \sum_{u'v' \in E(\Gamma_{n-1})} \left| n_{u'}(\Gamma_{n-1}) - n_{v'}(\Gamma_{n-1}) \right|$$

$$+ \sum_{u''v'' \in E(\Gamma_{n-2})} \left| n_{u''}(\Gamma_{n-2}) - n_{v''}(\Gamma_{n-2}) \right|.$$

Note that $\Gamma_{n-1} = 0\Gamma_{n-2} + 10\Gamma_{n-3}$ and the edge $u'v' \in E(\Gamma_{n-1})$ is an edge in the set $E(0\Gamma_{n-2})$. Furthermore $u''v'' \in E(\Gamma_{n-2})$ is an arbitrary edge. Then by the definition (7.3) of M_n we have

$$\sum_{u'v' \in E(\Gamma_{n-1})} \left| n_{u'}(\Gamma_{n-1}) - n_{v'}(\Gamma_{n-1}) \right| = M_{n-1}(1,0,0)$$

and

$$\sum_{u''v'' \in E(\Gamma_{n-2})} \left| n_{u''}(\Gamma_{n-2}) - n_{v''}(\Gamma_{n-2}) \right| = M_{n-2}(1,1,1).$$

Hence all of these edges $uv \in E(10\Gamma_{n-2})$ contribute $\left(M_{n-1}(1,0,0) + M_{n-2}(1,1,1) \right)z$ to $M_n(x, y, z)$.

Case 3: $uv \in E(0\Gamma_{n-1})$.

Since $0\Gamma_{n-1} = 00\Gamma_{n-2} + 010\Gamma_{n-3}$ we have three subcases to consider here. For each of them, we give only the conclusion and invite the reader to look at the arguments for it in the proof of [36, Proposition 1]. If $uv \in C_{n-1}$, where $u \in 00\Gamma_{n-2}$ and $v \in 010\Gamma_{n-3}$, then all of these edges contribute $F_{n-1}(F_n + F_{n-2})x$ to $M_n(x, y, z)$. The edges $uv \in E(010\Gamma_{n-3})$ contribute $\left(M_{n-1}(0,0,1)+M_{n-2}(1,0,0) \right)x$ to $M_n(x, y, z)$. Finally, the edges $uv \in E(00\Gamma_{n-2})$ contribute $\left(M_{n-1}(1,0,0) + M_{n-2}(1,1,1) \right)x$ to $M_n(x, y, z)$.

Combining all of the above cases and noting that $M_{n-1}(0,0,1)x = M_{n-1}(0,0,x)$, $M_{n-2}(1,0,0)x = M_{n-2}(x,0,0)$, and $M_{n-2}(1,1,1)x = M_{n-2}(x,x,x)$, we complete the proof. □

If we write $M_n(x, y, z) = a_n x + b_n y + c_n z$, then from the recursion in Proposition 7.15, we obtain for $n \geq 2$ the system of recursions

$$a_n = a_{n-1} + c_{n-1} + 2a_{n-1} + b_{n-2} + c_{n-2} + F_{n-1}(F_n + F_{n-2}),$$

$$b_n = F_n F_{n-1},$$

$$c_n = a_{n-1} + a_{n-2} + b_{n-2} + c_{n-2}.$$

Eliminating b_n, this is equivalent to the system

$$a_n = a_{n-1} + 2a_{n-1} + c_{n-1} + c_{n-2} + F_{n-2}F_{n-3} + F_{n-1}F_{n-2} + F_n F_{n-1}.$$
$$c_n = a_{n-1} + a_{n-2} + c_{n-2} + F_{n-2}F_{n-3}. \tag{7.4}$$

Let $A(t)$, $B(t)$, and $C(t)$ be the generating functions of the sequences a_n, b_n, and c_n, $(n \geq 2)$, respectively. It is already known ([98, A001654]) that

$$B(t) = \sum_{n \geq 2} F_n F_{n-1} t^n = \frac{t^2}{(1+t)(1-3t+t^2)}. \tag{7.5}$$

From (7.4) we obtain

$$A(t) = (t + 2t^2)A(t) + (t + t^2)C(t) + (1 + t + t^2)B(t) \tag{7.6}$$
$$C(t) = (t + t^2)A(t) + t^2 C(t) + t^2 B(t).$$

Solving the system (7.6) and using (7.5) we find

$$A(t) = \frac{t^2}{(1+t)^2(1-3t+t^2)^2} \quad \text{and} \quad C(t) = \frac{t^3 + 2t^4 - t^5}{(1+t)^2(1-3t+t^2)^2}. \tag{7.7}$$

Since $\mathrm{Mo}(\Gamma_n) = M_n(1,1,1) = a_n + b_n + c_n$, adding the generating functions $A(t)$, $B(t)$, and $C(t)$ we obtain

$$\sum_{n \geq 2} \mathrm{Mo}(\Gamma_n)t^n = \frac{(2-t)t^2}{(1+t)^2(1-3t+t^2)^2}. \tag{7.8}$$

Using partial fractions decomposition in (7.8) and the expansions

$$\frac{1}{1-3t+t^2} = \sum_{n \geq 0} F_{2n+2} t^n, \tag{7.9}$$

$$\frac{1}{(1-3t+t^2)^2} = \sum_{n \geq 0} \tfrac{1}{5}\big((4n+2)F_{2n+2} + (3n+3)F_{2n+1}\big)t^n, \tag{7.10}$$

we obtain

$$\mathrm{Mo}(\Gamma_n) = \tfrac{1}{25}\big((3n+2)(-1)^n + (4n-5)F_{2n+2}$$
$$+ (3n+3)F_{2n+1} - (4n-3)F_{2n} - 3nF_{2n-1}\big),$$

which can be simplified to the closed form expression for $\mathrm{Mo}(\Gamma_n)$ in Theorem 7.16. This is another way of writing the sum given in Theorem 7.14.

Theorem 7.16. [36, Theorem 3] *The Mostar index of Fibonacci cube Γ_n is given by*

$$\mathrm{Mo}(\Gamma_n) = \tfrac{1}{25}\big((3n-2)F_{2n+2} + nF_{2n+1} + (3n+2)(-1)^n\big).$$

7.4.3 Connection to Wiener Index

Here we point out a relation between the Mostar index and the Wiener index for Fibonacci cubes, giving an alternate expression to the closed formula for $W(\Gamma_n)$ given in Theorem 7.7. We recall that by Theorem 7.6,

$$W(\Gamma_n) = \sum_{i=1}^{n} F_i F_{i+1} F_{n-i+1} F_{n-i+2}. \tag{7.11}$$

In view of formula (7.2), of Theorem 7.14, and of (7.11), this means that

$$W(\Gamma_n) = \mathrm{Mo}(\Gamma_n) + \sum_{i=1}^{n} (F_i F_{n-i+1})^2.$$

The sum above is the sequence [98, A136429] with the generating function

$$\frac{t(1-t)^2}{(1+t)^2(1-3t+t^2)^2}.$$

Adding the generating function in (7.8) to this, we get

$$\sum_{n\geq1} W(\Gamma_n)t^n = \frac{t}{(1+t)^2(1-3t+t^2)^2}. \tag{7.12}$$

Using partial fractions and the expansions (7.9) and (7.10), $W(\Gamma_n)$ $(n \geq 2)$ is found to be

$$W(\Gamma_n) = \tfrac{1}{25}\big((3n+2)F_{2n+3} + (n-2)F_{2n+2} - (n+2)(-1)^n\big),$$

which is an alternate expression to the one given in Theorem 7.7.

It is also curious that in view of the generating functions (7.7) and (7.12), which differ only by the factor of t, we have

$$a_n = M_n(1,0,0) = W(\Gamma_{n-1}).$$

In Section 9.8.5 we will continue to explore the relation between Mostar index and Wiener index in the more general context of daisy cubes.

Chapter 8

Lucas Cubes

Eight years after the Fibonacci cubes were introduced, their cyclic version was proposed by Munarini, Perelli Cippo, and Zagaglia Salvi in [81] under the name Lucas cubes. In this chapter we will study the properties of Lucas cubes and their close variants.

Let $n \geq 1$. A binary string $b_1 \ldots b_n$ belongs to the set $\mathscr{L}_n$ of *Lucas strings of length* n if it does not contain two consecutive 1s, when the string is considered circularly like a necklace. Another way to define the set of Lucas strings of length n is:

$$\mathscr{L}_n = \{b_1 \ldots b_n : b_i b_{i+1} = 0 \text{ for } i \in [n-1] \text{ and } b_n b_1 = 0\}.$$

The n-*dimensional Lucas cube* Λ_n has $V(\Lambda_n) = \mathscr{L}_n$, and two vertices are adjacent if they differ in exactly one coordinate. It is thus the subgraph of Q_n induced by Lucas strings. For convenience we will assume that the empty string belongs to $\mathscr{L}_0$ and set $\Lambda_0 = Q_0 = K_1$. See Fig. 8.1 for the first four Lucas cubes.

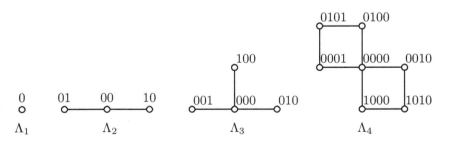

Fig. 8.1 Small Lucas cubes

8.1   Decomposition, Order, and Size

A Lucas string in $\mathscr{L}_n^{0\bullet}$ is a Fibonacci string. Furthermore, a Lucas string in $\mathscr{L}_n^{1\bullet}$ cannot start with 11 or end with 1. Therefore the set of Lucas strings of length n can be written for $n \geq 3$ as

$$\mathscr{L}_n = 0\mathscr{F}_{n-1} + 10\mathscr{F}_{n-3}0. \tag{8.1}$$

An immediate consequence is that $|\mathscr{L}_n| = F_{n+1} + F_{n-1}$ and therefore, by (1.10) we have the following fact.

Proposition 8.1. [81] *If $n \geq 1$, then $n(\Lambda_n) = L_n$.*

We can be more precise:

Proposition 8.2.   *The number of vertices of Hamming weight w in Λ_n is given by*

$$\binom{n-w}{w} + \binom{n-w-1}{w-1} = \frac{n}{n-w}\binom{n-w}{w}.$$

Proof. The mapping $s \mapsto 10s0$ is a bijection between Fibonacci strings of weight $w - 1$ in $\mathscr{F}_{n-3}$ and Lucas strings of weight w in $\mathscr{L}_n^{1\bullet}$. Similarly $s \mapsto 0s$ is a bijection between Fibonacci strings of weight w in $\mathscr{F}_{n-1}$ and Lucas strings of weight w in $\mathscr{L}_n^{0\bullet}$. The result follows.   □

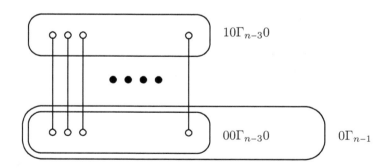

Fig. 8.2   Decomposition of the Lucas cube Λ_n in terms of Γ_{n-1} and Γ_{n-3}

From the partition (8.1) of $V(\Lambda_n)$ into $0\mathscr{F}_{n-1}$ and $10\mathscr{F}_{n-3}0$ we obtain a decomposition of Λ_n. Indeed there exist three kinds of edges in this decomposition:

(i) the edges of the Fibonacci cube $0\Gamma_{n-1}$,

(ii) the edges of the Fibonacci cube $10\Gamma_{n-3}0$,

(iii) the link edges between the two Fibonacci cubes.

More precisely, in case (iii), $10s0$ is adjacent to its mate $00s0$ for any $s \in \mathcal{F}_{n-3}$. See Fig. 8.2 and Fig. 8.3. We therefore have:

$$m(\Lambda_n) = m(\Gamma_{n-1}) + m(\Gamma_{n-3}) + n(\Gamma_{n-3}). \tag{8.2}$$

Lucas cubes can be also view as subgraphs of Fibonacci cubes obtained after removing all vertices that begin and end with 1; compare Fig. 8.3 and Fig. 3.6.

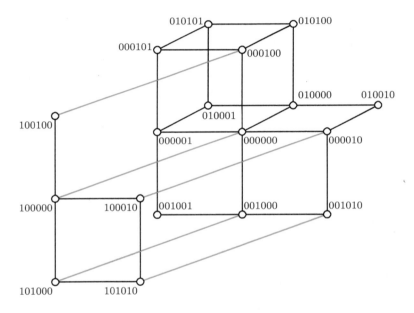

Fig. 8.3 The Lucas cube Λ_6

Most of the enumerative results about Fibonacci cubes use the fundamental recursive decomposition we introduced in Section 3.3. Note that the decomposition of Lucas cubes shown in Fig. 8.2 is not recursive but in terms of Fibonacci cubes. A consequence is that the proofs for the enumerative results for Lucas cubes are more varied. Some proofs are easy because they can use the cyclic nature of the constraint appearing in the definition of Lucas strings, whereas others are more technical because they use the decomposition of Lucas cubes and thus use results from Fibonacci cubes.

The determination of the size of Λ_n is an illustration of these two kinds of arguments.

Proposition 8.3. [81, Proposition 4] *If $n \geq 1$, then $m(\Lambda_n) = nF_{n-1}$.*

Proof. From the decomposition of Lucas cubes we deduce the relation (8.2). Using the expression on the size of Γ_n (Proposition 3.2) we obtain

$$m(\Lambda_n) = \tfrac{1}{5}((n-1)F_n + 2nF_{n-1}) + \tfrac{1}{5}((n-3)F_{n-2} + 2(n-2)F_{n-3}) + F_{n-1}.$$

After a quick calculation this number reduces to nF_{n-1}.   □

We can also give a bijection that illustrates the first kind of proof. Let $e = xy$ be an edge of Λ_n with $x_1 = 1$ and $y_1 = 0$. The string x can be decomposed as $x = 10s0$ where $s \in \mathcal{F}_{n-3}$. It is immediate that the mapping $e \mapsto s$ is one-to-one. Consequently, the number of edges using the first coordinate is $|\mathcal{F}_{n-3}| = F_{n-1}$. Because of the symmetry of the role of coordinates in the definition of Lucas cubes, the number of edges that use the direction i, $i \in [n]$, is the same and the result follows.

8.2   Sequence of Degrees

The Lucas cube Λ_n, $n \geq 2$, is not regular, the vertex 0^n is a vertex of maximum degree n. Using a technical computation similar to the proof of Theorem 3.4, the degree sequence of Lucas cubes can be determined.

Theorem 8.4. [65, Theorem 1.1] *For all $n \geq k \geq 0$ with $n \geq 2$, the number of vertices of Λ_n having degree k is*

$$\sum_{i=0}^{k} \left[2 \binom{i}{2i+k-n} \binom{n-2i-1}{k-i} + \binom{i-1}{2i+k-n} \binom{n-2i}{k-i} \right]. \qquad (8.3)$$

By our convention for the binomial coefficients, the expression under the summation sign is 0 when $i > \tfrac{1}{2}n$. In the same way as the corresponding result for Fibonacci cubes, we have a combinatorial interpretation of summands in (8.3).

Theorem 8.5. [65, Theorem 5.2] *For all n, k, w such that $n \geq k, w \geq 0$ and $n \geq 2$, the number of vertices of Λ_n of degree k and weight w is*

$$2 \binom{w}{2w+k-n} \binom{n-2w-1}{k-w} + \binom{w-1}{2w+k-n} \binom{n-2w}{k-w}.$$

Alternative proofs of the two previous theorems using generating functions are also proposed in [65].

From Theorem 8.5 we can also obtain the number of vertices of minimum degree in Lucas cubes.

Proposition 8.6. [65] *Let* $n \geq 2$. *The minimal degree of a vertex in* Λ_n *is* $\delta = \lfloor (n+2)/3 \rfloor$ *and the number of vertices of degree* δ *is*

$$\begin{cases} 3 & \text{if } n \equiv 0 \,(\text{mod}\,3), \\ \frac{1}{6}n(n+5) & \text{if } n \equiv 1 \,(\text{mod}\,3), \\ n & \text{if } n \equiv 2 \,(\text{mod}\,3). \end{cases}$$

8.3   Connectivity and Symmetry

In Theorem 3.7 we have determined the connectivity and the edge-connectivity of Fibonacci cubes. For Lucas cubes, these behave analogously, but with one exception: $\kappa(\Lambda_4) = 1$ and $\kappa'(\Lambda_4) = 2$.

Theorem 8.7. [7, Theorem 2.3] *If* $n \geq 1$ *and* $n \neq 4$, *then*

$$\kappa(\Lambda_n) = \kappa'(\Lambda_n) = \left\lfloor \frac{n+2}{3} \right\rfloor.$$

Proof. The proof proceeds similarly to the proof of Theorem 3.7, hence we only provide its sketch. First, the result has been checked for $n \leq 8$ by computer. Proceeding by induction, assume that the result is true for $n \leq 3k+2$, $k \geq 2$. Then the result is verified separately for the cases $n = 3k+3$, $n = 3k+4$, and $n = 3k+5$.

Let $n = 3k+3$. By (8.1) we have $\mathscr{L}_n = 0\mathscr{F}_{n-1} + 10\mathscr{F}_{n-3}0$. Let $X_{3k} \cong \Gamma_{3k}$ and $X_{3k+2} \cong \Gamma_{3k+2}$ be the subgraphs of Γ_{3k+3} induced by $10\mathscr{F}_{n-3}0$ and $0\mathscr{F}_{n-1}$, respectively. By Theorem 3.7, $\kappa(X_{3k}) = k$ and $\kappa(X_{3k+2}) = k + 1$. Then as in the proof of Theorem 3.7, we find that Λ_{3k+3} does not contain a separating set of cardinality k. Hence $\kappa(\Lambda_{3k+3}) \geq k + 1$ and by Proposition 8.6, $\kappa(\Lambda_{3k+3}) = k + 1$.

The cases $n = 3k + 4$ and $n = 3k + 5$ are treated similarly, where the first of these two cases requires a more careful, technical treatment. The omitted details can be found in [7]. □

The definition of Λ_n as a subgraph of Q_n induced by the binary strings of length n that have no two consecutive 1s in circular manner is more symmetric than the definition of Γ_n, hence one can intuitively expect that Lucas cubes have more symmetries than Fibonacci cubes. From Theorem 3.9 we know that $\mathrm{Aut}(\Gamma_n) \simeq \mathbb{Z}_2$ for every $n \geq 1$. To formulate the corresponding result for Lucas cubes, we need to recall from Page 49 that the dihedral group D_{2n} is the group of symmetries of a regular n-gon. D_{2n} is represented as $\langle x, y : x^2 = 1, y^n = 1, (xy)^2 = 1 \rangle$ (see Section 3.9).

Theorem 8.8. [20, Theorem 2.3] *If $n \geq 3$, then* $\mathrm{Aut}(\Lambda_n) \simeq D_{2n}$.

Proof. Recall from Section 3.8 that the reverse map $r : V(\Lambda_n) \to V(\Lambda_n)$ is defined by $r(b_1 b_2 \ldots b_n) = b^R = b_n b_{n-1} \ldots b_1$. Define further the map $s : \Lambda_n \to \Lambda_n$ by

$$s(b_1 b_2 \ldots b_n) = b_n b_1 \ldots b_{n-1}.$$

Let α be an arbitrary automorphism of Λ_n. As 0^n is the only vertex of degree n, we have $\alpha(0^n) = 0^n$. Hence α is bijective also when restricted to the set of neighbors of 0^n. Consider the neighbors 10^{n-1} and $0^{n-1}1$. Then α maps them into two neighbors of 0^n, say $\alpha(10^{n-1}) = 0^a 10^{n-a-1}$ and $\alpha(0^{n-1}1) = 0^b 10^{n-b-1}$, where $a, b \in \{0, 1, \ldots, n-1\}$ and computations are carried out mod n. We claim that then either $b = a - 1$ or $b = a + 1$. Indeed, if this would not be the case, then the vertices $\alpha(0^n) = 0^n$, $\alpha(10^{n-1})$ and $\alpha(0^{n-1}1)$ would lie in a 4-cycle, while the vertices 0^n, $\alpha(10^{n-1})$ and $\alpha(0^{n-1}1)$ do not lie in a 4-cycle, so α would not be an automorphism. Now, when $b = a - 1$ we get $\alpha = s^a$, and in the other case $\alpha = s^{a+1} \circ r$. We can conclude that $\mathrm{Aut}(\Lambda_n)$ is generated by r and s^a for $0 \leq a \leq n-1$, so $\mathrm{Aut}(\Lambda_n) \simeq D_{2n}$. $\qquad\square$

We can also count the number of orbits of Lucas cubes. As before, $o(\Lambda_n)$ denotes the number of orbits of Λ_n under the action of $\mathrm{Aut}(\Lambda_n)$ on $V(\Lambda_n)$, and $o_E(\Lambda_n)$ denotes the number of edge orbits of G under the action of $\mathrm{Aut}(\Lambda_n)$ on $E(\Lambda_n)$. To state the corresponding result, recall that the *Euler's phi function* (also know as the *Euler's totient function*) ϕ returns, for a given positive integer n, the number of integers in $[n]$ which are relatively prime to n. Now we have the following two formulas, the proofs of which are longer and somewhat technical, hence they are not included here.

Theorem 8.9. [20, Theorems 5.1 and 5.9] *If $n \geq 1$, then*

$$o_V(\Lambda_n) = \tfrac{1}{2} \left(\frac{1}{n} \sum_{d \mid n} \phi\left(\frac{n}{d}\right) L_d + F_{\lfloor n/2 \rfloor + 2} \right),$$

$$o_E(\Lambda_n) = \tfrac{1}{2} \left(F_{n-1} + F_{\left\lfloor \frac{n+1+(-1)^n}{2} \right\rfloor} \right).$$

8.4 Distance

By the same arguments we used for Γ_n in Section 4, it is immediate that if u and v are Lucas strings, then $d_{\Lambda_n}(u,v) = d_{\Gamma_n}(u,v) = d_{Q_n}(u,v) = H(u,v)$.

As noted in [81], the diameter of Λ_n is n for n even, and $n-1$ for n odd. Fixing a typo that appears therein, the following holds.

Proposition 8.10. [81, Proposition 1] *For n even, there exists a unique pair of vertices at distance n, the pair $\{(10)^{\frac{n}{2}}, (01)^{\frac{n}{2}}\}$. For n odd, there exist n pairs of vertices at distance $n-1$, which are the cyclic shifts of the pair $0(01)^{\frac{n-1}{2}}$ and $0(10)^{\frac{n-1}{2}}$.*

The authors of [81] proved also that the radius of Λ_n is $\lfloor n/2 \rfloor$. The eccentricity of a vertex in Λ_n thus lies between these bounds. The number of vertices with a given eccentricity have been determined as follows.

Theorem 8.11. [21, Theorem 5.16] *Let $\ell_{n,k}$ be the number of vertices of Λ_n having eccentricity k. Then the generating function for the eccentricity sequence is*

$$\ell(x,t) = \sum_{n,k \geq 0} \ell_{n,k}\, x^k t^n = \frac{1 + xt^2}{1 - xt - xt^2} + \frac{1}{1+xt} - \frac{1-t}{1-xt^2}. \tag{8.4}$$

We will give only a sketch of proof, for details we refer to the original paper [21]. Let us start by some notation.

Let $\mathcal{F}_n^{od\,ev^*}$ be the set of strings in $\mathcal{F}_n$ that begin with an odd number of 0s and end with a non-null even number of 0s. Let $\mathscr{L}_n^{od\,\varnothing}$ be the set of strings in $\mathscr{L}_n$ that begin with an odd number of 0's and do not end with 0. In the same way, we define $\mathcal{F}_n^{ab}$ and $\mathscr{L}_n^{ab}$ where $a, b \in \{od, ev^*, \varnothing\}$.

Note that $\mathcal{F}_n$ and $\mathscr{L}_n$ partition as

$$\mathcal{F}_n = \mathcal{F}_n^{od\,od} + \mathcal{F}_n^{od\,ev^*} + \mathcal{F}_n^{od\,\varnothing} + \mathcal{F}_n^{ev^*\,od}$$
$$+ \mathcal{F}_n^{ev^*\,ev^*} + \mathcal{F}_n^{ev^*\,\varnothing} + \mathcal{F}_n^{\varnothing\,od} + \mathcal{F}_n^{\varnothing\,ev^*} + \mathcal{F}_n^{\varnothing\,\varnothing},$$
$$\mathscr{L}_n = \mathscr{L}_n^{od\,od} + \mathscr{L}_n^{od\,ev^*} + \mathscr{L}_n^{od\,\varnothing} + \mathscr{L}_n^{ev^*\,od}$$
$$+ \mathscr{L}_n^{ev^*\,ev^*} + \mathscr{L}_n^{ev^*\,\varnothing} + \mathscr{L}_n^{\varnothing\,od} + \mathscr{L}_n^{\varnothing\,ev^*} + \mathscr{L}_n^{\varnothing\,\varnothing}.$$

Let $\mathcal{F}_{n,k}$ and $\mathscr{L}_{n,k}$ denote the set of vertices having eccentricity k in Γ_n and Λ_n.

For any $a, b \in \{od, ev^*, \varnothing\}$, let $\mathcal{F}_{n,k}^{ab} = \mathcal{F}_n^{ab} \cap \mathcal{F}_{n,k}$, $\mathscr{L}_{n,k}^{ab} = \mathscr{L}_n^{ab} \cap \mathscr{L}_{n,k}$, $f_{n,k}^{ab} = |\mathcal{F}_{n,k}^{ab}|$ and $\ell_{n,k}^{ab} = |\mathscr{L}_{n,k}^{ab}|$.

The following property can be easily proved.

Proposition 8.12. [21, Proposition 5.3] *If $n \geq 1$ and $x \in \mathscr{L}_n \setminus \mathscr{L}_n^{od\,od}$, then*

$$\mathrm{ecc}_{\Lambda_n}(x) = \mathrm{ecc}_{\Gamma_n}(x).$$

Since $\mathscr{L}_n^{a\,b} = \mathcal{F}_n^{a\,b}$ for $(a,b) \neq (\varnothing,\varnothing)$, we deduce:

Corollary 8.13. [21, Corollary 5.4] *Let $n,k \geq 0$. For $a,b \in \{od, ev^*, \varnothing\}$ such that $(a,b) \neq (od,od)$ and $(a,b) \neq (\varnothing,\varnothing)$ we have*

$$\mathscr{L}_{n,k}^{a\,b} = \mathcal{F}_{n,k}^{a\,b}.$$

We have thus

$$\ell_{n,k} = f_{n,k} - f_{n,k}^{od\,od} - f_{n,k}^{\varnothing\varnothing} + \ell_{n,k}^{od\,od} + \ell_{n,k}^{\varnothing\varnothing}. \tag{8.5}$$

Note that for $n \geq 1$, $\mathscr{L}_n^{\varnothing\varnothing} = \varnothing$ and thus, because of the null string, the generating function of $\ell_{n,k}^{\varnothing\varnothing}$ is $\ell^{\varnothing\varnothing}(x,y) = \sum_{n,k\geq 0} \ell_{n,k}^{\varnothing\varnothing} x^n y^k = 1$.

We know from Theorem 4.7 that the generating function of the sequence $f_{n,k}$ is

$$f(x,t) = \sum_{n,k\geq 0} f_{n,k}\, x^k t^n = \frac{1+xt}{1-xt(t+1)}.$$

The three other generating functions of the sequences that appear in equation (8.5) are determined by the following propositions.

Proposition 8.14. [21, Proposition 5.13] *The generating function of the sequence $f_{n,k}^{\varnothing\varnothing}$ is*

$$f^{\varnothing\varnothing}(x,t) = 1 + xt + \frac{x^3 t^3 (t+1)}{(1+xt)(1-xt-xt^2)}.$$

Proposition 8.15. [21, Proposition 5.8] *The generating function of the sequence $f_{n,k}^{od\,od}$ is*

$$f^{od\,od}(x,t) = \frac{xt(1-xt^2-x^2t^3)}{(1+xt)(1-xt^2)(1-xt-xt^2)}.$$

Proposition 8.16. [21, Proposition 5.14] *The generating function of the sequence $\ell_{n,k}^{od\,od}$ satisfies*

$$\ell^{od\,od}(x,t) = x^{-1} f^{od\,od}(x,t).$$

We can thus derive $\ell(x,t)$ from equation (8.5):

$$\ell(x,t) = f(x,t) - f^{od\,od}(x,t) - f^{\varnothing\varnothing}(x,t) + \ell^{od\,od}(x,t) + \ell^{\varnothing\varnothing}(x,t),$$

and after some algebraic manipulation we obtain the expression proposed in Theorem 8.11.

Expanding each term in the generating function $\ell(x,t)$ in (8.4) we obtain

Corollary 8.17. [21, Corollary 5.17] *If $n > k \geq 1$, then*

$$\ell_{n,k} = \binom{k}{n-k} + \binom{k-1}{n-k-1} + \varepsilon_{n,k},$$

where

$$\varepsilon_{n,k} = \begin{cases} -1 & \text{if } n = 2k, \\ 1 & \text{if } n = 2k+1, \\ 0 & \text{otherwise.} \end{cases}$$

Furthermore, $\ell_{0,0} = \ell_{1,0} = 1$, $\ell_{n,0} = 0$ for $n > 1$ and

$$\ell_{n,n} = \begin{cases} 2 & \text{if } n \text{ is even } (n \geq 2), \\ 0 & \text{if } n \text{ is odd.} \end{cases}$$

8.5 Hamiltonicity

In the seminal work [81] on Lucas cubes it is proved that Λ_n is not Hamiltonian. In 2005, Baril and Vajnovszki proved [12] that Λ_n has a Hamiltonian path if and only if $n \not\equiv 0 \,(\text{mod}\,3)$. Both results can be seen as straightforward consequences of the Hamiltonicity study of Fibonacci cubes we have done in Section 4.3.

Let us recall that we denote by $\mathcal{E}_n$ and $\mathcal{O}_n$ the set of strings in $\mathcal{F}_n$ of even and odd Hamming weight, respectively. Let $\mathcal{E}_n^L$ and $\mathcal{O}_n^L$ denote the analogous sets for the Lucas strings.

Theorem 8.18. [81, Theorem 3] *For any positive integer n,*

$$\begin{aligned} |\mathcal{E}_n^L| &= |\mathcal{O}_n^L| + 2 && \text{if } n \equiv 0 \,(\text{mod}\,6), \\ |\mathcal{O}_n^L| &= |\mathcal{E}_n^L| + 2 && \text{if } n \equiv 3 \,(\text{mod}\,6), \\ |\mathcal{E}_n^L| &= |\mathcal{O}_n^L| + 1 && \text{if } n \equiv 1, 5 \,(\text{mod}\,6), \\ |\mathcal{O}_n^L| &= |\mathcal{E}_n^L| + 1 && \text{if } n \equiv 2, 4 \,(\text{mod}\,6). \end{aligned}$$

Proof. This is immediate by direct inspection for $n \leq 3$. Assume thus $n \geq 4$. From the decomposition of Lucas strings in terms of Fibonacci strings we get

$$\mathcal{E}_n^L = 0\mathcal{E}_{n-1} + 10\mathcal{O}_{n-3}0,$$

$$\mathcal{O}_n^L = 0\mathcal{O}_{n-1} + 10\mathcal{E}_{n-3}0.$$

Therefore

$$|\mathcal{E}_n^L| - |\mathcal{O}_n^L| = |\mathcal{E}_{n-1}| - |\mathcal{O}_{n-1}| - (|\mathcal{E}_{n-3}| - |\mathcal{O}_{n-3}|).$$

The result now follows using the values of $|\mathcal{E}_n| - |\mathcal{O}_n|$ we determined in Proposition 4.14. □

Since a cycle in a bipartite graph has to have even length we infer

Corollary 8.19. [81, Corollary 1] Λ_n *is not Hamiltonian.*

Theorem 8.20. [12, Corollary 12] *There exists a Hamiltonian path in* Λ_n *if and only if* $n \not\equiv 0 \,(\mathrm{mod}\, 3)$.

Proof. The necessary condition is immediate since a path visits alternatively vertices of $\mathcal{E}_n^L$ and $\mathcal{O}_n^L$.

By direct inspection the result is true for $n \leq 4$.

Consider the sequence of strings in $\mathcal{F}_n$ defined recursively by

$$V_0 = \lambda$$
$$V_1 = 0, 1$$
$$V_n = 0V_{n-1}^R, 10V_{n-2}^R, \ n \geq 2.$$

We have proved in Section 4.3 that V_n defines a Hamiltonian path in Γ_n with endpoints

$$(010)^m \text{ and } (100)^m \text{ for } n = 3m,$$
$$(010)^m 0 \text{ and } (100)^m 1 \text{ for } n = 3m+1,$$
$$(010)^m 01 \text{ and } (100)^m 10 \text{ for } n = 3m+2.$$

The sequence of strings $0V_{n-1}$ defines a Hamiltonian path Q in $0\Gamma_{n-1}$. Similarly $S = 10V_{n-3}0$ is a Hamiltonian path in $10\Gamma_{n-3}0$.

Assume $n = 3p + 1$ with $p \geq 1$. The endpoints of V_{n-1} are $(010)^p$ and $(100)^p$, thus those of Q are $u = 0(010)^p$ and $0(100)^p$. Likewise the endpoints of S are $10(010)^{p-1}00$ and $v = 10(100)^{p-1}10 = 1(010)^p$. Joining the paths Q and S by the edge uv belonging to the matching between $00\Gamma_{n-3}0$ and $10\Gamma_{n-3}0$ we obtain the required Hamiltonian path of Λ_n.

Assume now $n = 3p+2$. By the same construction, we have a path Q in $0\Gamma_{n-1}$ with end points $u = 0(010)^p 0 = 00(100)^p$ and $0(100)^p 1$. We have also a path S in $10\Gamma_{n-3}0$ with endpoints $10(010)^{p-1}010$ and $v = 10(100)^{p-1}100 = 10(100)^p$. Finally, the vertices u and v can be linked by an edge of the matching. □

Theorem 8.20 has the following consequence.

Corollary 8.21. *For any integer* $n \geq 1$ *not divisible by 3,* $\alpha(\Lambda_n) = \lceil \frac{1}{2}L_n \rceil$.

8.6 Diametral Shortest Paths

Here we follow the terminology and the ideas of Section 4.4 which dealt with diametral shortest paths in Γ_n.

We have noted in Section 8.4 that

$$\mathrm{diam}(\Lambda_n) = \begin{cases} n & \text{if } n \text{ is even}, \\ n-1 & \text{if } n \text{ is odd}. \end{cases}$$

Rephrasing Proposition 8.10 in the manner of Proposition 4.16 we have:

Proposition 8.22. [38, Proposition 2] *The number of diametrically oppo-site vertices u, v in Λ_n is 1 if n is even, and n if n is odd. They are*

(i) $u = (01)^{\frac{n}{2}}$ *and* $v = (10)^{\frac{n}{2}}$ *(n even),*
(ii) *cyclic shifts of the pair* $u = 0(01)^{\frac{n-1}{2}}$ *and* $v = 0(10)^{\frac{n-1}{2}}$ *(n odd).*

For Γ_n, we have denoted the number of diametral shortest paths by c_n. We let d_n denote the number of diametral shortest paths in Λ_n in this section. This is unambiguous; the diametrically opposite pair is unique for n even, and the number of paths is equinumerous for any diametrically opposite pair for n odd, since cyclic shifts of the paths give a bijection between the shortest paths in question.

Similar to Theorem 4.17, Eğecioğlu, E. Saygı and Z. Saygı proved the following result, where E_n is the Euler number defined in Section 4.4.

Theorem 8.23. [38, Theorem 2] *Let d_n be the number of diametral shortest paths in Λ_n. Then for $n \geq 1$,*

$$d_n = \begin{cases} \frac{n}{2} E_{n-1} & \text{if } n \text{ is even}, \\ E_{n-1} & \text{if } n \text{ is odd}, \end{cases}$$

where E_n is the Euler number.

Proof. First assume that n is even. From Proposition 8.22 we only need to consider the vertices $u = (01)^{\frac{n}{2}}$ and $v = (10)^{\frac{n}{2}}$. Mimicking the bijective proof of Theorem 4.17 we arrive at permutations σ of $[n]$ satisfying $\sigma_i > \sigma_{i+1}$ for any odd index i with $1 \leq i < n$, $\sigma_i > \sigma_{i-1}$ for any odd index i with $1 < i \leq n$ and the extra condition $\sigma_1 > \sigma_n$ since in Λ_n we have $b_1 b_n = 0$. This last requirement is easily verified by tracing the first appearance of a 1 in the first and the last columns of the table of paths that define the bijection for Γ_n. Therefore, σ must be a circular alternating permutation of $[n]$, and these were enumerated by Kreweras in [71].

For n odd, without loss of generality take $u = 0(01)^{\frac{n-1}{2}}$ and $v = 0(10)^{\frac{n-1}{2}}$. Then $u, v \in 0\Gamma_{n-1}$ and since $\Lambda_n = 0\Gamma_{n-1} + 10\Gamma_{n-3}0$ we have $d_n = c_{n-1} = E_{n-1}$, which yields the assertion. $\qquad\square$

8.7 Counting Substructures

In this section we consider a number of substructures of Λ_n in the spirit of the treatment of the case of Fibonacci cubes in Chapter 5.

8.7.1 *Cube Polynomial*

Results about the cube polynomial of Lucas cubes can be compared to the results for Fibonacci cubes from Section 5.1. Proofs are similar to those in the previous section and hence we omit most of the details but confine ourselves to pointing out the main differences. To begin with, by direct inspection of Fig 8.1 we find $C_{\Lambda_0}(x) = C_{\Lambda_1}(x) = 1$ and $C_{\Lambda_2}(x) = 3 + 2x$.

We next find the generating function for the sequence of cube polynomials of Lucas cubes.

Theorem 8.24. [61, Proposition 5.1] *The generating function of the sequence* $(C_{\Lambda_n}(x))_{n \geq 0}$ *is*

$$\sum_{n \geq 0} C_{\Lambda_n}(x)t^n = \frac{1 + (1+x)t^2}{1 - t - (1+x)t^2}.$$

Proof. Let $n \geq 3$ and partition the vertex set of Λ_n into vertices that start with 0 and those that start with 1. The latter vertices are then of the form $10\ldots0$. Similarly to the proof of Theorem 5.2 we now get that for $n \geq 3$,

$$C_{\Lambda_n}(x) = C_{\Gamma_{n-1}}(x) + (1+x)C_{\Gamma_{n-3}}(x). \tag{8.6}$$

To complete the proof combine Theorem 5.2 with (8.6) and the initial conditions $C_{\Gamma_0}(x) = C_{\Gamma_1}(x) = 1$ and $C_{\Gamma_2}(x) = 3 + 2x$. □

Using (8.6) we can quickly generate the first few polynomials:

$$\begin{aligned}
C_{\Lambda_0}(x) &= C_{\Lambda_1}(x) = 1 \\
C_{\Lambda_2}(x) &= 3 + 2x \\
C_{\Lambda_3}(x) &= 4 + 3x \\
C_{\Lambda_4}(x) &= 7 + 8x + 2x^2 \\
C_{\Lambda_5}(x) &= 11 + 15x + 5x^2 \\
C_{\Lambda_6}(x) &= 18 + 30x + 15x^2 + 2x^3 \\
C_{\Lambda_7}(x) &= 29 + 56x + 35x^2 + 7x^3.
\end{aligned} \tag{8.7}$$

Corollary 8.25. [61, Theorems 5.2 and Corollary 5.3] *If* $n \geq 3$, *then* $C_{\Lambda_n}(x)$ *is of degree* $\lfloor n/2 \rfloor$ *and is given by*

$$C_{\Lambda_n}(x) = \sum_{j=0}^{\lfloor n/2 \rfloor} \left[2\binom{n-j}{j} - \binom{n-j-1}{j} \right] (1+x)^j.$$

Moreover, the number of induced subgraphs of Γ_n isomorphic to Q_k is

$$c_k(\Lambda_n) = \sum_{i=k}^{\lfloor n/2 \rfloor} \left[2\binom{n-i}{i} - \binom{n-i-1}{i} \right] \binom{i}{k}.$$

Proof. Rewrite (5.3) as $C_{\Gamma_{n-1}}(x) = C_{\Gamma_{n-2}}(x) + (1+x)C_{\Gamma_{n-3}}(x)$ and subtract this equality from (8.6) to obtain

$$C_{\Lambda_n}(x) = 2C_{\Gamma_{n-1}}(x) - C_{\Gamma_{n-2}}(x) \quad (n \geq 3). \tag{8.8}$$

The result now follows from Theorem 5.3. $\qquad\square$

Like in Section 5.1, for any positive integer k it is possible to determine the generating function of the sequence $(c_k(\Lambda_n))_{n \geq 0}$. From its form we see that this sequence is the convolution of the sequence $(L_n)_{n \geq 0}$ with k-fold convolutions of the sequence $(F_{n+1})_{n \geq 0}$ with itself. With this observation we obtain:

Corollary 8.26. [61, Corollary 5.6] *For any $k \geq 1$,*

$$c_k(\Lambda_n) = \sum_{\substack{i_0, i_1, \ldots, i_k \geq 0 \\ i_0 + i_1 + \cdots + i_k = n-k}} L_{i_0} F_{i_1} \cdots F_{i_k} = \sum_{i=0}^{n-k} L_i c_{k-1}(\Gamma_{n-i-3}).$$

Note that the first equality reduces for $k = 1$ to

$$c_1(\Lambda_n) = \sum_{i=1}^{n-1} F_i L_{n-1-i},$$

which is the expression for the size of Λ_n that first appeared in [58, Proposition 7], while the second equality for $k = 2$ was obtained in [58, Proposition 8].

We have also a Binet-like formula for $C_{\Lambda_n}(x)$.

Theorem 8.27. [61, Theorem 6.2] *If $n \geq 1$, then*

$$C_{\Lambda_n}(x) = \left(\frac{1 + \sqrt{5 + 4x}}{2} \right)^n + \left(\frac{1 - \sqrt{5 + 4x}}{2} \right)^n.$$

It is now easy to determine the zeros of $C_{\Lambda_n}(x)$.

Proposition 8.28. [61, Proposition 6.4] *If $n \geq 1$, then the zeros of $C_{\Lambda_n}(x)$ are*

$$-\frac{\tan^2\left(\frac{(2r+1)\pi}{2n} \right) + 5}{4}, \quad 0 \leq r \leq \lfloor n/2 \rfloor - 1.$$

In particular, the zeros are simple and are negative real numbers.

As a consequence, the sequence of coefficients of $C_{\Lambda_n}(x)$ is unimodal.
    Theorem 8.27 leads to divisibility consequences.

Corollary 8.29.

   (i) If $p \geq 1$, then $C_{\Gamma_{2p}}(x) = C_{\Gamma_{p-1}}(x) C_{\Lambda_{p+1}}(x)$.
   (ii) If $n \geq 1$ and k is odd, then $C_{\Lambda_n}(x)$ divides $C_{\Lambda_{kn}}(x)$.

Proof. Set

$$f(x) = \frac{1 + \sqrt{5 + 4x}}{2} \quad \text{and} \quad g(x) = \frac{1 - \sqrt{5 + 4x}}{2}.$$

(i) By Theorem 5.5,

$$
\begin{aligned}
C_{\Gamma_{2p}}(x) &= \frac{1}{\sqrt{5 + 4x}} \left[f^{2p+2}(x) - g^{2p+2}(x) \right] \\
&= \frac{1}{\sqrt{5 + 4x}} \left[f^{p+1}(x) - g^{p+1}(x) \right] \left[f^{p+1}(x) + g^{p+1}(x) \right] \\
&= C(\Gamma_{p-1}, x) C(\Lambda_{p+1}, x).
\end{aligned}
$$

(ii) $C_{\Lambda_n}(x_0) = 0$ means that $f^n(x_0) = -g^n(x_0)$. Therefore $f^{kn}(x_0) = -g^{kn}(x_0)$ which in turn implies $C_{\Lambda_{kn}}(x_0) = 0$. Since the zeros of C_{Λ_n} are simple, divisibility follows.   □

8.7.2   *Maximal Hypercubes*

Let $h_k(\Lambda_n)$ denote the number of maximal hypercubes of dimension k of Λ_n, and let

$$H_{\Lambda_n}(x) = \sum_{k \geq 0} h_k(\Lambda_n) x^k$$

be corresponding enumerator polynomial.
    The study of maximal hypercubes in Lucas cubes is very similar to that of maximal hypercubes in Fibonacci cubes. Like Fibonacci strings, Lucas strings can be viewed as blocks of 0s separated by isolated 1s, or as single 0s possibly separated by isolated 1s. Considering the constraint on the extremities of a Lucas string, these points of view give the following two decompositions of the vertices of Λ_n.

Proposition 8.30. *Any vertex of weight w in Λ_n can be uniquely decomposed as*

$$0^{l_0} 1 0^{l_1} \ldots 1 0^{l_i} \ldots 1 0^{l_p}$$

where $p = w$, $\sum_{i=0}^{p} l_i = n - w$, $l_0, l_p \geq 0$, $l_0 + l_p \geq 1$, and $l_1, \ldots, l_{p-1} \geq 1$.

Proposition 8.31. *Any vertex of weight w in Λ_n can be uniquely decomposed as*

$$1^{k_0} 01^{k_1} \ldots 01^{k_i} \ldots 01^{k_q},$$

where $q = n - w$, $\sum_{i=0}^{q} k_i = w$, $k_0 + k_q \leq 1$, and $k_0, \ldots, k_q \leq 1$.

Using the same arguments as in the proof of Lemma 5.9, it is immediate to deduce from the decomposition of Lucas strings as blocks of 0s separated by isolated 1s a characterization of the bottom and top vertices of maximal hypercubes in Λ_n.

Proposition 8.32. [73, Proposition 2.10] *If H is a maximal hypercube of dimension $k \geq 1$ in Λ_n, then $b(H) = 0^n$ and $t(H) = 0^{l_0} 10^{l_1} \ldots 10^{l_i} \ldots 10^{l_k}$, where $\sum_{i=0}^{k} l_i = n - k$, $l_0, l_k \in \{0, 1, 2\}$, $l_0 + l_k \in \mathcal{B}$, and $l_i \in [2]$ for $i \in [k - 1]$. Furthermore, any such vertex is the top vertex of a maximal hypercube.*

Theorem 8.33. [73, Theorem 2.12] *If $k \in [n]$, then*

$$h_k(\Lambda_n) = \frac{n}{k} \binom{k}{n - 2k}.$$

Proof. The proof is similar to that of Theorem 5.10, the case of Fibonacci cubes, with three cases according to the value of l_0.

Case 1: By Proposition 8.32, the set T of top vertices that begin with 1 is the set of strings which can be written as $10^{l_1} \ldots 10^{l_i} \ldots 10^{l_k}$, where $\sum_{i=1}^{k} l_i = n - k$ and $1 \leq l_i \leq 2$ for $i \in [k]$. Let $l_i' = l_i - 1$ for $i \in [k]$. We have thus a one to one mapping between T and the set of strings $D = \{10^{l_1'} \ldots 10^{l_i'} \ldots 10^{l_k'}\}$, where $\sum_{i=1}^{k} l_i' = n - 2k$ and $l_i' \in \mathcal{B}$ for $i \in [k]$. Removing the first 1, and by complement, this set is in bijection with the set $E = \{1^{l_1'} \ldots 01^{l_i'} \ldots 01^{l_k'}\}$. By Proposition 5.8, E is the set of Fibonacci strings of length $n - k - 1$ and weight $n - 2k$. Thus

$$|T| = \binom{k}{n - 2k}.$$

Case 2: The set U of top vertices that begin with 01 is the set of strings which can be written as $010^{l_1} \ldots 10^{l_i} \ldots 10^{l_k}$, where $\sum_{i=1}^{k} l_i = n - k - 1$, $1 \leq l_i \leq 2$ for $i \in [k - 1]$, and $l_k \leq 1$. Let $l_i' = l_i - 1$ for $i \in [k - 1]$ and $l_k' = l_k$. We have thus a one to one mapping between U and the set of strings $F = \{010^{l_1'} \ldots 10^{l_i'} \ldots 10^{l_k'}\}$, where $\sum_{i=1}^{k} l_i' = n - 2k$ and $l_i' \leq 1$ for $i \in [k]$. Removing the first 01, and by complement, this set is in bijection with the set $G = \{1^{l_1'} \ldots 01^{l_i'} \ldots 01^{l_k'}\}$. By Proposition 5.8, G is the set of Fibonacci strings of length $n - k - 1$ and weight $n - 2k$. Thus

$$|U| = \binom{k}{n - 2k}.$$

Case 3: The last set V of top vertices that begin with 001, is the set of strings which can be written as $0010^{l_1} \ldots 10^{l_i} \ldots 0^{l_{k-1}}1$, where $\sum_{i=1}^{k-1} l_i = n - k - 2$ and $1 \le l_i \le 2$ for $i \in [k - 1]$. Let $l_i' = l_i - 1$, $i \in [k - 1]$. We have thus a one to one mapping between V and the set of strings $H = \{0010^{l_1'} \ldots 10^{l_i'} \ldots 0^{l_{k-1}'}1\}$ where $\sum_{i=1}^{k-1} l_i' = n - 2k - 1$ and $l_i' \le 1$ for $i \in [k - 1]$. Removing the first 001 and the last 1, this set, again by complement, is in bijection with the set $K = \{1^{l_1'} \ldots 01^{l_i'} \ldots 01^{l_{k-1}'}\}$. The set K is the set of Fibonacci strings of length $n - k - 3$ and weight $n - 2k - 1$. Thus

$$|V| = \binom{k - 1}{n - 2k - 1}.$$

Therefore

$$h_k(\Lambda_n) = 2\binom{k}{n - 2k} + \binom{k - 1}{n - 2k - 1} = \frac{n}{k}\binom{k}{n - 2k}.$$

$\square$

Note that for $n \ne 1$, $h_k(\Lambda_n) \ne 0$ if and only if $\lceil n/3 \rceil \le k \le \lfloor n/2 \rfloor$.

Corollary 8.34. [73, Corollary 2.13] *If $n \ge 5$, then the enumerator polynomial $H_{\Lambda_n}(x)$ of the number of maximal hypercubes of dimension k in Λ_n satisfies*

$$H_{\Lambda_n}(x) = x\left(H_{\Lambda_{n-2}}(x) + H_{\Lambda_{n-3}}(x)\right),$$

with $H_{\Lambda_0}(x) = 1$, $H_{\Lambda_1}(x) = 1$, $H_{\Lambda_2}(x) = 2x$, $H_{\Lambda_3}(x) = 3x$, and $H_{\Lambda_4}(x) = 2x^2$. The generating function of the sequence $(H_{\Lambda_n}(x))_{n \ge 0}$ is

$$\sum_{n \ge 0} H_{\Lambda_n}(x)t^n = \frac{1 + t + xt^2 + xt^3 - xt^4}{1 - xt^2(1 + t)}. \tag{8.9}$$

Proof. Assume $n \ge 5$. By Theorem 8.33 and Pascal identity we get $h_k(\Lambda_n) = h_{k-1}(\Lambda_{n-2}) + h_{k-1}(\Lambda_{n-3})$ for $n \ge 5$ and $k \ge 2$. Notice that when $n \ge 5$, this equality holds also for $k = 1$, and $h_0(\Lambda_n) = 0$. The recurrence relation for $H_{\Lambda_n}(x)$ follows. If $g = g(x, t)$ denotes the left hand side of (8.9), then

$$g - 1 - t - 2xt^2 - 3xt^3 - 2x^2t^4 = x(t^2(g - 1 - t - 2xt^2) + t^3(g - 1 - t)),$$

and the corollary follows.

$\square$

8.7.3 *q-Cube Polynomial*

The study of a generalization of the enumerator polynomial of the hyper-cubes in Lucas cubes which q-counts them by their distance to the all 0 vertex is similar to the treatment of the Fibonacci cube case in Section 5.4. Here we follow the treatment by E. Saygı and Eğecioğlu from [93].

$C_{\Lambda_n}(x,q)$ is defined as the sum of all terms of the form $q^d x^k$, one for each subcube of Λ_n. The exponent k is the dimension of subcube and the exponent d is the distance of the subcube to the all 0 vertex in Λ_n.

As an example, we consider the structure of $C_{\Lambda_4}(x,q)$. For $k = 0$ there are seven vertices in the graph giving 0-dimensional hypercubes. The vertex 0000 has distance 0, the vertices 0001, 0010, 0100 and 1000 each have distance 1 and the vertices 0101 and 1010 have distance 2 to 0000. So the coefficient of x^0 is $1 + 4q + 2q^2$.

Now consider $k = 1$, that is, 1-dimensional hypercubes in the graph. These are the edges of the graph. From Fig. 8.4 we see that there are four edges with distance 0 and four edges with distance 1 to the vertex 0000. So the coefficient of x in $C_{\Lambda_4}(x,q)$ is $4 + 4q$.

Finally there are only two 2-dimensional hypercubes in Λ_4 and these hypercubes contain the vertex 0000, giving $2x^2$. Adding these contributions, we get

$$C_{\Lambda_4}(x,q) = (1 + 4q + 2q^2) + (4 + 4q)x + 2x^2.$$

A graphical presentation of these hypercubes in Λ_4 and their individual contributions to $C_{\Lambda_4}(x,q)$ is presented in Fig. 8.4.

$C_{\Lambda_n}(x,q)$ satisfies a simple recursion similar to the one for the cube polynomial. As a consequence, its computation is relatively straightfor-ward.

Lemma 8.35. [93, Lemma 1] *If $n \geq 3$, then*

$$C_{\Lambda_n}(x,q) = C_{\Lambda_{n-1}}(x,q) + (q + x)C_{\Lambda_{n-2}}(x,q) \tag{8.10}$$

with $C_{\Lambda_1}(x,q) = 1$ and $C_{\Lambda_2}(x,q) = 1 + 2q + 2x$.

Using (8.10) we can quickly compute the first few $C_{\Lambda_n}(x,q)$. These are

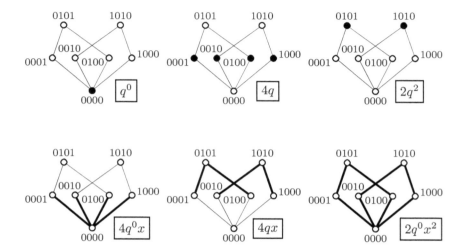

Fig. 8.4   Calculation of $C_{\Lambda_4}(x,q) = (1 + 4q + 2q^2) + (4 + 4q)x + 2x^2$.

the "q-analogues" of the cube polynomials in (8.7):

$$C_{\Lambda_0}(x,q) = 1,$$
$$C_{\Lambda_1}(x,q) = 1,$$
$$C_{\Lambda_2}(x,q) = 1 + 2q + 2x,$$
$$C_{\Lambda_3}(x,q) = 1 + 3q + 3x,$$
$$C_{\Lambda_4}(x,q) = 1 + 4q + 2q^2 + (4 + 4q)x + 2x^2,$$
$$C_{\Lambda_5}(x,q) = 1 + 5q + 5q^2 + (5 + 10q)x + 5x^2,$$
$$C_{\Lambda_6}(x,q) = 1 + 6q + 9q^2 + 2q^3 + (6 + 18q + 6q^2)x + (9 + 6q)x^2 + 2x^3,$$
$$C_{\Lambda_7}(x,q) = 1 + 7q + 14q^2 + 7q^3 + (7 + 28q + 21q^2)x + (14 + 21q)x^2 + 7x^3.$$

Also from recursion (8.10) we find:

Proposition 8.36. [93, Proposition 1] *The generating function of the q-cube polynomial $C_{\Lambda_n}(x,q)$ is*

$$\sum_{n\geq 0} C_{\Lambda_n}(x,q)t^n = \frac{1 + (q + x)t^2}{1 - t - (q + x)t^2}.$$

The recursion in (8.10) can be solved directly to find $C_{\Lambda_n}(x,q)$ in explicit form.

Theorem 8.37. [93, Theorem 1] *For any positive integer n, the q-cube polynomial $C_{\Lambda_n}(x,q)$ of the Lucas cube has degree $\lfloor n/2 \rfloor$ in x and it is* *given explicitly as*

$$C_{\Lambda_n}(x,q) = \frac{1}{2^{n-1}} \sum_{i=0}^{\lfloor n/2 \rfloor} \binom{n}{2i} (1 + 4(q+x))^i .$$

Writing

$$C_{\Lambda_n}(x,q) = \sum_{k \geq 0} \bar{c}_{n,k}(q) x^k ,$$

thus thinking of $C_{\Lambda_n}(x,q)$ as a polynomial in x whose coefficients of x^k are polynomials in q, we obtain

Corollary 8.38. *For any positive integer n, the coefficient polynomials of the q-cube polynomial $C_{\Lambda_n}(x,q)$ are given by*

$$\bar{c}_{n,k}(q) = \frac{1}{2^{n-1}} \left(\frac{4}{1+4q} \right)^k \sum_{i=k}^{\lfloor \frac{n}{2} \rfloor} \binom{n}{2i}\binom{i}{k} (1+4q)^i .$$

A few of the polynomials $\bar{c}_{n,k}(q)$ are given in Table 8.1.

$n \backslash k$	0	1	2	3	4
0	1	0	0	0	0
1	1	0	0	0	0
2	$1 + 2q$	2	0	0	0
3	$1 + 3q$	3	0	0	0
4	$1 + 4q + 2q^2$	$4 + 4q$	2	0	0
5	$1 + 5q + 5q^2$	$5 + 10q$	5	0	0
6	$1 + 6q + 9q^2 + 2q^3$	$6 + 18q + 6q^2$	$9 + 6q$	2	0
7	$1 + 7q + 14q^2 + 7q^3$	$7 + 28q + 21q^2$	$14 + 21q$	7	0

Table 8.1 The table of coefficients of the q-cube polynomials $C_{\Lambda_n}(x,q)$ by rows. The entry in row n, column k is the coefficient polynomial $\bar{c}_{n,k}(q)$

Using the properties of convolutions we also obtain a convolution characterization of $\bar{c}_{n,k}(q)$.

First we need to define q-Lucas numbers. Similar to the q-analogue of the Fibonacci numbers in (5.12) with generating function (5.13), a q-analogue of the Lucas numbers can be defined by $L_0(q) = 2, L_1(q) = 1$, and

$$L_n(q) = L_{n-1}(q) + qL_{n-2}(q) \quad (n \geq 2). \tag{8.11}$$

The generating function of $(L_n(q))_{n\geq 0}$ is

$$\sum_{n\geq 0} L_n(q)t^n = \frac{2-t}{1-t-qt^2}. \tag{8.12}$$

Proposition 8.39. [93, Proposition 2] *For* $n \geq 1$ *the coefficient polynomials* $\overline{c}_{n,k}(q)$ *of the* q-*cube enumerator* $C_{\Lambda_n}(x,q)$ *are given by*

$$\overline{c}_{n,k}(q) = \sum_{\substack{i_0,i_1,\ldots,i_k \geq 0 \\ i_0+i_1+\cdots+i_k=n-k}} L_{i_0}(q)F_{i_1}(q)\cdots F_{i_k}(q).$$

Proof. From (8.12) and (5.18), the convolution of $L_n(q)$ with the k-fold convolutions of $F_n(q)$ has the generating function

$$\frac{(2-t)t^k}{(1-t-qt^2)^{k+1}}.$$

Setting

$$g_0(t,q) = \frac{2-t}{(1-t-qt^2)} - 1 \quad \text{and} \quad g_k(t,q) = \frac{(2-t)t^{2k}}{(1-t-qt^2)^{k+1}} \quad (k \geq 1)$$

we find

$$\sum_{k\geq 0} g_k(t,q)x^k = -1 + \frac{2-t}{(1-t-qt^2)} \sum_{k\geq 0} \left(\frac{xt^2}{1-t-qt^2}\right)^k$$

$$= \frac{1+(q+x)t^2}{1-t-(q+x)t^2}.$$

This is identical to the generating function of the $C_{\Lambda_n}(x,q)$ of Proposition 8.36. It follows that the $g_k(t,q)$ are the generating functions of the columns of Table 8.1. The proposition now follows by equating the coefficients of $t^n x^k$ in the two expressions as we have

$$\sum_{k\geq 0} g_k(t,q)x^k = \sum_{k\geq 0} \left(\left(\sum_{i_0\geq 0} L_{i_0}(q)t^{i_0}\right)\left(\sum_{i\geq 0} f_i(q)t^i\right)^k\right)t^k x^k$$

$$= \sum_{n\geq 0} \left(\sum_{k\geq 0} \overline{c}_{n,k}(q)x^k\right)t^n.$$

$\square$

We saw in Proposition 8.2 that there are

$$\frac{n}{n-i}\binom{n-i}{i} = 2\binom{n-i}{i} - \binom{n-i-1}{i}$$

vertices in Λ_n of Hamming weight i. The distance between such a vertex and the all zero vertex is obviously i. Using this, the polynomials in the first column ($k = 0$) of Table 8.1 can be written for $n \geq 1$ as

$$L_n(q) = \bar{c}_{n,0}(q) = \sum_{i=0}^{\lfloor n/2 \rfloor} \frac{n}{n-i} \binom{n-i}{i} q^i.$$

In general, we have the following expression for the entry in row n, column k of Table 8.1:

Proposition 8.40. [93, Proposition 3] *The coefficient polynomials $\bar{c}_{n,k}(q)$ of the q-cube enumerator $C_{\Lambda_n}(x,q)$ of the Lucas cube Λ_n are given explicitly by*

$$\bar{c}_{n,k}(q) = \sum_{i=k}^{\lfloor n/2 \rfloor} \frac{n}{n-i} \binom{n-i}{i} \binom{i}{k} q^{i-k}.$$

Next we consider divisibility properties of $C_{\Lambda_n}(x,q)$. These are mostly consequences of Binet formulas for the q-cube polynomials.

Proposition 8.41. [93, Proposition 4] *Let $C_{\Gamma_n}(x,q)$ and $C_{\Lambda_n}(x,q)$ be the q-cube polynomials of the Fibonacci cubes Γ_n and the Lucas cubes Λ_n, respectively. Then the following assertions hold.*

(i) *If $n, m \geq 0$ and m is odd, then $C_{\Lambda_n}(x,q)$ divides $C_{\Lambda_{mn}}(x,q)$ as a polynomial in x. Furthermore, the coefficients of powers of x in this quotient are polynomials in q with non-negative integer coefficients.*

(ii) *If $m \geq 1$, then $C_{\Gamma_{2m}}(x,q) = C_{\Gamma_{m-1}}(x,q) C_{\Lambda_{m+1}}(x,q)$.*

(iii) *If $n, m \geq 1$ and m is even, then $C_{\Lambda_n}(x,q)$ divides $C_{\Gamma_{mn-2}}(x,q)$ as a polynomial in x.*

Incidentally, similar to the case of the Fibonacci cubes, the values $a_n = C_{\Lambda_n}(1,1)$ satisfy the recurrence

$$a_n = a_{n-1} + 2a_{n-2}$$

with the initial values $a_0 = a_1 = 1$, giving the shifted Jacobsthal sequence [50]:

$$1, 1, 3, 5, 11, 21, 43, 85, 171, 341, 683, 1365, 2731, \ldots$$

Write

$$C_{\Lambda_n}(x,q) = \sum_{k \geq 0} \bar{c}_{n,k}(q) x^k \quad \text{and} \quad C_{\Gamma_n}(x,q) = \sum_{k \geq 0} c_{n,k}(q) x^k,$$

and let $D : \mathbb{Z}[q] \to \mathbb{Z}[q]$ denote the differentiation operator.

Proposition 8.42. [93, Proposition 6] *The coefficient polynomials* $\bar{c}_{n,k}(q)$ *and* $c_{n,k}(q)$ *of the q-cube polynomials of* $C_{\Lambda_n}(x,q)$ *and* $C_{\Gamma_n}(x,q)$ *satisfy*

$$\frac{1}{k} D\bar{c}_{n,k-1}(q) = \bar{c}_{n,k}(q) \quad \text{and} \quad \frac{1}{k} Dc_{n,k-1}(q) = c_{n,k}(q).$$

In particular,

$$\frac{1}{k!} D^k \bar{c}_{n,0}(q) = \bar{c}_{n,k}(q) \quad \text{and} \quad \frac{1}{k!} D^k c_{n,0}(q) = c_{n,k}(q).$$

Using operator notation we can write

$$C_{\Lambda_n}(x,q) = e^{xD} L_n(q) \quad \text{and} \quad C_{\Gamma_n}(x,q) = e^{xD} F_{n+2}(q).$$

Therefore Taylor's theorem gives the following expressions for the q-cube polynomials.

Proposition 8.43. [93, Proposition 7] *Let* $C_{\Lambda_n}(x,q)$ *and* $C_{\Gamma_n}(x,q)$ *be the q-cube polynomials of the Lucas cubes* Λ_n *and the Fibonacci cubes* Γ_n *respectively. Then*

$$C_{\Lambda_n}(x,q) = L_n(x+q) \quad \text{and} \quad C_{\Gamma_n}(x,q) = F_{n+2}(x+q),$$

where $L_n(q)$ *and* $F_n(q)$ *are as defined in (8.11) and (5.12).*

8.8 Characterizations and Recognition

Taranenko [102] reduced the recognition of Lucas cubes to the recognition of Fibonacci cubes by the following theorem which is similar to Theorem 6.9. Recall that the latter was the key tool for fast recognition of Fibonacci cubes as presented in Section 6.3.3. Before stating the corresponding theorem for Lucas cubes, we recall from Section 6.3 the following sets defined with respect to an edge ab of a connected graph G:

$$W_{ab} = \{w \in V(G) : d(a,w) < d(b,w)\},$$
$$W_{ba} = \{w \in V(G) : d(w,b) < d(w,a)\},$$
$$U_{ab} = \{w \in W_{ab} : w \text{ has a neighbor in } W_{ba}\},$$
$$U_{ba} = \{w \in W_{ba} : w \text{ has a neighbor in } W_{ab}\},$$
$$F_{ab} = \{e = uv \in E(G) : u \in U_{ab}, v \in U_{ba}\}.$$

Taranenko's theorem now reads as follows.

Theorem 8.44. [102, Theorem 3.7] *Let* ab *be an edge of a connected, bipartite graph* G *with* $\deg_G(a) = n$. *Then* $G \cong \Lambda_n$ *if and only if the following conditions are satisfied:*

(i) *All the neighbors of a are of degree $n-2$.*

(ii) *$G[U_{ab}]$ is convex in $G[W_{ab}]$.*

(iii) *F_{ab} is a matching defining an isomorphism between $G[U_{ab}]$ and $G[U_{ba}]$.*

(iv) *$G[W_{ab}]$ is isomorphic to Γ_{n-1}, and $G[W_{ba}]$ is isomorphic to Γ_{n-3}.*

(v) *$W_{ba} = U_{ba}$.*

Theorem 8.44 together with Theorem 6.11 yields the following result.

Theorem 8.45. [102, Theorem 4.2] *If G is a graph, then it can be checked in $\mathcal{O}(m(G))$ time whether G is a Lucas cube.*

While Taranenko was working out Theorem 8.44, he found the next result, which is very interesting in its own right. To formulate it, we need some preparation. Assume that we have the situation as in Mulder's convex expansion theorem (Theorem 6.5). Let H be the graph obtained from G by identifying each pair of vertices u and v such that $uv \in F_{ab}$. Let X be the set of these identified vertices. Then H is a smaller median graph and X induces a convex subgraph of H. We say that G is obtained from H by an *expansion* over X. Moreover, in case when X induces a peripheral subgraph of H, we say that G is obtained from H by a *peripheral expansion* over X. The announced result of Taranenko now reads as follows.

Theorem 8.46. [102, Theorem 3.6] *If $n \geq 3$, then Γ_n contains a unique convex subgraph $H \cong \Gamma_{n-2}$, such that the peripheral expansion of Γ_n over H is isomorphic to Λ_{n+1}.*

We sketch the way Theorem 8.46 is proved. Let H be an arbitrary convex subgraph of Γ_n (assuming it exists) such that the peripheral expansion of G over H is isomorphic to Λ_{n+1}. Then by degree conditions we infer that $a = 0^n \in V(H)$, but $b = 10^{n-1} \notin V(H)$ and $c = 0^{n-1}1 \notin V(H)$. Using the Convexity Lemma from [55] which we already applied in the proof of Theorem 6.8, we next infer that none of the vertices from W_{ba} as well as none of the vertices from W_{ca} lies in H. Set now

$$S = V(\Gamma_n) \setminus (W_{ba} \cup W_{ca}) = W_{ab} \cap W_{ac}.$$

Then the subgraph of Γ_n induced by S is the unique subgraph as required by the theorem. This constructive proof is illustrated in Fig. 8.5, where Λ_5 is obtained from Γ_4 by a peripheral expansion over Γ_2.

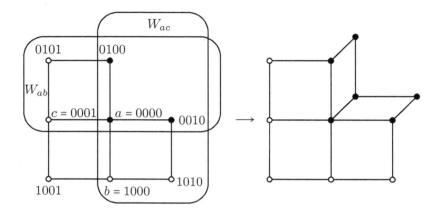

Fig. 8.5 Λ_5 (right) obtained from Γ_4 (left) by a peripheral expansion over Γ_2 (black vertices left)

8.8.1   *Lucas Cubes as Resonance Graphs*

in Theorem 6.2 we have presented a surprising connection that Fibonacci cubes can be characterized as the resonance graphs of fibonaccenes. Lucas cubes play a similar, important role in chemical graph theory. Indeed, as it can be deduced from [122, Theorem 3.4.(2)] due to Yao and Zhang, Lucas cubes are also resonance graphs. Moreover, in [126], Žigert Pleteršek and Berlič investigated the resonance graphs of the so-called armchair carbon nanotubes, also known as cyclic polypyrenes and proved that their resonance graphs are almost Lucas cubes. More precisely, the resonance graph of a cyclic polypyrene is an amalgam of two Lucas cubes, together with a Cartesian product power of the path P_3 and one isolated vertex.

8.9   Invariants

We next consider the domination related invariants of Lucas cubes along with irregularity, followed by the computation of Wiener and Mostar indices.

8.9.1   *Domination-Type Invariants*

In Table 8.2   all known exact values of domination numbers and total domination numbers of Lucas cubes are listed. The values of $\gamma(\Lambda_n)$ for $n \leq 8$ are obtained by brute force in [20]. Integer linear programming can be used exactly the same way as for Fibonacci cubes. Values of $\gamma(\Lambda_n)$ for $n \le 11$ and of $\gamma_t(\Lambda_n)$, for $n \le 12$, are obtained in this manner in [54] and by Z. Saygı in [95], respectively. For other values of n only bounds are known.

n	1	2	3	4	5	6	7	8	9	10	11	12
$\gamma(\Lambda_n)$	1	1	1	3	4	5	7	11	16	23	35	
$\gamma_t(\Lambda_n)$		2	2	3	4	7	9	13	19	27	41	58

Table 8.2 Known domination numbers and total domination numbers of Λ_n

We can first deduce interleaving relations from decompositions of Λ_n.

Proposition 8.47. [20, Proposition 3.1] *If $n \ge 4$, then*

(i) $\gamma(\Lambda_n) \le \gamma(\Gamma_{n-1}) + \gamma(\Gamma_{n-3})$,
(ii) $\gamma(\Lambda_n) \le \gamma(\Gamma_n) \le \gamma(\Lambda_n) + \gamma(\Gamma_{n-4})$.

Proof. *(i)*: $V(\Lambda_n)$ can be partitioned into vertices that start with 0 and vertices that start with 1. The latter are of the form $10\mathcal{F}_{n-3}0$ and hence can be dominated by $\{10b0 : b \in U\}$ where U is a minimum dominating set of Γ_{n-3} with $\gamma(\Gamma_{n-3})$ vertices. While the former vertices can be dominated by $\gamma(\Gamma_{n-1})$ vertices.

(ii): Let D be a minimum dominating set of Γ_n and set

$$D' = \{u : u \text{ is a Lucas string from } D\} \cup \{0b_2\ldots b_{n-1}0 : 1b_2\ldots b_{n-1}1 \in D\}.$$

A vertex $1b_2\ldots b_{n-1}1$ dominates two Lucas vertices, namely $0b_2\ldots b_{n-1}1$ and $1b_2\ldots b_{n-1}0$. Since these two vertices are dominated by $0b_2\ldots b_{n-1}0$, we infer that D' is a dominating set of Λ_n. It follows that $\gamma(\Lambda_n) \le \gamma(\Gamma_n)$.

A dominating set of Λ_n dominates all vertices of Γ_n but the vertices of the form $10b_3\ldots b_{n-2}01$. These vertices in turn are dominated by $\gamma(\Gamma_{n-4})$ vertices. □

With a similar proof we obtain the following parallel result for the total domination number.

Proposition 8.48. [95, Proposition 3.2] *If $n \ge 4$, then*

(i) $\gamma_t(\Lambda_n) \le \gamma_t(\Gamma_{n-1}) + \gamma_t(\Gamma_{n-3})$,
(ii) $\gamma_t(\Lambda_n) \le \gamma_t(\Gamma_n) \le \gamma_t(\Lambda_n) + \gamma_t(\Gamma_{n-4})$.

A general lower bound on the domination number of Lucas cubes is established in [20]. This result is parallel to the bound of Pike and Zou for Fibonacci cubes, Theorem 7.1, but the proof is rather different. The starting point is the following lemma and some specific notations.

We will denote by $\mathscr{L}_{n,w}$ the set of all the vertices of Λ_n of Hamming weight w. In addition, for $n \geq 4$ set $\mathscr{L}'_{n,2} = \{0^a 1010^{n-a-3} : 0 \leq a \leq n-1\}$.

Lemma 8.49. [20, Lemma 3.3] *Let $n \geq 7$. Then for the Lucas cube Λ_n the following hold.*

(i) *The vertex 0^n is the only vertex of maximum degree n.*
(ii) *The vertices of $\mathscr{L}_{n,1}$ have degree $n-2$.*
(iii) *Among the vertices with at least two 1s, only the vertices of $\mathscr{L}'_{n,2}$ have degree $n-3$. All the other vertices have degree at most $n-4$.*

Proof. Facts (i) and (ii) are immediate. Assertion (iii) is easy by a straightforward case study or, alternatively, can be seen as a consequence of Theorem 8.5.   □

Lemma 8.50. *Let $n \geq 1$. Then any ℓ vertices from $\mathscr{L}'_{n,2}$ have at least ℓ down-neighbors, that is, at least ℓ neighbors in $\mathscr{L}_{n,1}$.*

Proof. For $i \in [\ell]$, let A_i be the set of down-neighbors of some $v_i \in \mathscr{L}'_{n,2}$. Then $|A_i| = 2$ for each i. Considering bits by modulo n, each vertex $0^a 10^{n-a-1}$ in $\mathscr{L}_{n,1}$ can be a down-neighbor of at most two vertices $0^a 1010^{n-a-3}$ and $0^{a-2}1010^{n-a-1}$, and hence at most two of $v_1, \ldots, v_l$. The assertion follows by the pigeonhole principle.   □

To establish the lower bound, we apply the concept of over-domination introduced in Section 7.1. Recall from there that the over-domination of G with respect to D is:

$$\mathrm{OD}_G(D) = \left(\sum_{u \in D} (\deg_G(u) + 1) \right) - n(G). \tag{8.13}$$

Theorem 8.51. [20, Theorem 3.5] *If $n \geq 7$, then*

$$\gamma(\Lambda_n) \geq \left\lceil \frac{L_n - 2n}{n - 3} \right\rceil.$$

Proof. Let D be a minimum dominating set of Λ_n. Set $D_1 = D \cap \mathscr{L}_{n,1}$ and $D_2 = D \cap \mathscr{L}'_{n,2}$, and let $k = |D_1|$ and $l = |D_2|$. Then clearly $0 \leq k$ and $l \leq n$. Note that the over-domination of G with respect to D can be rewritten as

$$\mathrm{OD}(G) = \sum_{u \in V(\Lambda_n)} (|\{v \in D : d(u,v) \leq 1\}| - 1) . \tag{8.14}$$

For a vertex u of Λ_n, set $t(u) = |\{v \in D : d(u,v) \le 1\}| - 1$. As D is a dominating set, $t(u) \ge 0$ for all $u \in V(\Lambda_n)$. We now distinguish two cases.

Case 1: $0^n \in D$.

Combining Lemma 8.49 with Equation (8.13) we get

$$
\begin{aligned}
\mathrm{OD}(D) &\le (n+1) + k(n-1) + l(n-2) + (\gamma(\Lambda_n) - k - l - 1)(n-3) - L_n \\
&= \gamma(\Lambda_n)(n-3) + 2k + l + 4 - L_n .
\end{aligned}
$$

Since $t(u) \ge 0$ for all $u \in V(\Lambda_n)$, (8.14) implies

$$
\mathrm{OD}(D) \ge t(0^n) + \sum_{v \in D_1} t(v) \ge 2k .
$$

Therefore

$$
\gamma(\Lambda_n) \ge \left\lceil \frac{L_n - l - 4}{n-3} \right\rceil \ge \left\lceil \frac{L_n - n - 4}{n-3} \right\rceil .
$$

Case 2: $0^n \notin D$.

Again, combining Lemma 8.49 with (8.13) we infer

$$
\begin{aligned}
\mathrm{OD}(D) &\le k(n-1) + l(n-2) + (\gamma(\Lambda_n) - k - l)(n-3) - L_n \\
&= \gamma(\Lambda_n)(n-3) + 2k + l - L_n .
\end{aligned}
$$

Let A be the set of down-neighbors of D_2. Then for $u \in D_1 \cap A$, $t(u) \ge 1$. By Lemma 8.50, $|A| \ge l$ and hence $|D_1 \cap A| \ge k + l - n$. Therefore by (8.14),

$$
\mathrm{OD}(D) \ge \sum_{v \in D_1 \cap A} t(v) \ge k + l - n .
$$

Thus

$$
\gamma(\Lambda_n) \ge \left\lceil \frac{L_n - k - n}{n-3} \right\rceil \ge \left\lceil \frac{L_n - 2n}{n-3} \right\rceil .
$$

The conclusions of the two cases gives the theorem. $\qquad\square$

Other domination-type invariants for Lucas cubes have also been investigated, as for instance the 2-packing number in [20,54] and the independent domination number in [54].

8.9.2 *Irregularity*

To simplify the notation, in the rest of the section let $I_n(x) = I_{\Gamma_n}(x)$ and $J_n(x) = I_{\Lambda_n}(x)$ denote the irregularity polynomials of Γ_n and Λ_n, respectively. Using the decomposition of Lucas cubes in terms of Fibonacci cubes and proceeding along the lines the argument given for Fibonacci cubes but with more cases to consider, the following relation for the irregularity polynomial of Lucas cubes was established.

Theorem 8.52. [35, Theorem 2] *If $n \geq 3$, then*

$$J_{n+2}(x) - J_{n+1}(x) - J_n(x) = I_{n+1}(x) - I_n(x) - I_{n-2}(x) - I_{n-3}(x), \quad (8.15)$$

with $J_1(x) = 0$, $J_2(x) = 2x$, $J_3(x) = 3x^2$, $J_4(x) = 4x^2 + 4$, and $J_5(x) = 5x^2 + 10x$.

If we multiply identity (8.15) by t^{n+2} and sum for $n \geq 4$, then using the generating function $I(x,t)$ obtained in Corollary 7.10 we obtain the generating function of the irregularity polynomials of Λ_n.

Corollary 8.53. [35, Corollary 3] *The generating function of the sequence $(J_n(x))_{n\geq 0}$ of the irregularity polynomials of Λ_n is given by*

$$\sum_{n\geq 0} J_n(x)t^n = \frac{t\big(c_1(x)t + c_2(x)t^2 + c_3(x)t^3 + c_4(x)t^4 + c_5(x)t^5 + c_6(x)t^6\big)}{(1 - t - t^2)^2},$$

where $c_1(x) = 2x$, $c_2(x) = x(3x - 4)$, $c_3(x) = -2(x - 1)(x + 2)$, $c_4(x) = -2(x - 1)(3x - 4)$, $c_5(x) = 2(x - 1)(2x - 1)$, and $c_6(x) = 3(x - 1)^2$.

After calculations similar to those involved in Corollary 7.11 we derive an expression for the irregularity polynomial itself from the generating function in Corollary 8.53.

Corollary 8.54. [35, Corollary 4] *If $n \geq 4$, then the irregularity polynomial $J_n(x)$ of the Lucas cube Λ_n is given by*

$$J_n(x) = nF_{n-3}x^2 + 2nF_{n-4}x + nF_{n-5},$$

with $J_1(x) = 0$, $J_2(x) = 2x$, and $J_3(x) = 3x^2$.

By evaluation in $x = 1$ of the derivative of $J_n(x)$, we deduce the following expression for irr(Λ_n).

Corollary 8.55. [35, Corollary 5] *If $n \geq 3$, then* irr(Λ_n) = $2nF_{n-2}$.

The above expressions for $J_n(x)$ and irr(Λ_n) are obtained after a long and technical path (for details see [35]), hence it is astonishing that the resulting expressions are surprisingly simple. It is thus attractive to show a bijective proof as Mollard did in [76] and as we did for Fibonacci cubes in Section 7.3.2.

Taking into account the cyclic nature of the definition of Lucas strings, coordinates are to be considered cyclically in $[n]$. For example, in the following, the coordinate $i+1$ must be understood as 1 when $i = n$ and $i-1$ means n when $i = 1$.

Let $i \in [n]$. Consider an edge $e = xy$ that uses coordinate i, where $x_i = 1$, and let us compare $\deg_{\Lambda_n}(x)$ and $\deg_{\Lambda_n}(y)$.

For some $j \neq i$, an edge of Λ_n that uses coordinate j is incident to x if and only if $x + \delta_j \in \mathscr{L}_n$. Since $x_{j-1} = y_{j-1}$ and $x_{j+1} = y_{j+1}$, for $j \notin \{i-1, i+1\}$ an edge using the coordinate j is incident to x if and only if an edge using the same coordinate is incident to y. Therefore the contribution of the edge e to the irregularity of Λ_n depends only of the existence of edges using coordinates $i-1$ and $i+1$.

Since $x_{i-1} = y_{i-1} = 0$, $x_{i+1} = y_{i+1} = 0$ and $x_i \neq y_i$, this contribution, i.e., $\mathrm{imb}_{\Lambda_n}(e) = |\deg_{\Lambda_n}(x) - \deg_{\Lambda_n}(y)|$, can be determined according to the following result.

Theorem 8.56. [76, Theorem 4.6] *Let $n \geq 4$ and let $e = xy$ be an edge of Λ_n with $y = x + \delta_i$. Then $\mathrm{imb}(e)$ is given by Table 8.3, where the coordinates $i-2$ and $i+2$ are taken cyclically in $[n]$.*

$\mathrm{imb}(x(x+\delta_i))$	x_{i-2}	x_{i+2}
0	1	1
1	0	1
	1	0
2	0	0

Table 8.3 $\mathrm{imb}(e)$ in Λ_n

In Section 7.3.2 we have defined right and left imbalanced edges for Fibonacci cubes. The same can be done for Lucas cubes. More precisely, let $e = xy \in E(\Lambda_n)$, where $x_i = 1$ and $y_i = 0$. Then an edge $e' = y(y + \delta_j)$ is a right imbalanced edge for e if $j = i+1$, otherwise e' a left imbalanced edge for e. Set now

$$R_i = \{(e, e') : e \in E(\Lambda_n), \ e \text{ uses coordinate } i,$$
$$e' \text{ is a right imbalanced edge for } e\},$$
$$L_i = \{(e, e') : e \in E(\Lambda_n), \ e \text{ uses coordinate } i,$$
$$e' \text{ is a left imbalanced edge for } e\}.$$

If $e' = y(y + \delta_j)$ is a right imbalanced edge for e, then $x_{i-1}x_i x_{i+1}x_{i+2} = 0100$ and thus $x_{i+3} \ldots x_n x_1 \ldots x_{i-2} \in \mathcal{F}_{n-4}$. It is immediate that we can define this way a one-to-one mapping between R_i and $\mathcal{F}_{n-4}$. We have thus $|R_i| = F_{n-2}$ and similarly $|L_i| = F_{n-2}$. Since i can be chosen arbitrary in $[n]$ we obtain irr$(\Lambda_n) = 2nF_{n-2}$.

Observing Table 8.3, imb$(e) = 2$ if and only if $x_{i-2} = x_{i+2} = 0$. We can thus associate to any edge xy that uses coordinate i with imbalance 2 a Fibonacci string $x_{i+3} \ldots x_n x_1 \ldots x_{i-3}$ in $\mathcal{F}_{n-5}$ and this mapping is one-to-one. We thus obtain a bijective proof that the coefficient of x^2 in the irregularity polynomial of Λ_n is nF_{n-3}. Similar bijective proofs are immediate for the other coefficients [76].

8.9.3   *Wiener Index*

Obtaining the Wiener index of Lucas cubes is significantly simpler than the corresponding one for Fibonacci cubes. The intrinsic reason for it is that in Lucas cubes all the coordinates of vertices are cylically equivalent, while in Fibonacci cubes the first and the last coordinate behave differently from the other coordinates.

Theorem 8.57. [62, Theorem 3.4] *If $n \geq 1$, then $W(\Lambda_n) = n\,F_{n-1}\,F_{n+1}$.*

Proof. We use the fact that Lucas cubes are partial cubes [58]. This fact can be deduced similarly as Proposition 4.2, hence we do not repeat the argument here. This means Theorem 7.5 can be applied, that is,

$$W(\Lambda_n) = \sum_{i=1}^{n} |W_{(i,1)}(\Lambda_n)| \cdot |W_{(i,0)}(\Lambda_n)|,$$

where $W_{(i,\chi)}(G) = \{u = u_1 u_2 \ldots u_n \in V(G) : u_i = \chi\}$ for $\chi \in \mathcal{B}$. By the symmetry of Lucas strings $|W_{(i,1)}| \cdot |W_{(i,0)}|$ does not depend of i. So we may assume that $i = 1$. There are $|\mathcal{F}_{n-3}|$ Lucas strings whose first coordinate is 1, and there are $|\mathcal{F}_{n-1}|$ Lucas strings whose first coordinate is 0.   □

8.9.4   *Mostar Index*

The symmetry of Lucas cubes also enables a simpler derivation of a closed formula (Theorem 8.59) for Mo(Λ_n) than Mo(Γ_n).

Since $\Lambda_2 = \Gamma_2$, we have Mo$(\Gamma_2) =$ Mo$(\Lambda_2) = 2$. For $n \geq 3$ we have the following result, which is similar to Lemma 7.12 and Lemma 7.13.

Lemma 8.58. [36, Lemma 3] *If $n \geq 3$ and $uv \in E(\Lambda_n)$ with $u_k = 0$ and $v_k = 1$ for some $k \in [n]$, then $n_u(\Lambda_n) = F_{n+1}$ and $n_v(\Lambda_n) = F_{n-1}$.*

Proof. Assume that $1 < k < n$ and let $\alpha \in V(\Lambda_n)$ have the string representation $b_1 b_2 \ldots b_n$. Since $uv \in E(\Lambda_n)$, the binary representations of u and v must be of the form $a_1 \ldots a_{k-2}000a_{k+2}\ldots a_n$ and $a_1 \ldots a_{k-2}010a_{k+2}\ldots a_n$, respectively. Then, if $b_k = 0$ we have $d(\alpha, u) = d(\alpha, v) - 1$ and if $b_k = 1$ we have $d(\alpha, u) = d(\alpha, v) + 1$. Thus $n_u(\Lambda_n)$ and $n_v(\Lambda_n)$ are equal to the number of vertices in Λ_n whose k^{th} coordinate is 0 and 1, respectively. Therefore we need to count the number of Lucas strings of the form $\beta_1 0 \beta_2$ and $\beta_3 010 \beta_4$, which gives $n_u(\Lambda_n) = F_{n+1}$ and $n_v(\Lambda_n) = F_{n-1}$.

For the case $k = 1$, using the decomposition of Λ_n in terms of Fibonacci cubes, we have $u \in V(0\Gamma_{n-1})$ and $v \in V(10\Gamma_{n-3}0)$. It follows that $n_u(\Lambda_n) = |V(0\Lambda_n)| = F_{n+1}$ and $n_v(\Lambda_n) = |V(10\Gamma_{n-3}0)| = F_{n-1}$. Similarly, for $k = n$ we have the same results $n_u(\Lambda_n) = F_{n+1}$ and $n_v(\Lambda_n) = F_{n-1}$. $\qquad\square$

Using Lemma 8.58 for any $uv \in E(\Lambda_n)$ we have

$$\left| n_u(\Lambda_n) - n_v(\Lambda_n) \right| = F_{n+1} - F_{n-1} = F_n \,.$$

Since the size of Λ_n is nF_{n-1}, a computation similar to the one that was used in the proof of Theorem 7.14 gives

Theorem 8.59. [36, Theorem 2] *If $n \geq 2$, then* $\mathrm{Mo}(\Lambda_n) = nF_n F_{n-1}$.

8.10 Alternate Lucas Cubes

Since Lucas numbers satisfy the same recurrence as Fibonacci numbers, we may wonder if there is a way to construct a family of graphs mimicking that of Fibonacci cubes, with a fundamental decomposition similar to that of Fibonacci cubes. In other words the family should be constructed in terms of two previous graphs and a perfect matching as is the case for Fibonacci cubes, but the orders should be given by the Lucas sequence instead of the Fibonacci sequence.

With this in mind, the family of graphs called *alternate Lucas cubes* was introduced and studied by Eğecioğlu, E. Saygı, and Z. Saygı in [34] as an alternative for Lucas cubes. These interconnection networks are subgraphs of Fibonacci cubes and have a fundamental decomposition similar to the one for Fibonacci cubes. The vertices of alternate Lucas cubes are constructed from binary strings that are encodings of Lucas representation of integers. The order and the size of alternate Lucas cubes are identical to those of Lucas cubes.

Every positive integer n can be expressed uniquely [16] as a sum of distinct Lucas numbers in the form

$$n = \sum_{i \geq 0} b_{i+1} L_i \,,$$

where $b_i b_{i+1} = 0$ for $i \geq 1$ and $b_1 b_3 = 0$. We call this representation the *Lucas representation* of integers. Lucas representations of the integers $n \in \{0, 1, \ldots, 6\}$ and their corresponding binary encodings are given in Table 8.4.

n	Lucas representation	Binary encoding $b_4 b_3 b_2 b_1$
0	0	0000
1	L_1	0010
2	L_0	0001
3	L_2	0100
4	L_3	1000
5	$L_3 + L_1$	1010
6	$L_3 + L_0$	1001

Table 8.4 Lucas representations of $n \in \{0, 1, \ldots, 6\}$ and their binary encodings as used as vertex labels in the construction of the alternate Lucas cubes

The n-dimensional alternate Lucas cube $\mathcal{L}_n$ is defined as the induced subgraph of the hypercube Q_n obtained by removing vertices from Q_n that do not correspond to a Lucas representation. More precisely,

$$V(\mathcal{L}_n) = \{b_n \ldots b_2 b_1 \mid b_i b_{i+1} = 0 \text{ for } 1 \leq i < n \text{ and } b_1 b_3 = 0\} \,.$$

At the top of Fig. 8.6, the first four Lucas cubes are presented with their vertices labeled with the corresponding binary strings in the hypercube graph. At the bottom of Fig. 8.6, the first four alternate Lucas cubes are presented with their labels that are their digits in the Lucas representation. The first three cubes $\mathcal{L}_1$, $\mathcal{L}_2$, $\mathcal{L}_3$ are identical to the first three Lucas cubes Λ_1, Λ_2, Λ_3. However $\mathcal{L}_4$ is not isomorphic to Λ_4 because of the existence of a vertex of degree 3 in $\mathcal{L}_4$. This vertex has label 1000 as shown in Fig. 8.6. In fact, comparing the degree sequences of the families $\mathcal{L}_n$ and Λ_n shows that $\mathcal{L}_n$ is not isomorphic to Λ_n for $n \geq 4$ [34, Proposition 9].

It is worth emphasizing that the n-bit binary representations of the integer labels $0, 1, \ldots, 2^n - 1$ correspond to the binary labels of the vertices

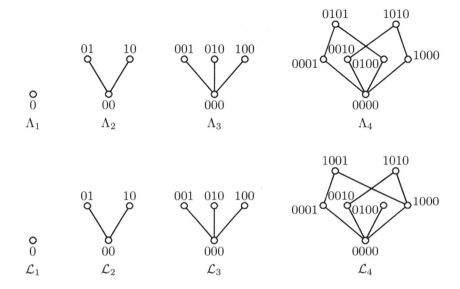

Fig. 8.6 Lucas cubes $\Lambda_1, \Lambda_2, \Lambda_3, \Lambda_4$ and the alternate Lucas cubes $\mathcal{L}_1, \mathcal{L}_2, \mathcal{L}_3, \mathcal{L}_4$

of the hypercube Q_n. Similarly, the n-bit Zeckendorf representations of the integer labels $0, 1, \ldots, F_{n+2} - 1$ correspond to the binary labels of the vertices of the Fibonacci cube Γ_n. This property is carried over to alternate Lucas cubes; the n-bit Lucas representations of the integer labels $0, 1, \ldots, L_n - 1$ correspond to the binary labels of the vertices of the alternate Lucas cube $\mathcal{L}_n$. This pleasing property is missing in the classical Lucas cubes.

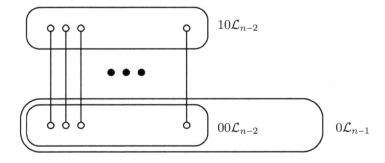

Fig. 8.7 Recursive decomposition of the alternate Lucas cube $\mathcal{L}_n$ in terms of $\mathcal{L}_{n-1}$ and $\mathcal{L}_{n-2}$

The alternate Lucas cube $\mathcal{L}_n$ can be decomposed into two subgraphs induced by the vertices that start with 0 and 10 respectively. The vertices that start with 0 constitute a graph isomorphic to $\mathcal{L}_{n-1}$ and the vertices that start with 10 constitute a graph isomorphic to $\mathcal{L}_{n-2}$. Additionally, there is a perfect matching between these two subgraphs, analogous to the decomposition of Fibonacci cubes. For $n \geq 3$ we denote this decomposition of $\mathcal{L}_n$ symbolically as

$$\mathcal{L}_n = 0\mathcal{L}_{n-1} + 10\mathcal{L}_{n-2}. \tag{8.16}$$

In (8.16), there are L_{n-2} edges in the perfect matching between the vertices in $10\mathcal{L}_{n-2}$ and the corresponding vertices in $00\mathcal{L}_{n-2} \subset 0\mathcal{L}_{n-1}$, in complete analogy with the Fibonacci decomposition but with different initial conditions since $\mathcal{L}_1 \neq \Gamma_1$. Of course in the case of Γ_n, the corresponding perfect matching is enumerated by Fibonacci numbers.

The fundamental decomposition of Γ_n reflects the recursion $F_n = F_{n-1} + F_{n-2}$ whereas the corresponding decomposition of Λ_n reflects the identity $L_n = F_{n-1} + F_{n+1}$ given in (1.10). The decomposition of alternate Lucas cubes corresponds to the recursion $L_n = L_{n-1} + L_{n-2}$ of (1.8).

8.10.1   *Enumerative Properties*

By the definition of alternate Lucas cubes, $n(\mathcal{L}_n) = n(\Lambda_n) = L_n$.

8.10.1.1   *The Size*

The first few values of $m(\mathcal{L}_n)$ for $n \geq 2$ are

$$2, 3, 8, 15, 30, 56, 104, 189, 340, 605, \ldots$$

Proposition 8.60. [34, Proposition 3] *If $n \geq 2$, then $m(\mathcal{L}_n) = nF_{n-1}$.*

Proof. By the fundamental decomposition (8.16), the edges of $\mathcal{L}_n$ are of three types: those that are from $\mathcal{L}_{n-1}$, those that are from $\mathcal{L}_{n-2}$, and the L_{n-2} link edges that are added between the twin nodes in the two copies of $\mathcal{L}_{n-2}$. This gives the recursion

$$m(\mathcal{L}_n) = m(\mathcal{L}_{n-1}) + m(\mathcal{L}_{n-2}) + L_{n-2} \tag{8.17}$$

for $n \geq 3$. Using $L_{n-2} = F_{n-1} + F_{n-3}$ and the initial values, we find that the solution to the recursion (8.17) is given by $m(\mathcal{L}_n) = nF_{n-1}$. $\square$

Therefore, the size of $\mathcal{L}_n$ is the same as the size of the Lucas cube Λ_n (see Proposition 8.3).

8.10.1.2 *Number of Vertices by Weight*

The next result is parallel to Proposition 8.2.

Proposition 8.61. [34, Proposition 4] *The number of vertices of Hamming weight w in $\mathcal{L}_n$ is given by*

$$\frac{n}{n-w}\binom{n-w}{w}.$$

Proof. Let $r_{n,w}$ denote the number of vertices of Hamming weight w in $\mathcal{L}_n$. From the fundamental decomposition (8.16),

$$r_{n,w} = r_{n-1,w} + r_{n-2,w-1}$$

for $n \geq w \geq 1$ with $r_{n,0} = 1$ for $n \geq 1$, and $r_{n,1} = n$ for $n \geq 2$. The solution to this recurrence gives the result. □

8.10.1.3 *Degree Sequences*

Using technical computations along the lines of the proof of Theorem 3.4, the following result can be shown.

Theorem 8.62. [34, Theorem 5] *If $n \geq 1$ and $k \in [n]$, then the number of vertices of $\mathcal{L}_n$ of degree k is*

$$\sum_{j=0}^{k}\left[2\binom{n-2j-3}{k-j-1}\binom{j+1}{n-k-j-1} + \binom{n-2j-2}{k-j-2}\binom{j}{n-k-j}\right.$$
$$\left. + \binom{n-2j-2}{k-j}\binom{j}{n-k-j-1}\right].$$

We can also incorporate the Hamming weight into this count.

Proposition 8.63. [34, Proposition 6] *For $0 \leq w \leq k \leq n$, the number of vertices of $\mathcal{L}_n$ having degree k and weight w is*

$$\binom{w}{n-k-w}\left[2\binom{n-2w-1}{k-w} + \binom{n-2w-2}{k-w-2}\right] + \binom{w}{n-k-w-1}\binom{n-2w-2}{k-w}.$$

We consider a refinement of the degree polynomial of $\mathcal{L}_n$. This generalization keeps track of the number of down-neighbors of v (vertices obtained by changing a 1 to a 0), and the number of up-neighbors (vertices obtained by changing a 0 to a 1 in v). Denoting these two quantities by $\deg_{\text{down}}(v)$ and $\deg_{\text{up}}(v)$, respectively, we now set

$$G_n(u,z) = \sum_{v \in \mathcal{L}_n} u^{\deg_{\text{up}}(v)} z^{\deg_{\text{down}}(v)},$$

and define the generating function

$$G(t) = G(u, z, t) = \sum_{n \geq 1} G_n(u, z) t^n.$$

A closed for expression for $G(t)$ is the following.

Theorem 8.64. [34, Theorem 11] *The generating function of the bivariate polynomials $G_n(u, z)$ is given by*

$$G(t) = \frac{t(1 + (2z - u(1 - u))t + 2z(1 - u)t^2)}{(1 - ut)(1 - zt^2) - zt^3}. \tag{8.18}$$

As demonstrated in [34], Theorem 8.64 can be specialized to give a number of results. Here a include a few of these.

(i) Taking $u = z = 1$, in (8.18), we have the generating function of the Lucas numbers:

$$\frac{t + 2t^2}{1 - t - t^2}.$$

(ii) Taking $u = z = y$, we have the generating function of the degree polynomials.

(iii) Taking $u = 1$ in $G_n(u, z)$, we obtain the weight enumerator polynomial $G_n(1, z)$ of $\mathcal{L}_n$. This specialization gives

$$\frac{t(1 + 2zt)}{1 - t - zt^2} = t + (1 + 2z)t^2 + (1 + 3z)t^3 + (1 + 4z + 2z^2)t^4$$

$$+(1 + 5z + 5z^2)t^5 + (1 + 6z + 9z^2 + 2z^3)t^6 + \cdots$$

(iv) Similarly, $G_n(u, 1)$ has the generating function

$$\frac{t(1 + (2 - u(1 - u))t + 2(1 - u)t^2)}{(1 - ut)(1 - t^2) - t^3} = t + (2 + u^2)t^2 + (3 + u^3)t^3$$

$$+ (3 + 2u + u^2 + u^4)t^4 + (5 + u + 3u^2 + u^3 + u^5)t^5 + \cdots$$

8.10.2   *q-Cube Polynomial*

Let $c_{n,k,d}$ denote the number of k-cubes in $\mathcal{L}_n$ whose distance to the all 0 vertex in $\mathcal{L}_n$ is d. Analogous to the q-cube polynomial of Γ_n (see Section 5.4) we define

$$C_{\mathcal{L}_n}(x, q) = \sum_{d, k \geq 0} c_{n,k,d} q^d x^k.$$

Note that by taking $q = 1$ one obtains the cube polynomial of $\mathcal{L}_n$. In Fig. 8.8, the calculation of $c_{\mathcal{L}_4}(x, q)$ is illustrated.

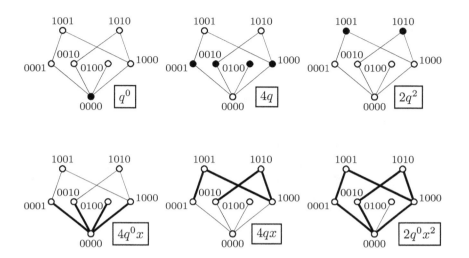

Fig. 8.8 The calculation of the q-cube polynomial $C_{\mathcal{L}_4}(x,q) = 1+4q+2q^2+(4+4q)x+2x^2$ indicating the contribution of each hypercube in $\mathcal{L}_4$

Proposition 8.65. [34, Proposition 13] *If $n \geq 3$, then*
$$C_{\mathcal{L}_n}(x,q) = C_{\mathcal{L}_{n-1}}(x,q) + (q+x)C_{\mathcal{L}_{n-2}}(x,q)$$
with $C_{\mathcal{L}_1} = 1$ and $C_{\mathcal{L}_2} = 1 + 2q + 2x$. The generating function of $(c_{\mathcal{L}_n})_{n \geq 1}$ is given by
$$\sum_{n \geq 1} C_{\mathcal{L}_n}(x,q)t^n = \frac{t + (2q + 2x)t^2}{1 - t - (q+x)t^2}.$$

We have determined the q-cube polynomial of Λ_n in Section 8.7.3. From the generating function given therein, we see that for $n \geq 1$, the q-cube polynomials of Λ_n and $\mathcal{L}_n$ are identical. This is a curious fact as Λ_n and $\mathcal{L}_n$ are non-isomorphic for $n \geq 4$. So not only does $\mathcal{L}_n$ have the same order and size as Λ_n, but the number of induced hypercubes of every dimension is also the same for both, even when we take into account their distance to the all zero vertex in each.

In fact we will see in Section 9.8 that this is a consequence of the fact that Λ_n and $\mathcal{L}_n$ are daisy cubes with the same number of vertices with a given Hamming weight.

8.10.3 *Maximal Hypercubes and Irregularity Polynomial*

The number of maximal hypercubes isomorphic to Q_k in Fibonacci cubes and in Lucas cubes were studied in Section 5.2 and Section 8.7.2, respectively. Recall that $h_k(G)$ denotes the number of maximal hypercubes of dimension k of G, so that the enumerator polynomial is

$$H_{\mathcal{L}_n}(x) = \sum_{k \geq 0} h_k(\mathcal{L}_n) x^k \,.$$

Since the decomposition of Γ_n and $\mathcal{L}_n$ follow the same pattern, we have the following recurrence relation. It can be proved along the same lines as Corollary 5.11.

Proposition 8.66. [34, Proposition 16] *If $n \geq 4$, then*

$$H_{\mathcal{L}_n}(x) = x\left(H_{\mathcal{L}_{n-2}}(x) + H_{\mathcal{L}_{n-3}}(x)\right)$$

with $H_{\mathcal{L}_1}(x) = 1$, $H_{\mathcal{L}_2}(x) = 2x$, and $H_{\mathcal{L}_3}(x) = 3x$. Furthermore, the generating function of $(H_{\mathcal{L}_n}(x))_{n \geq 1}$ is

$$\sum_{n \geq 1} H_{\mathcal{L}_n}(x)t^n = \frac{t + 2xt^2(1+t)}{1 - xt^2(1+t)} \,.$$

Note that although the recursive relations for $\mathcal{L}_n$, Λ_n and Γ_n are the same for the maximal hypercubes, the initial conditions are different, and consequently the enumerator polynomials are not the same.

Recall from Section 7.3.1 that the irregularity polynomial $I_G(x)$ of a graph G is defined by

$$I_G(x) = \sum_{uv \in E(G)} x^{|\deg_G(u) - \deg_G(v)|} \,.$$

Using (8.16) we can write

$$\mathcal{L}_n = 0\mathcal{L}_{n-1} + 10\mathcal{L}_{n-2} \tag{8.19}$$

$$= (00\mathcal{L}_{n-2} + 010\mathcal{L}_{n-3}) + 10\mathcal{L}_{n-2} \tag{8.20}$$

$$= ((000\mathcal{L}_{n-3} + 0010\mathcal{L}_{n-4}) + 010\mathcal{L}_{n-3}) + (100\mathcal{L}_{n-3} + 1010\mathcal{L}_{n-4}) \tag{8.21}$$

where there are perfect matchings (see Fig. 8.9) between

- $10\mathcal{L}_{n-2}$ and $00\mathcal{L}_{n-2} \subset 0\mathcal{L}_{n-1}$ in (8.19),
- $10\mathcal{L}_{n-2}$ and $00\mathcal{L}_{n-2}$; $010\mathcal{L}_{n-3}$ and $000\mathcal{L}_{n-3} \subset 00\mathcal{L}_{n-2}$ in (8.20),
- $010\mathcal{L}_{n-3}$ and $000\mathcal{L}_{n-3}$; $100\mathcal{L}_{n-3}$ and $000\mathcal{L}_{n-3}$; $1010\mathcal{L}_{n-4}$ and $0010\mathcal{L}_{n-4}$; $0010\mathcal{L}_{n-4}$ and $0000\mathcal{L}_{n-4} \subset 000\mathcal{L}_{n-3}$; $1010\mathcal{L}_{n-4}$, and $1000\mathcal{L}_{n-4} \subset 100\mathcal{L}_{n-3}$ in (8.21).

Setting $I_n(x) = I_{\mathcal{L}_n}(x)$, we have the following result.

Theorem 8.67. [34, Theorem 18] *If $n \geq 6$, then*

$$I_n(x) = 2I_{n-1}(x) + I_{n-2}(x) - 2I_{n-3}(x) - I_{n-4}(x),$$

with $I_1(x) = 0$, $I_2(x) = 2x$, $I_3(x) = 3x^2$, $I_4(x) = x^3 + 2x^2 + 3x + 2$ and $I_5(x) = x^3 + 6x^2 + 7x + 1$.

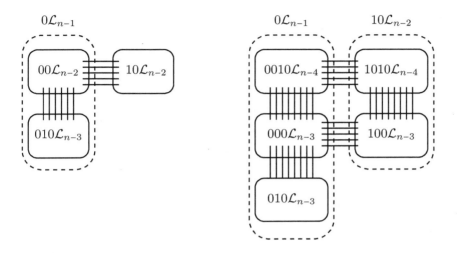

Fig. 8.9 Fundamental decomposition and perfect matchings in the alternate Lucas cube $\mathcal{L}_n$, $n \geq 4$

Corollary 8.68. [34, Corollary 20] *If $n \geq 2$, then*

$$I_{\mathcal{L}_n}(x) = nF_{n-1} + 2\Big(F_{n-1} + (n-1)F_{n-2}\Big)(x-1)$$
$$+\Big((n+1)F_{n-3} + 3F_{n-4}\Big)(x-1)^2$$
$$+\tfrac{1}{5}\Big(nF_{n-4} + (2n-3)F_{n-5}\Big)(x-1)^3 ,$$
$$\text{irr}(\mathcal{L}_n) = 2\Big(F_{n-1} + (n-1)F_{n-2}\Big) = 2m(\mathcal{L}_{n-1}) + 2F_{n-1} .$$

8.10.4 Additional Properties

Several other properties of alternate Lucas cubes are proved in [34], here we summarize some of them.

$\mathcal{L}_n$ never has a Hamiltonian cycle, while $\mathcal{L}_n$ has a Hamiltonian path if and only if n is not divisible by 3. A consequence of this is the independence number of $\mathcal{L}_n$, which is identical to the one given in Corollary 8.21 for Lucas cubes.

Corollary 8.69. [34, Corollary 24] *If $n \geq 1$ is not divisible by 3, then* $\alpha(\mathcal{L}_n) = \left\lceil \frac{L_n}{2} \right\rceil$.

The diameter, the radius, and the center of $\mathcal{L}_n$ are as follows.

Proposition 8.70. [34, Proposition 25] *If $n \geq 3$, then $\operatorname{diam}(\mathcal{L}_n) = n - 1$, $\operatorname{rad}(\mathcal{L}_n) = \lfloor n/2 \rfloor$, and*

$$C(\mathcal{L}_n) = \begin{cases} \{0^n\} & \text{if } n \text{ is odd,} \\ \{0^n, 10^{n-1}\} & \text{if } n \text{ is even.} \end{cases}$$

8.10.5   *Wiener Index and Mostar Index*

The fundamental decomposition of $\mathcal{L}_n$ suggests that the calculation of the Mostar index and the Wiener index for alternate Lucas cubes should be similar to the corresponding calculation for Fibonacci cubes. This is indeed the case.

By direct inspection we observe that $\operatorname{Mo}(\mathcal{L}_1) = 0$, $\operatorname{Mo}(\mathcal{L}_2) = 2$, and $\operatorname{Mo}(\mathcal{L}_3) = 6$. Using the same ideas as in Lemma 7.12, Eğecioğlu, E. Saygı, and Z. Saygı obtained:

Lemma 8.71. [39, Lemma 3.1] *For $n \geq 3$, assume that $uv \in E(\mathcal{L}_n)$ with $u_k = 0$ and $v_k = 1$ for some $k \in [n]$. Then for $k \leq n - 2$ we have $n_u(\mathcal{L}_n) = F_{k+1}L_{n-k}$ and $n_v(\mathcal{L}_n) = F_k L_{n-k-1}$; and for $k \in \{n-1, n\}$ we have $n_u(\mathcal{L}_n) = F_{n+1}$ and $n_v(\mathcal{L}_n) = F_{n-1}$.*

To find $\operatorname{Mo}(\mathcal{L}_n)$, we need to find the number of edges $uv \in E(\mathcal{L}_n)$ for which $u_k = 0$ and $v_k = 1$ for each fixed $k \in [n]$ and add up these contributions over k. Similar to Lemma 7.13, we have:

Lemma 8.72. [39, Lemma 3.2] *For $n \geq 3$, assume that $uv \in E(\mathcal{L}_n)$ with $u_k = 0$ and $v_k = 1$ for some $k \in [n]$. Then the number of such edges in $\mathcal{L}_n$ is equal to $F_k L_{n-k-1}$ for $k \leq n - 2$, and is equal to F_{n-1} for $k \in \{n-1, n\}$.*

Just as these two lemmas are parallel the related ones for Fibonacci cubes, the following theorem can be proved along the lines of Theorem 7.14.

Theorem 8.73. [39, Theorem 3.3] *If $n \geq 1$, then*

$$\operatorname{Mo}(\mathcal{L}_n) = 2F_{n-1}F_n + \sum_{k=1}^{n-2} F_k L_{n-k-1} \left(F_k L_{n-k-2} + F_{k-1} L_{n-k} \right).$$

A closed form evaluation of the sum in Theorem 8.73 is:

Theorem 8.74. [39, Theorem 4.2] *If $n \geq 1$, then*

$$\operatorname{Mo}(\mathcal{L}_n) = \tfrac{1}{25}\left(16L_{2n} + (5n - 28)L_{2n-1} - (15n - 40)(-1)^n \right). \tag{8.22}$$

For the calculation of the Wiener index $W(\mathcal{L}_n)$, we use Lemma 8.71 and mimic the proof of Theorem 7.6.

Theorem 8.75. *If $n \geq 1$, then*

$$W(\mathcal{L}_n) = 2F_{n+1}F_{n-1} + \sum_{k=1}^{n-2} F_k F_{k+1} L_{n-k-1} L_{n-k}. \tag{8.23}$$

The generating function of the sequence $(W(\mathcal{L}_n))_{n \geq 1}$ was found in [39, Equation (5.2)].

$$\sum_{n \geq 1} W(\mathcal{L}_n) t^n = \frac{t^2(4 - 7t + 2t^2 + 6t^3 - 2t^4)}{(1+t)^2(1 - 3t + t^2)^2}.$$

The first few terms of the sequence $(W(\mathcal{L}_n))_{n \geq 1}$ are

$$0, 4, 9, 38, 118, 380, 1156, 3476, 10247, 29862, 86090, 246134, 698664, \ldots,$$

in agreement with the values obtained from (8.23).

A closed form expression for the formula (8.23) is given by the following result.

Theorem 8.76. [39, Theorem 5.2] *If $n \geq 1$, then*

$$W(\mathcal{L}_n) = \tfrac{1}{25}\Big((5n - 6)L_{2n-1} + (5n + 8)L_{2n-2} + (5n + 20)(-1)^n\Big). \tag{8.24}$$

8.10.6 *Diametral Shortest Paths*

Here we follow the terminology and the ideas of Section 4.4 which dealt with the case of Γ_n, and also Section 8.6 that dealt with Λ_n. The results in this section are from [38] and are due to Eğecioğlu, E. Saygı, and Z. Saygı.

If $n \geq 3$, then we know from Proposition 8.70 that $\mathrm{diam}(\mathcal{L}_n) = n - 1$. This fact is complemented by the following result.

Proposition 8.77. [38, Proposition 3] *For any integer $n \geq 4$, the number of diametrically opposite pair of vertices in $\mathcal{L}_n$ is 4. These pairs are:*

(i) $u = 0^s(10)^k 001$ *and* $v = 1^s(01)^k 010$,
(ii) $u = 0^s(10)^k 010$ *and* $v = 1^s(01)^k 001$,
(iii) $u = 0^s(10)^k 100$ *and* $v = 1^s(01)^k 001$,
(iv) $u = 0^s(10)^k 100$ *and* $v = 1^s(01)^k 010$,

where $n = 2k + 3 + s$, k is a non-negative integer, and $s \in \{0, 1\}$.

For a pair of diametrically opposite vertices u and v of a graph G, let $c(u, v; G)$ denote the number of diametral u, v-paths. Recalling that E_n is the Euler number as defined in Section 4.4, we can state the following result.

Theorem 8.78. [38, Theorem 3] *If* $n = 2k + 3 + s$, *where* $n \geq 4$, k *is a non-negative integer, and* $s \in \{0, 1\}$, *then*

$$c(0^s(10)^k100, 1^s(01)^k001; \mathcal{L}_n)$$
$$= c(0^s(10)^k100, 1^s(01)^k010; \mathcal{L}_n) = E_{n-1}, \quad and$$
$$c(0^s(10)^k001, 1^s(01)^k010; \mathcal{L}_n)$$
$$= c(0^s(10)^k010, 1^s(01)^k001; \mathcal{L}_n) = \binom{n-1}{2}E_{n-3}.$$

Proof. We sketch the proof. We consider the permutations σ of $[n]$ satisfying extra conditions depending on the pair of vertices. We will give the proof for n even $(s = 1)$ and only for the pairs $u = 0^s(10)^k100$ and $v = 1^s(01)^k001$ and $u = 0^s(10)^k001$ and $v = 1^s(01)^k010$. The other cases can be obtained similarly.

For the pair $u = 0(10)^k100$ and $v = 1(01)^k001$ as we consider the shortest paths we will not change the $(n-1)^{\text{st}}$ position since it is 0 for each vertex. Therefore we need to consider the permutations σ of $[n] \setminus \{n-1\}$ satisfying $\sigma_i > \sigma_{i+1}$ for any odd index i with $1 \leq i \leq n-3$, $\sigma_i > \sigma_{i-1}$ for any odd index i with $1 < i \leq n-3$ and $\sigma_n > \sigma_{n-2}$, since in $\mathcal{L}_n$ we have $b_{n-2}b_n = 0$. By setting $\tau_i = \sigma_i$ for $i \in [n-2]$ and $\tau_{n-1} = \sigma_n$ we observe that τ is an alternating permutation of $[n-1]$.

Now consider the pair $u = 0(10)^k001$ and $v = 1(01)^k010$. In the shortest paths under consideration, we will not change the $(n-2)^{\text{nd}}$ position since it is 0 for each vertex. Therefore we need to consider the permutations σ of $[n] \setminus \{n-2\}$ satisfying $\sigma_i > \sigma_{i+1}$ for any odd index i with $1 \leq i < n-3$, $\sigma_i > \sigma_{i-1}$ for any odd index i with $1 < i \leq n-3$ and $\sigma_{n-1} > \sigma_n$. By setting $\tau_i = \sigma_i$ for $i \in [n-3]$ we observe that τ is an alternating permutation of $[n-3]$ and we have $\binom{n-1}{2}$ different choices for σ_{n-1}, σ_n which gives the desired result. $\square$

Chapter 9

Variations on Fibonacci Cubes

Not only the investigation of the properties of Fibonacci cubes attracted many researchers, but it has also led to the development of a variety of interesting generalizations and variations. We have already considered Lucas cubes and alternate Lucas cubes in detail in Chapter 8. In this chapter, we further consider the basic properties of a number of interesting classes of graphs brought about by the study of Fibonacci cubes. Among these families of graphs are generalized Fibonacci cubes, Pell graphs, k-Fibonacci cubes, Fibonacci-run graphs, cube-complements of Fibonacci cubes, daisy cubes, and Fibonacci p-cubes. One way or another, the study of all of these graph families were inspired and initiated by the idea of Fibonacci cubes.

9.1 Generalized Fibonacci Cubes

Recall from Chapter 2 that if $f = f_1 \ldots f_k \in \mathcal{B}_k$, then

$$\mathcal{B}_n(f) = \{w \in \{0,1\}^n : \not\exists\, u, v \in \{0,1\}^* \text{ with } w = ufv\}\,.$$

That is, $\mathcal{B}_n(f)$ is the set of binary strings of length n that do not contain f as a substring. Γ_n is then the subgraph of Q_n induced by the vertex set $\mathcal{F}_n = \mathcal{B}_n(11)$, hence the following generalization of Fibonacci cubes is natural.

Given $f = f_1 \ldots f_k \in \mathcal{B}_k$, the *generalized Fibonacci cube* $Q_n(f)$ is the subgraph of Q_n induced by $\mathcal{B}_n(f)$, that is,

$$Q_n(f) = Q_n[\mathcal{B}_n(f)]\,.$$

In other words, $Q_n(f)$ is obtained from Q_n by removing all the vertices that contain f as a substring. Fibonacci cubes are thus the following instance of generalized Fibonacci cubes:

$$\Gamma_n = Q_n(11)\,.$$

183

As another example, consider $Q_n(01)$. Let $b = b_1 \ldots b_n \in V(Q_n(01))$ and let b_i be the first coordinate which is equal to 0. By the definition of i we then have $b_1 = \cdots = b_{i-1} = 1$, and since 01 is not a substring of b, we have $b_{i+1} = \cdots = b_n = 0$. It follows that $V(Q_n(01)) = \{1^j 0^{n-j} : j \in \{0, 1, \ldots, n\}\}$ and consequently $Q_n(01) \cong P_{n+1}$. We show in the same way (or using Proposition 9.1 for that matter) that $Q_n(10) \cong P_{n+1}$, so that

$$Q_n(01) \cong Q_n(10) \cong P_{n+1}. \tag{9.1}$$

For a sporadic example of a generalized Fibonacci cube see Fig. 9.1, where $Q_4(110)$ is drawn. Note that the binary strings of length 4 that contain 110 are $\underline{110}0$, $\underline{110}1$, $0\underline{110}$, and $1\underline{110}$, so that $Q_4(110)$ is obtained from Q_4 by removing these four vertices.

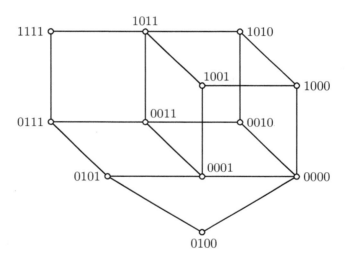

Fig. 9.1 The generalized Fibonacci cube $Q_4(110)$

Generalized Fibonacci cubes were introduced by Ilić, Klavžar, and Rho [52]. The guiding line of research put forward in this seminal paper is the question of isometric embeddability of generalized Fibonacci cubes into hypercubes. Before heading there, we note that when studying generalized Fibonacci cubes $Q_n(f)$, we do not need to consider all binary strings f, as different generalized Fibonacci cubes may be isomorphic to each other. To this end, recall from Section 2.2 that for a binary string $b = b_1 b_2 \ldots b_n$, the reverse of b is $b^R = b_n b_{n-1} \ldots b_1$ and the complement of f is $\overline{f}$. Then we have the following isomorphism cases.

Proposition 9.1. *If f is a binary string and $n \geq 1$, then*

$$Q_n(f) \cong Q_n(f^R) \cong Q_n(\overline{f}).$$

Proof. Note that f is a substring of a binary string b if and only if f^R is a substring of b^R. Hence the assignment $b \mapsto b^R$ is an isomorphism between $Q_n(f)$ and $Q_n(f^R)$. Similarly, f is a substring of b if and only if $\overline{f}$ is a substring of $\overline{b}$. Hence the assignment $b \mapsto \overline{b}$ is an isomorphism between $Q_n(f)$ and $Q_n(\overline{f})$. $\square$

As an example, $\Gamma_n \cong Q_n(00) \cong Q_n(11)$, a fact implicitly or explicitly used elsewhere in this book. Notably this is done in Fig. 9.6 where an isomorphic copy of Γ_4 is found in Π_4 and the standard roles of 0 and 1 in Γ_4 are interchanged.

Before we turn to isometric embeddability, we would like to add that the generalized Fibonacci cubes $Q_n(111)$ can also be recognized in linear time. This result due to Rho and Vesel [89] nicely complements Theorem 6.11.

Recall that a subgraph H of G is isometric if the distances are the same when considered in H or G and that isometric subgraphs of hypercubes are called partial cubes. We further introduce the notation $H \hookrightarrow G$ to denote that H is an isometric subgraph of G and $H \not\hookrightarrow G$ that this is not the case. For instance, it follows from Theorem 6.3 that Fibonacci cubes are partial cubes, that is, if $n \geq 0$, then

$$\Gamma_n \hookrightarrow Q_n.$$

We can directly verify this fact as follows. Let $b = b_1 \ldots b_n$ and $b' = b'_1 \ldots b'_n$ be arbitrary vertices of Γ_n. Then first changing each coordinate of b from 1 to 0 for which $b_i = 1$ and $b'_i = 0$, and afterwards changing from 0 to 1 the other coordinates in which b and b' differ, yields a shortest b, b'-path in Q_n which lies completely in Γ_n.

A simple feature that applies to all generalized Fibonacci cubes which are partial cubes is the following.

Proposition 9.2. [52, Proposition 6.1] *Let $f \notin \{01, 10\}$ be a binary string of length at least 2. If $Q_n(f) \hookrightarrow Q_n$, then*

$$\Delta(Q_n(f)) = \operatorname{diam}(Q_n(f)) = n.$$

Proof. In view of Proposition 9.1 we may without loss of generality assume that f contains at least two 1s. Since 0^n as well as all its neighbors in Q_n belong to $Q_n(f)$, we get $\Delta(Q_n(f)) = n$.

To prove that $\mathrm{diam}(Q_n(f)) = n$, we first observe that $\mathrm{diam}(Q_n(f)) \le n$ because $Q_n(f) \hookrightarrow Q_n$ and $\mathrm{diam}(Q_n) = n$. It remains to show that $\mathrm{diam}(Q_n(f)) \ge n$. To do it, we distinguish three cases. Suppose first that f contains two adjacent 1s. Then consider a path from $b = 10101\ldots$ to $\bar{b}$ by passing through the vertex 0^n. Similarly, if f contains two adjacent 0s, consider a shortest path of length n passing through the vertex 1^n. Assume finally that f does not have two equal consecutive coordinates, that is, $f \in \{1010\ldots, 0101\ldots\}$. Then consider a path from 0^n to 1^n by complementing digits from left to right. In each of the three cases we have constructed a shortest path in $Q_n(f)$ of length n, hence $\mathrm{diam}(Q_n(f)) \ge n$.   □

It is not difficult to prove that if $s \ge 1$, then $Q_n(1^s) \hookrightarrow Q_n$, and if $r, s, t \ge 1$ and $n \ge r + s + t + 1$, then $Q_n(1^r 0^s 1^t) \not\hookrightarrow Q_n$ (see [52, Propositions 3.1 and 3.2]). To prove a characterization of the strings of the form $1^r 0^s$, for which $Q_n(f) \hookrightarrow Q_n$ holds, we need some preparation.

If G is a connected graph and $u, v \in V(G)$, then the *interval between u and v*, denoted by $I_G(u, v)$, is the set of all vertices which lie on shortest u, v-paths. If $b, b' \in Q_n(f)$, $n \ge 2$, then b and b' are *d-critical strings for* $Q_n(f)$ if $d_{Q_n}(b, b') = d$, but none of the neighbors of b in $I_{Q_n}(b, b')$ belongs to $Q_n(f)$, or none of the neighbors of b' in $I_{Q_n}(b, b')$ belongs to $Q_n(f)$. The following lemma is clear.

Lemma 9.3. *If there exist d-critical strings for* $Q_n(f)$, $n \ge 2$, *then* $Q_n(f) \not\hookrightarrow Q_n$.

The announced embeddability characterization now reads as follows.

Theorem 9.4. [52, Theorem 3.3] *If* $n \ge 2$, *then the following hold.*

  (i) *If* $r \ge 1$, *then* $Q_n(1^r 0) \hookrightarrow Q_n$.
  (ii) *If* $s \ge 2$, *then* $Q_n(1^2 0^s) \hookrightarrow Q_n$ *if and only if* $n \le s + 4$.
  (iii) *If* $r, s \ge 3$, *then* $Q_n(1^r 0^s) \hookrightarrow Q_n$ *if and only if* $n \le 2r + 2s - 3$.

Proof. (i): If $r = 1$, then the assertion follows by (9.1). Assume $r \ge 2$, and let $b, b' \in V(Q_n(1^r 0))$. We proceed by induction on $d = d_{Q_n}(b, b')$. If $d = 1$, then b is clearly adjacent to b' in $Q_n(1^r 0)$. Let $d \ge 2$ and let i be the smallest index such that $b_i \ne b_i'$. We may assume that $b_i = 1$ and $b_i' = 0$. In b, change the ith coordinate to 0 and denote the new vertex by b''. The only possibility that b'' does not belong to $Q_n(1^r 0)$ is that b_i'' is preceded by s 1s. By the way the index i is selected, $b_i' = 0$ is then also preceded by r 1s. As this would mean that $b' \notin Q_n(1^r 0)$, we infer that $b'' \in Q_n(1^r 0)$.

Since b'' differs from b' in $d-1$ coordinates, induction implies that there exists a b, b'-path in $Q_n(1^r0)$ of length d.

(ii) and (iii): Let $r, s \geq 2$.

Claim: If $r, s \geq 2$ and $n \leq 2r + 2s - 3$, then $Q_n(1^r0^s) \hookrightarrow Q_n$ if and only if it is not the case that $r = 2$, $s \geq 4$, and $n > s + 4$.

Let again $b, b' \in V(Q_n(1^r0))$ and let i be the smallest index such that $b_i \neq b'_i$, where $b_i = 1$ and $b'_i = 0$. Let further b'' be the neighbor of b as above. Then $d_{Q_n}(b'', b') < d_{Q_n}(b, b')$. If $b'' \in Q_n(1^r0^s)$, then induction yields $d_{Q_n(1^r0^s)}(b, b') = d_{Q_n}(b, b')$. Suppose that $b'' \notin Q_n(1^r0^s)$. Then b'' contains a substring $x_{b''} = 1^r0^k b''_i 0^{s-1-k}$, where $b''_i = 0$ and the corresponding substring x_b of b is $1^r0^k10^{s-1-k}$. In the corresponding substring $x_{b'}$ of b', at least one of the last $s - 1 - k$ coordinates is 1, for otherwise $b' \notin Q_n(1^r0^s)$. We now distinguish two cases.

Case 1: $x_{b'}$ contains a coordinate 1 which is not the last coordinate of $x_{b'}$. In this case, $s - 1 - k \geq 2$ and therefore $k \leq s - 3$. Then we can change this bit in b to obtain a vertex from $Q_n(1^r0^s)$ at distance $d_{Q_n}(b, b') - 1$ from b' unless $r = 2$, $s \geq 4$ and $n > s + 4$. Assume $r = 2$, $s \geq 4$ and $n > s + 4$. Let $k = n - s - 4$. Then $k \in [s-3]$. Select vertices $b = 1^20^k100^s$ and $b' = 1^20^k010^s$. Note that $b, b' \in Q_n(1^20^s)$ and that they differ in two coordinates. The only neighbors of b in $I_{Q_n}(b, b')$ are $1^20^k000^s$ and $1^20^k110^s$. Since none of these two vertices lies in $Q_n(1^20^s)$, the vertices b and b' are 2-critical for $Q_n(1^r0^s)$ and hence $Q_n(1^r0^s) \not\hookrightarrow Q_n$ by Lemma 9.3.

Case 2: The last coordinate of $x_{b'}$ is 1, and it is preceded with $s - 1$ zeros. Change the last coordinate of x_b in b. If the new vertex is not in $Q_n(1^r0^s)$, then the length of b is at least $r + (s - 2) + r + s = 2r + 2s - 2$ if $s - 1 - k = 1$, while if $s - 1 - k \geq 2$, the length of b is at least $r + (s - 1) + r + s = 2r + 2s - 1$. Hence $Q_n(1^r0^s) \hookrightarrow Q_n$ for each $n \leq 2r + 2s - 3$. This proves the claim.

By the just proved claim, (ii) holds for $s = 3$ if $n \leq s + 4 = 2r + 2s - 3$, and (iii) holds if $n \leq 2r + 2s - 3$.

For the remaining subcases of (ii), assume first $s = 2$. Then $s + 4 = 6 > 2r + 2s - 3 = 5$, thus we need to prove that $Q_n(1^20^2) \hookrightarrow Q_n$ if $n = 6$, and that $Q_n(1^20^2) \not\hookrightarrow Q_n$ if $n > 6$. The latter subcase will be proved in Subcase 1 below, while for $n = 6$ the assertion has been checked by computer. When $s \geq 4$, we have $s + 4 < 2r + 2s - 3$ and by the claim it remains to demonstrate that for $r \neq 2$ or $s \neq 2$ we have $Q_n(1^r0^s) \not\hookrightarrow Q_n$ if $n > 2r + 2s - 3$. This will be done in Subcase 2 below.

Subcase 1: $r = s = 2$.

Suppose first that $n = 7$. Set $b = 1^21010^2$ and $b' = 1^20100^2$ and observe that

$b, b' \in Q_n(1^20^2)$. Moreover, b and b' differ in three coordinates. The only neighbors of b in $I_{Q_n}(b, b')$ are 1^20010^2, 1^21110^2, and 1^21000^2. As none of them belongs to $Q_n(1^20^2)$, the vertices b and b' are 3-critical strings for $Q_n(1^20^2)$. Attaching an appropriate number of 1s to the front of b and b', we get 3-critical strings for $Q_n(1^20^2)$ for $n > 7$. Now apply Lemma 9.3 for the desired conclusion.

Subcase 2: $r > 2$ or $s > 2$.
Suppose first that $n = 2r + 2s - 2$. Then $b = 1^r0^{s-2}101^{r-2}0^s$ and $b' = 1^r0^{s-2}011^{r-2}0^s$ are 2-critical for $Q_n(1^r0^s)$ and hence Lemma 9.3 gives that $Q_n(1^r0^s) \not\hookrightarrow Q_n$. Attaching an appropriate number of 1s to the front of b and b', we then get 2-critical strings for $Q_n(1^r0^s)$ for each $n > 2r+2s-2$. $\square$

Many other results on isometric (non-)embeddability of generalized Fibonacci cubes into hypercubes have been demonstrated. Here we list only a selection of these results.

In [52], a classification of when $Q_n(f) \hookrightarrow Q_n$ holds was provided for all strings f with $|f| \leq 5$. In [112], Wei proposed a necessary condition for an isometric embeddability of $Q_n(f)$ into Q_n for strings f consisting of odd number of blocks, and determined a classification of all strings consisting of 5 blocks (by a block we mean a run; i.e., a maximal substring consisting of the same bit). As a final result, we present the following theorem proved by Wei, Yang, and Wang, where f^n denotes the concatenation of n copies of a given string f.

Theorem 9.5. [116, Theorem 3.3] *Let f be a binary string and $n \geq 2$. Then $Q_n(f) \hookrightarrow Q_n$ if and only if $Q_n(f^n) \hookrightarrow Q_n$.*

9.2   Good and Bad Words

Based on what has been said in the previous section, the following terminology introduced by Klavžar and Shpectorov [67] is very natural. A binary word f is *bad* if there exists $n \in \mathbb{N}$ such that $Q_n(f) \not\hookrightarrow Q_n$. For bad words we have the following fact.

Lemma 9.6. *If $Q_n(f) \not\hookrightarrow Q_n$ for some $n \in \mathbb{N}$, then $Q_{n'}(f) \not\hookrightarrow Q_{n'}$ for all $n' \geq n$.*

Proof. Let $n' = n + r$, $r \geq 1$. Since $Q_n(f) \not\hookrightarrow Q_n$, there exist vertices b, b' of $Q_n(f)$ such that $d_{Q_n(f)}(b, b') > d_{Q_n}(b, b')$. If f starts with 1, then set $\widehat{b} = 0^r b$ and $\widehat{b'} = 0^r b'$, while if f starts with 0, then set $\widehat{b} = 1^r b$ and $\widehat{b'} = 1^r b'$.

In either case, the vertices $\widehat{b}$ and $\widehat{b'}$ lie in $Q_{d'}(f)$ and

$$d_{Q_{n'}(f)}(\widehat{b},\widehat{b'}) = d_{Q_n(f)}(b,b') > d_{Q_n}(b,b') = d_{Q_{n'}}(\widehat{b},\widehat{b'}),$$

which means that $Q_{n'}(f) \not\hookrightarrow Q_{n'}$. $\qquad\square$

Thus for every bad word f there exists the smallest integer n for which non-isometricity holds; it is called the *index of* f and denoted by $B(f)$. On the other hand, assuming that f is bad and hence $Q_{B(f)}(f) \not\hookrightarrow Q_{B(f)}$, it could still be possible that there exits $n' > B(f)$ such that $Q_{B(f)}(f) \hookrightarrow Q_{n'}$. However, Wei and Zhang proved that this cannot happen.

Theorem 9.7. [119, Theorem 1.2] *If f is a bad word and $n \geq B(f)$, then $Q_n(f)$ cannot be isometrically embedded into any hypercube.*

To paraphrase Theorem 9.7, bad words are really bad. On the other hand we say that the word f is *good* if it is not bad, that is, if $Q_n(f) \hookrightarrow Q_n$ for all $n \in \mathbb{N}$. For instance, the word 11 is good (Fibonacci cubes are partial cubes!) as well as are the words 1^r0 for every $r \geq 1$ by Theorem 9.4 *(i)*. On the negative side, Theorem 9.4 *(ii)* says that 1^r0^s, $r,s \geq 2$, are bad words. Set

$$\mathcal{GV}_n = \{f \in \mathcal{B}_n : f \text{ is good}\},$$
$$\mathcal{BV}_n = \{f \in \mathcal{B}_n : f \text{ is bad}\}.$$

Clearly, a word is either good or bad, hence $\mathcal{B}_n$ partitions into $\mathcal{GV}_n$ and $\mathcal{BV}_n$, so that

$$|\mathcal{GV}_n| + |\mathcal{BV}_n| = |\mathcal{GV}_n \cup \mathcal{BV}_n| = |\mathcal{B}_n| = 2^n.$$

In graph theory it is often the case that when we look at a given graph property, asymptotically almost all graphs have that property, or almost all graphs do not have that property. For instance, if the property in question is to have a non-trivial automorphism, then it is well-known that asymptotically almost all graphs have no non-trivial symmetries (non-identity automorphisms). Another such property is that almost all graphs have diameter 2. Hence it would be natural to expect that asymptotically almost all words are bad or almost all words are good. As a surprise, we have the following impressive result.

Theorem 9.8. [67, Corollary 4.4, Theorem 6.1] *The sequence $\frac{|\mathcal{BV}_n|}{2^n}$ converges to α, where α is between 0.919975 and 0.924156.*

Theorem 9.8 thus asserts that for large n, the number of good words is approximately 8% of all words of that length, that is, the number of bad words is approximately 92% of all words of that length. So asymptotically a significant proportion of words are good words!

To derive Theorem 9.8, several ideas and concepts are needed, a key one is the following. For a given binary word f, let $b_k(f)$ be the prefix of f of length k, and let $e_k(f)$ be the suffix of f of length k. Then f has an *r-error overlap*, if for some k, the words $b_k(f)$ and $e_k(f)$ agree in all but r coordinates. As a step to derive Theorem 9.8, it was proved in [67] that a bad word has a 2-error overlap, while in [113] a proof that the converse is also true was given. Hence we have the following result.

Theorem 9.9. [67, Theorem 5.1], [113, Theorem 1.1] *A word is bad if and only if it has a 2-error overlap.*

Here we give a proof of the left-to-right implication of the theorem. The proof for the reverse implication is quite lengthy and technical and hence not given here.

Suppose that f is a bad word and choose n so that $Q_n(f) \not\hookrightarrow Q_n$. Let $b, b' \in V(Q_n(f))$ with $d_{Q_n(f)}(b, b') > d_{Q_n}(b, b')$. Assume that b and b' are selected such that $m = d_{Q_n}(b, b')$ is as small as possible. Clearly, $m \geq 2$. Let $i_1 < i_2 < \cdots < i_m$ be the positions in which b and b' differ. For a subset S of $V = \{i_1, i_2, \ldots, i_m\}$, let $b(S)$ be the word obtained from b by switching the bits in all positions contained in S. Note that $b(\varnothing) = b$ and $b(V) = b'$. For simplicity we will write $b(i)$ instead of $b(\{i\})$.

Clearly, each word $b(S)$ lies on a shortest b, b'-path in Q_n. By the way m is selected, none of the words $b(S)$, where $\varnothing \neq S \neq V$, is contained in $Q_n(f)$. Hence all these words contain occurrences of f. For each $i \in \{i_1, i_2, \ldots, i_m\}$, let f_i be one occurrence of f in $b(i)$. Let also $s_i + 1$ be the first position that f_i occupies within $b(i)$. Every f_i contains the corresponding position i. Now, define a digraph D with the vertex set V, where there is an arc from i to j if and only if f_i covers the position j.

Claim: *There exist $i, j \in V$ with arcs both from i to j and from j to i.*

Since b' does not contain f, every $i \in V$ is a source of an arc. Furthermore, all arcs from i_1 are directed to the right, and all the arcs from i_m to the left. Let $j = i_s$ be the first vertex from which there is an arc pointing left. Then $i = i_{s-1}$ and j fulfill the assertion of the claim.

Let now i and j be as in the claim. Then the factor f_i of $b(i)$ and the factor f_j of $w(j)$ are both are equal to f, and they both contain positions

i and j. So they have an overlap and within this overlap, they disagree exactly in positions i and j. We have thus proved that each bad word has a 2-error overlap.

Using Theorem 9.9 we can use a computer to determine the first few values of $|\mathcal{BV}_n|$ and $|\mathcal{BV}_n|/2^n$. These results are presented in Table 9.1. Interestingly, the sequence $|\mathcal{BV}_n|/2^n$ is not monotone.

n	$|\mathcal{BV}_n|$	$|\mathcal{BV}_n|/2^n$	n	$|\mathcal{BV}_n|$	$|\mathcal{BV}_n|/2^n$
3	2	0.250000	17	119802	0.914017
4	8	0.500000	18	240362	0.916908
5	22	0.687500	19	480966	0.917370
6	46	0.718750	20	963302	0.918676
7	98	0.765625	21	1927382	0.919047
8	210	0.820313	22	3857746	0.919758
9	430	0.839844	23	7715446	0.919753
10	886	0.865234	24	15437078	0.920122
11	1790	0.874023	25	30873042	0.920088
12	3638	0.888184	26	61759618	0.920290
13	7350	0.897217	27	123512490	0.920240
14	14830	0.905151	28	247051278	0.920338
15	29758	0.908142	29	494077866	0.920292
16	59802	0.912506	30	988213906	0.920346

Table 9.1 The first few values of the sequences $|\mathcal{BV}_n|$ and $|\mathcal{BV}_n|/2^n$. The latter converges to $\alpha \in (0.919975, 0.924156)$

In [113], Wei proved several additional characterizations of bad words, out of which we select the following.

Theorem 9.10. [113, Corollary 1.4] *A word f is bad if and only if for every $n \geq B(f)$ there exist 2-critical words or 3-critical words.*

With respect to the index $B(f)$ of a bad word f, it is natural to wonder whether $B(f)$ can be bounded as a function of f. In [53, Theorem 2.1], Ilić, Klavžar and Rho proved that if f is a bad word, then $B(f) < |f|^2$. Moreover, in [53, Theorem 2.2] it was established that for almost all bad words f we actually have $B(f) < 2|f|$. It was further conjectured that the same conclusion holds for all bad words. The conjecture was confirmed by Wei and Zhang.

Theorem 9.11. [118, Corollary 1.4] *If f is a bad word, then $B(f) < 2|f|$.*

Wei, Yang, and Zhu [117] continued the investigation of the index of bad words. Among other results they characterized the bad words with the smallest and with the largest possible index. The smallest possible index is $B(f) = |f| + 1$ and is achieved if and only if $f = 1^k 0^s 1^t$ (or $\overline{f}$) for some $k, s, t \geq 1$. The largest possible index of a bad word f is $2|f| - 1$. In the case when f contains exactly two 0s, the word 0011 (or its reverse) is the unique such word.

9.3   Perfect Codes in Generalized Fibonacci Cubes

Perfect 1-error-correcting codes appeared first in coding theory, and later the concept was extended to arbitrary graphs by Biggs [13].

A 1-*perfect code* of a graph G is a subset $C \subseteq V(G)$ such that every vertex of G is either in C or adjacent to precisely one member of C. This concept generalizes to r-perfect codes, $r \geq 1$, but since we will exclusively deal with 1-perfect codes, we will call them simply *perfect codes*. A perfect code is thus a dominating set such that any vertex is dominated exactly once, for this reason another name frequently used for it is an *efficient dominating set*, a concept we briefly encountered just before Theorem 7.1.

Proposition 9.12. *A dominating set D of G is a perfect code if and only if $x \neq y$ implies $d_G(x, y) \geq 3$ for every $x, y \in D$.*

Proof. This is immediate since the existence of a vertex u dominated by two vertices x and y implies $d_G(x, y) \leq 2$.   □

The existence or non-existence of perfect codes have been considered for many classes of graphs. See the introduction of [4] for some references.

The (classical) perfect codes of coding theory correspond to codes in Q_n. Let us recall some basic results about them we will need in the sequel.

It will be convenient to consider the binary strings of length n as vectors of $\mathbb{F}^n$, the vector space of dimension n over the field $\mathbb{F} = \mathbb{Z}_2$, that is, to associate to a string $x = x_1 x_2 \ldots x_n$ the vector $\theta(x_1 x_2 \ldots x_n) = (x_1, x_2, \ldots, x_n)$. The *parity function* is the linear mapping from $\mathbb{F}^n$ to $\mathbb{Z}_2$ defined by $\pi(x_1, x_2, \ldots, x_n) = x_1 + x_2 + \cdots + x_n$. By the correspondence θ we can define the binary sum $x + y = \theta^{-1}(\theta(x) + \theta(y))$, and the parity $\pi(x) = \pi(\theta(x))$ of strings in $\mathcal{B}_n$. The complement of a string $x \in \mathcal{B}_n$ is thus the string $\overline{x} = x + 1^n$.

In this section, the concatenation of strings x and y is denoted explicitly by $x \cdot y$ instead of just xy when there is a risk of ambiguity.

Since Q_n is n-regular, the existence of a perfect code of cardinality $|C|$ implies $|C|(n + 1) = 2^n$, thus a necessary condition of existence is that $n + 1$ is a power of 2. In other words $n = 2^p - 1$ for some integer p.

For any integer p, Hamming [47] constructed a linear subspace of $\mathbb{F}^{2^p-1}$ which is a perfect code. Such a code is called a binary *linear* code. It is easy to prove that all binary linear perfect codes are Hamming codes.

In 1961, Vasil'ev [106] constructed the first family of perfect codes which are not linear codes. Let us recall Vasil'ev's construction.

Theorem 9.13. [106] *Let C_r be a perfect code of Q_r, let $f : C_r \to \mathbb{Z}_2$, and let π be the parity function. Then the set*

$$C_{2r+1} = \{x \cdot \pi(x) + f(c) \cdot x + c : x \in \mathcal{B}_r, c \in C_r\}$$

is a perfect code of Q_{2r+1}.

Proof. First notice that $|C_{2r+1}| = 2^r |C_r| = 2^r \frac{2^r}{r+1} = \frac{2^{2r+1}}{2r+2}$. Thus, in view of Proposition 9.12, if suffices to prove that the Hamming distance between two different elements of C_{2r+1} is at least 3. Indeed any vertex of Q_{2r+1} will be dominated by at most one vertex of C_{2r+1}, thus vertices of C_{2r+1} will dominate $(2r + 2)|C_{2r+1}| = n(Q_{2r+1})$ vertices.

Assume $(x, c) \neq (x', c')$ and consider the distance

$$d(x \cdot \pi(x) + f(c) \cdot x + c, x' \cdot \pi(x') + f(c') \cdot x' + c') = d_1 + d_2 + d_3,$$

where $d_1 = d(x, x')$, $d_2 = d(\pi(x)+f(c), \pi(x')+f(c'))$, and $d_3 = d(x+c, x'+c')$.

   (i) If $d_1 = 0$, then $x = x'$, thus $d_3 = d(c, c') \geq 3$.
   (ii) If $d_1 = 1$ and $c = c'$, then $\pi(x) \neq \pi(x')$, thus $d_2 = d_3 = 1$.
   (iii) If $d_1 = 1$ and $c \neq c'$, then $d_3 \geq 2$, otherwise $d(c, c') \leq 2$.
   (iv) If $d_1 = 2$, then $d_3 \neq 0$, otherwise $d(c, c') = 2$.

Thus we always have $d = d_1 + d_2 + d_3 \geq 3$ and C_{2r+1} is a perfect code. $\square$

If $f(c) = 0$ for any $c \in C_r$ we obtain the classical inductive construction of Hamming codes with $C_1 = \{0\}$ as basis. For $n \geq 7$ other choices of f can give perfect codes not isomorphic to Hamming codes by the automorphisms of Q_n.

Since Fibonacci cubes are close to hypercubes, it is natural to study the existence of perfect codes for them. We first prove a non-existence result due to Ashrafi, Azarija, Babai, Fathalikhani, and Klavžar.

Theorem 9.14. [4, Theorem 1.1] Γ_n *admits a perfect code if and only if* $n \le 3$.

Proof. It can be easily checked by hand that each of $\Gamma_0, \Gamma_1, \Gamma_2, \Gamma_3$ contains a perfect code and that neither of Γ_4 and Γ_5 does. It remains to prove that Γ_n does not admit a perfect code for any $n \ge 6$.

By $\mathcal{F}_{n,k}$ we denote the vertices of Γ_n of Hamming weight k. We have thus

$$|\mathcal{F}_{n,k}| = \binom{n-k+1}{k}.$$

We denote by $\mathcal{F}_{n,k}^{0\bullet}$ and $\mathcal{F}_{n,k}^{1\bullet}$ the vertices of $\Gamma_{n,k}$ that start with 0 and 1, respectively. It is immediate that

$$|\mathcal{F}_{n,k}^{0\bullet}| = |\mathcal{F}_{n-1,k}| = \binom{n-k}{k} \quad \text{and} \quad |\mathcal{F}_{n,k}^{1\bullet}| = |\mathcal{F}_{n-2,k-1}| = \binom{n-k}{k-1}.$$

Claim: *If* $n \ge 6$ *and* C *is a perfect code of* Γ_n, *then* $0^n \notin C$.

Suppose on the contrary that $0^n \in C$. Then all the vertices in $\mathcal{F}_{n,1}$ are dominated by 0^n. Hence $\mathcal{F}_{n,2} \cap C = \varnothing$. Consequently, each vertex of $\mathcal{F}_{n,2}$ must be dominated by a vertex of $\mathcal{F}_{n,3}$. The only vertices in $\mathcal{F}_{n,3}$ that dominate the vertices in $\mathcal{F}_{n,2}^{1\bullet}$ are in $\mathcal{F}_{n,3}^{1\bullet}$. Since each vertex $v \in \mathcal{F}_{n,3}^{1\bullet}$ has precisely two neighbors in $\mathcal{F}_{n,2}^{1\bullet}$ we have

$$|C \cap \mathcal{F}_{n,3}^{1\bullet}| = \tfrac{1}{2}|\mathcal{F}_{n,2}^{1\bullet}| = \tfrac{1}{2}(n-2).$$

Therefore, the number of undominated vertices in $\mathcal{F}_{n,3}^{1\bullet}$ so far is

$$|\mathcal{F}_{n,3}^{1\bullet}| - \tfrac{1}{2}(n-2) = \binom{n-3}{2} - \tfrac{1}{2}(n-2) = \tfrac{1}{2}(n^2 - 8n + 14).$$

These vertices can only be dominated by the vertices of $\mathcal{F}_{n,4}^{1\bullet}$. Moreover, each such vertex dominates precisely three of the undominated vertices of $\mathcal{F}_{n,3}^{1\bullet}$. Hence we have that

$$|C \cap \mathcal{F}_{n,4}^{1\bullet}| = \tfrac{1}{6}(n^2 - 8n + 14).$$

But the last expression is not an integer. This contradiction proves the claim.

Suppose now that C is a perfect code of Γ_n. Then by our Claim we have that $0^n \notin C$. This implies that $|C \cap \mathcal{F}_{n,1}| = 1$. Denote by a this unique vertex. The remaining $n-1$ vertices of $\mathcal{F}_{n,1}$ must be dominated by the vertices of $\mathcal{F}_{n,2}$. Since a vertex of $\mathcal{F}_{n,2}$ dominates precisely two vertices of $\mathcal{F}_{n,1}$, it follows that n is odd and that there are

$$|\mathcal{F}_{n,2}| - \tfrac{1}{2}(n-1) - (d-1) = \binom{n-1}{2} - \tfrac{1}{2}(n-1) - (d-1)$$

$$= \tfrac{1}{2}(n^2 - 4n - 2d + 5) \qquad (9.2)$$

undominated vertices in $\mathcal{F}_{n,2}$, where $d \in \{n-2, n-1\}$ is the degree of a. These vertices must be dominated by the vertices of $\mathcal{F}_{n,3}$ and hence the expression in (9.2) must be divisible by 3. Setting $d = n-1$ and using the fact that $n = 2k+1$ for some integer k, (9.2) is reduced to $2k^2 - 4k + 1$. Since 3 does not divide $2k^2 - 4k + 1$ for any $k > 0$, it follows that $d = n-2$. Consequently, $a \notin \{10^{n-1}, 0^{n-1}1\}$. The fact that $d = n-2$ implies that there are $\tfrac{1}{2}(n-3)^2$ undominated vertices in $\mathcal{F}_{n,2}$ that need to be dominated by the vertices of $\mathcal{F}_{n,3}$. This implies that 6 divides $(n-3)^2$, that is, $n = 6k+3$ for some $k > 0$. In what follows we split the proof into two parts depending

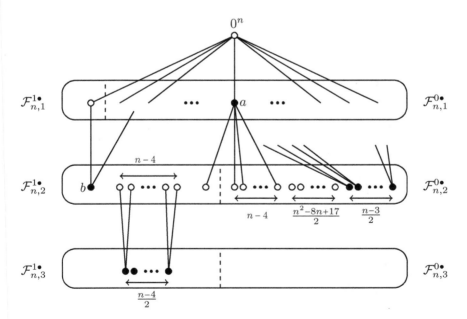

Fig. 9.2 The case when a starts with 00

on whether a starts with 00 or 01.

Case 1: a starts with 00.

In this case a it dominates precisely $n-4$ vertices of $\mathcal{F}^0_{n,2}$ and a single vertex of $\mathcal{F}^1_{n,2}$ (see Fig. 9.2.) In order to dominate $\mathcal{F}^{1\bullet}_{n,1} = \{10^{n-1}\}$, the perfect code C must contain at least one vertex of $\mathcal{F}^{1\bullet}_{n,2}$. Moreover, since every vertex of $\mathcal{F}^{1\bullet}_{n,2}$ is adjacent to 10^{n-1}, we must have $|C \cap \mathcal{F}^{1\bullet}_{n,2}| = 1$. Since the vertex a dominates precisely one vertex in $\mathcal{F}^{1\bullet}_{n,2}$, there are $|\mathcal{F}^{1\bullet}_{n,2}| - 2 = n-4$ vertices in $\mathcal{F}^{1\bullet}_{n,2}$ that must be dominated by the vertices in $\mathcal{F}^{1\bullet}_{n,3}$, and since each such vertex dominates precisely two elements of $\mathcal{F}^{1\bullet}_{n,2}$, it follows that C must contain $\frac{1}{2}(n-4)$ vertices of $\mathcal{F}^{1\bullet}_{n,3}$. The fact that n is odd implies that the last expression is not an integer thus deriving a contradiction.

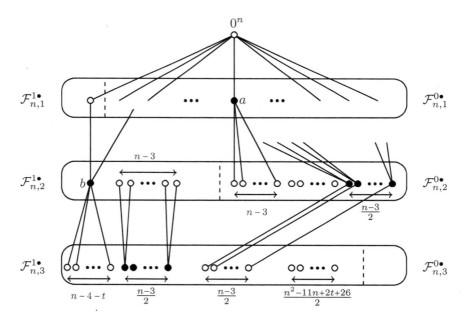

Fig. 9.3   The case when a starts with 01

Case 2: a starts with 01.

In this case $a = 0100^{n-3}$ and dominates precisely $n-3$ vertices of $\mathcal{F}^{0\bullet}_{n,2}$. As before, in order to dominate $\{10^{n-1}\} = \mathcal{F}^{1\bullet}_{n,1}$, the set C must contain precisely one vertex of $\mathcal{F}^{1\bullet}_{n,2}$, call it b (see Fig. 9.3.) Notice that this vertex dominates 10^{n-1} as well as precisely one vertex in $\mathcal{F}^{0\bullet}_{n,1}$. Observe furthermore that the number of undominated vertices in $\mathcal{F}^{1\bullet}_{n,2}$ is $(n-2)-1$ which in turn implies that

$$|C \cap \mathcal{F}_{n,3}^{1\bullet}| = \tfrac{1}{2}(n-3).$$

Finally, we compute the number of undominated vertices of $\mathcal{F}_{n,3}^{1\bullet}$. Observe that b dominates $n-4-t$ vertices in $\mathcal{F}_{n,3}^{1\bullet}$, where $t=0$ when b starts 101 or when $b = 10\ldots01$, and $t=1$ when b starts 100 and ends 0. Since $a \in C$, every vertex of $C \cap \mathcal{F}_{n,2}^{0\bullet}$ starts with 00 and hence has precisely one neighbor in $\mathcal{F}_{n,3}^{1\bullet}$. The set $\mathcal{F}_{n,1}$ contains precisely one vertex of C namely a. In addition, the vertex b dominates precisely two vertices of $\mathcal{F}_{n,1}$. Therefore there are $n-3$ undominated vertices in $\mathcal{F}_{n,1}$ implying that $|C \cap \mathcal{F}_{n,2}^{0\bullet}| = \tfrac{1}{2}(n-3)$. It thus follows that $\tfrac{1}{2}(n-3)$ vertices of $\mathcal{F}_{n,3}^{1\bullet}$ are dominated by $\mathcal{F}_{n,2}^{0\bullet}$ and that consequently

$$|\mathcal{F}_{n,3}^{1\bullet}| - (n-3) - (n-4-t) = \binom{n-3}{2} - \tfrac{1}{2}(n-3) - \tfrac{1}{2}(n-3) - (n-4-t)$$

$$= \tfrac{1}{2}(n^2 - 11n + 2t + 26) \tag{9.3}$$

vertices of $\mathcal{F}_{n,3}^{1\bullet}$ remain undominated by C. These vertices must be dominated by the vertices in $\mathcal{F}_{n,4}^{1}$, each vertex dominating precisely 3 vertices. Since $n = 6k+3$ for some integer k the expression (9.3) reduces to $18k^2 - 15k + t + 1$ which is equivalent to $t+1 \pmod 3 \not\equiv 0$ for $t \in \{0,1\}$. Hence the expression (9.3) is not divisible by 3 and we have derived a final contradiction which proves Theorem 9.14. $\qquad\square$

We continue with an existence result given by Mollard [75]. Indeed when $n = 2^p - 1$, for some integer p, and s is large enough, there exits a perfect code in the generalized Fibonacci cube $Q_n(1^s)$. The idea is to construct, using Vasil'ev's approach, a perfect code of Q_n without elements that contains 1^s as substring.

Lemma 9.15. *Let m be an integer. Let A_0 be the set of strings $A_0 = \{0^{m+1}y : y \in \mathcal{B}_m\}$. For $i \in [m]$, let $A_i = \{z10^{m+1}y : z \in \mathcal{B}_{i-1}, y \in \mathcal{B}_{m-i}\}$. Then the sets A_i, $i \in \{0,\ldots,n\}$, are disjoint and any string of $\mathcal{B}_{2m+1}$ containing 0^{m+1} as substring belongs to some A_i.*

Proof. Let x be a string of $\mathcal{B}_{2m+1}$ containing 0^{m+1} as substring and i be the minimum integer such that $x_{i+1}x_{i+2}\ldots x_{i+m+1} = 0^{m+1}$. Then either $i = 0$, and x belongs to A_0, or $m \geq i \geq 1$. In this case $x_i = 1$ thus $x \in A_i$. Assume $x \in A_i \cap A_j$ with $m \geq j > i \geq 0$ then $x_j = 1$ thus $j \geq i+m+2 > m$, a contradiction. $\qquad\square$

Theorem 9.16. [75, Theorem 2.2] *Let* $n = 2^p - 1$ *where* $p \geq 2$ *and let* $s = 3.2^{p-2}$. *There exists a perfect code* C *in* Q_n *such that no element of* C *contains* 1^s *as substring.*

Proof. Let $m = 2^{p-2} - 1$ thus $2m + 1 = 2^{p-1} - 1$ and $s = 3m + 3$. Let C_{2m+1} be a perfect code in Q_{2m+1}. Let f be the function from $\mathcal{B}_{2m+1}$ to $\mathbb{Z}_2$ defined by

   (i) $f(0^{m+1}y) = 1$ for $y \in \mathcal{B}_m$
   (ii) $f(10^{m+1}y) = 0$ for $y \in \mathcal{B}_{m-1}$
   (iii) $f(z10^{m+1}y) = \pi(z)$ for $z \in \mathcal{B}_{i-1}$ and $y \in \mathcal{B}_{m-i}$ for $i = 2$ to m.
   (iv) $f = 0$ otherwise.

Note that by the previous lemma the function f is well-defined. Let C be the perfect code of Q_{4m+3} obtained from Vasil'ev's construction from C_{2m+1} and f. Assume there exists a string d in C with 1^{3m+3} as substring. This means d is obtained from $x = d_1 d_2 \ldots d_{2m+1}$ and $c \in C_{2m+1}$. Since $n = 4m + 3$, note first that $d_{m+1}d_{m+2}\ldots d_{3m+3} = 1^{2m+3}$. Let i be the minimum integer such that $d_i d_{i+1} \ldots d_{3m+i+2} = 1^{3m+3}$. We consider three cases.

Case 1: $i = 1$.
Then $x = d_1 d_2 \ldots d_{2m+1} = 1^{2m+1}$ and $d_{2m+2}d_{2m+3}\ldots d_{3m+3} = 1^{m+2}$. Since $c + x = 1^{m+1}d_{3m+4}d_{3m+5}\ldots d_{4m+3}$ we have $c = 0^{m+1}y$ for some $y \in \mathcal{B}_m$. Thus $f(c) = 1$ and since $\pi(x) = 1$ we obtain $d_{2m+2} = f(c) + \pi(x) = 0$, a contradiction.

Case 1: $i = 2$.
Then $x = 01^{2m}$ and $d_{2m+2}d_{2m+3}\ldots d_{3m+4} = 1^{m+3}$. Since $c + x = 1^{m+2}d_{3m+5}d_{3m+6}\ldots d_{4m+3}$ we have $c = 10^{m+1}y$ for some $y \in \mathcal{B}_{m-1}$. Thus $f(c) = 0$ and since $\pi(x) = 0$ we obtain $d_{2m+2} = f(c) + \pi(x) = 0$, a contradiction.

Case 3: $i \geq 3$. In this case $x = z01^{2m-i+2}$ for $z \in \mathcal{B}_{i-2}$ and $d_{2m+2}d_{2m+3}\ldots d_{3m+2+i} = 1^{m+i+1}$. Since $c + x = 1^{m+i}d_{3m+i+3}d_{3m+i+4}\ldots d_{4m+3}$ we have $c = \overline{z}10^{m+1}y$ for some $y \in \mathcal{B}_{m-i+1}$. Thus $f(c) = \pi(\overline{z})$. Since $\pi(x) = \pi(z) + \pi(1^{2m-i+2})$ and $\pi(\overline{z}) + \pi(z) = \pi(1^{i-2})$ we obtain $d_{2m+2} = f(c) + \pi(x) = \pi(1^{2m}) = 0$, again a contradiction.

Therefore, there exists no string d in C with 1^{3m+3} as substring. □

Corollary 9.17. [75, Corollary 2.3] *Let* $n = 2^p - 1$, *where* $p \geq 2$, *and let* $s \geq 3 \, 2^{p-2}$. *Then there exists a perfect code in* $Q_n(1^s)$.

Proof. Indeed, let C be a perfect code in Q_n such that no element of C contains $1^3 2^{p-2}$ as substring. The strings of C are in $V(Q_n(1^s))$. Let x be a vertex of $V(Q_n(1^s))$. If $x \notin C$ then x is adjacent in Q_n to a vertex c in C. Note that x and c are also adjacent in $Q_n(1^s)$ thus C is a dominating set of $Q_n(1^s)$. If c and c' are two strings of C then $d_{Q_n(1^s)}(c,c') \geq d_{Q_n}(c,c') \geq 3$. Therefore C is a perfect code in $Q_n(1^s)$. $\square$

For $n = 2^p - 1$, it is of interest to determine the minimum s such that there exists a perfect code in $Q_n(1^s)$. From this point of view, Corollary 9.17 is not always the best result possible. For example, for $n = 7$, it gives a perfect code in $Q_7(1^s)$ for $s \geq 6$. But the code C_7 obtained in Vasil'ev's construction starting from $C_3 = \{000, 111\}$ with $f(000) = f(111) = 1$ is a perfect code in $Q_7(1^5)$. Indeed

(i) $11111ab$ or 0011111 cannot be in C_7 since $P(111)+1 = P(001)+1 = 0$.
(ii) $011111a$ cannot be in C_7 since the possible codewords beginning with 011 are 0111011 and 0111100.

Consider now perfect codes in Lucas cubes.

It can be easily checked by hand that $\{0^n\}$ is a perfect code in Λ_n for $n \leq 3$ as shown in Fig. 8.1, and that Λ_4 and Λ_5 do not contain a perfect code. Mollard proved [77] the non-existence of perfect codes in Λ_n for $n \geq 4$.

By $\mathscr{L}_{n,k}$ we denote the vertices of Λ_n with Hamming weight k. From Proposition 8.2 we obtain

$$|\mathscr{L}_{n,2}| = \tfrac{1}{2}n(n-3) \quad \text{and} \quad |\mathscr{L}_{n,3}| = \tfrac{1}{6}n(n-4)(n-5).$$

Assume $n \geq 3$ and $k \geq 1$. Let $\mathscr{L}_{n,k}^{1\bullet}$ be the vertices of $\Lambda_{n,k}$ that start with 1. Since $\mathscr{L}_{n,k}^{1\bullet} = \{10s0 : s \in \mathcal{F}_{n-3,k-1}\}$ it is immediate that

$$|\mathscr{L}_{n,k}^{1\bullet}| = |\mathcal{F}_{n-3,k-1}| = \binom{n-1-k}{k-1}.$$

Lemma 9.18. [77, Lemma 2.1] *If $n \geq 6$ and C is a perfect code of Λ_n, then $0^n \in C$.*

Proof. Suppose on the contrary that $0^n \notin C$. Since 0^n must be dominated there exists a vertex in $\mathscr{L}_{n,1} \cap C$. This vertex is unique and because of the circular symmetry of Λ_n we can assume $10^{n-1} \in C$.

Since $0^n \notin C$ the other vertices of $\mathscr{L}_{n,1}$ must be dominated by vertices in $\mathscr{L}_{n,2}$. But a vertex in $\mathscr{L}_{n,2}$ has precisely two neighbors in $\mathscr{L}_{n,1}$, thus n must be odd and

$$|\mathscr{L}_{n,2} \cap C| = \tfrac{1}{2}(n-1).$$

The unique vertex 10^{n-1} in $\mathscr{L}_{n,1} \cap C$ has exactly $n-3$ neighbors in $\mathscr{L}_{n,2}$. Let D be the vertices of $\mathscr{L}_{n,2}$ not in C and not dominated by 10^{n-1}. Vertices in D must be dominated by vertices in $\mathscr{L}_{n,3} \cap C$. Each vertex of $\mathscr{L}_{n,3} \cap C$ has exactly exactly three neighbors in $\mathscr{L}_{n,2}$. Thus 3 divides the number of vertices in D. This number is

$$|D| = |\mathscr{L}_{n,2}| - (n-3) - \tfrac{1}{2}(n-1) = \tfrac{1}{2}(n^2 + 1) - 3(n+1).$$

But this quantity is not divisible by 3 since for n odd, $n^2 + 1$ modulo 6 is either 2 or 4. □

We are now able to prove the following result.

Theorem 9.19. [77, Theorem 1.2] *The Lucas cube Λ_n admits a perfect code if and only if $n \le 3$.*

Proof. Let $n \ge 6$ and C be a perfect code. Since $0^n \in C$ all vertices of $\mathscr{L}_{n,1}$ are dominated by 0^n and thus $\mathscr{L}_{n,2} \cap C = \mathscr{L}_{n,1} \cap C = \varnothing$. Consequently, each vertex of $\mathscr{L}_{n,2}$ must be dominated by a vertex in $\mathscr{L}_{n,3}$. Since each vertex in $\mathscr{L}_{n,3}$ has precisely three neighbors in $\mathscr{L}_{n,2}$ we obtain

$$|\mathscr{L}_{n,3} \cap C| = \tfrac{1}{3}|\mathscr{L}_{n,2}|.$$

This number must be an integer thus 3 divides $|\mathscr{L}_{n,2}| = \tfrac{1}{2}n(n-3)$ and therefore 3 divides $n(n-3)$. This is only possible when n is a multiple of 3.

Each vertex of $\mathscr{L}_{n,2}^1$ must be dominated by a vertex in $\mathscr{L}_{n,3}^1$. Furthermore a vertex in $\mathscr{L}_{n,3}^1$ has precisely two neighbors in $\mathscr{L}_{n,2}^1$. Therefore $|\mathscr{L}_{n,2}^1| = n - 3$ must be even and thus $n = 6p + 3$ for some integer $p \ge 1$.

Let E be the set of vertices of $\mathscr{L}_{n,3}$ not in C. Vertices in E must be dominated by a vertex in $\mathscr{L}_{n,4}$. Furthermore each vertex in $\mathscr{L}_{n,4}$ has precisely four neighbors in $\mathscr{L}_{n,3}$. Therefore 4 divides $|E|$. Since

$$|E| = |\mathscr{L}_{n,3}| - |\mathscr{L}_{n,3} \cap C| = \tfrac{1}{6}n(n-4)(n-5) - \tfrac{1}{6}n(n-3) = \tfrac{1}{6}n(n^2 - 10n + 23).$$

Replacing n by $6p+3$ we obtain that 4 divides the odd number $(2p+1)(18p^2 - 12p + 1)$. This contradiction proves the theorem. □

9.4   Pell Graphs

Pell graphs form an interesting family of graphs that are defined similarly to Fibonacci cubes, extend our treatment from binary to ternary, and are at the same time intrinsically related to Fibonacci cubes. More than enough reasons to present Pell graphs in this section!

Recalling that for the binary alphabet we use $\mathcal{B} = \{0, 1\}$, we set

$$\mathcal{T} = \{0, 1, 2\},$$

where $\mathcal{T}$ stands for ternary. For each $n \geq 1$, we collect the ternary strings of length n into the set

$$\mathcal{T}_n = \{t_1 \ldots t_n : t_i \in \mathcal{T}, i \in [n]\}.$$

Clearly $|\mathcal{T}_n| = 3^n$. A *Pell string* is a ternary string in which each run of 2s is of even length. Equivalently, a Pell string is a string over the alphabet $\{0, 1, 22\}$. Let $\mathcal{P}_n$ be the set of all Pell strings of length n. $\mathcal{P}_1 = \{0, 1\}$ and $\mathcal{P}_2 = \{00, 01, 10, 11, 22\}$.

Let $\mathcal{C}_n \subseteq \mathcal{T}_n$. Recall our convention from Chapter 3 that the notation $\mathcal{C}_n^{f\bullet}$, where $f = f_1 \ldots f_k$ is a ternary string of length $k \in [n]$, stands for the set of the all strings from $\mathcal{C}_n$ which have f as a prefix, that is

$$\mathcal{C}_n^{f\bullet} = \{t_1 \ldots t_n \in \mathcal{C}_n : t_1 = f_1, \ldots, t_k = f_k\}.$$

Since a non-null Pell string begins either with 0, 1 or 22 followed by a Pell string, for $n \geq 3$ we have

$$\mathcal{P}_n = \mathcal{P}_n^{0\bullet} + \mathcal{P}_n^{1\bullet} + \mathcal{P}_n^{22\bullet},$$

where the operation + stands for the disjoint union. This can equivalently be written

$$\mathcal{P}_n = 0\mathcal{P}_{n-1} + 1\mathcal{P}_{n-1} + 22\mathcal{P}_{n-2}. \tag{9.4}$$

The *Pell numbers* P_n are defined by the recursion

$$P_n = 2P_{n-1} + P_{n-2}$$

for $n \geq 2$ with $P_0 = 0$ and $P_1 = 1$. The identity (9.4) leads to the same recurrence for $|\mathcal{P}_n|$ and hence we have

$$|\mathcal{P}_n| = P_{n+1}, \quad n \geq 1. \tag{9.5}$$

In [80], Munarini introduced the Pell graphs Π_n as follows. Set first $\Pi_0 = K_1$. For $n \geq 1$, let $V(\Pi_n) = \mathcal{P}_n$. Two vertices of Π_n are adjacent if either one of them can be obtained from the other by replacing one 0 with 1 (or the other way around), or by replacing one substring 11 with 22 (or the other way around). Note that when the latter change is performed, the two 2s replaced by two 1s must be selected such that the obtained string remains a Pell string. For instance, given the Pell string 01222200, we may replace the first two 2s to obtain the Pell string 01112200, or the last two 2s to obtain 01221100, but we are not allowed to replace the middle two 2s,

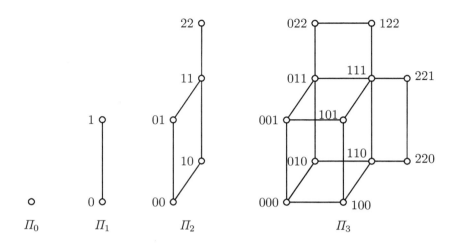

Fig. 9.4   The Pell graphs Π_0, Π_1, Π_2, Π_3

as the string 01211200 obtained by this substitution is not a Pell string. In Fig. 9.4, the first four Π_n are drawn.

Just as the intrinsic recursive structure of Fibonacci cubes leads to their fundamental decomposition, Pell graphs also have such a decomposition. Indeed, since for $n \geq 3$ we have

$$V(\Pi_n) = \mathcal{P}_n = \mathcal{P}_n^{0\bullet} + \mathcal{P}_n^{1\bullet} + \mathcal{P}_n^{22\bullet},$$

each of the subsets of vertices $\mathcal{P}_n^{0\bullet}$ and $\mathcal{P}_n^{1\bullet}$ induces a subgraph of Π_n isomorphic to Π_{n-1}, while the subset $\mathcal{P}_n^{22\bullet}$ induces a subgraph of Π_n isomorphic to Π_{n-2}. Moreover, each vertex $0x$ of $\mathcal{P}_n^{0\bullet}$ has exactly one neighbor in $\mathcal{P}_n^{1\bullet}$, that is, the vertex $1x$. This means that the subgraph of Π_n induced by the set $\mathcal{P}_n^{0\bullet} + \mathcal{P}_n^{1\bullet}$ is isomorphic to the Cartesian product $\Pi_{n-1} \,\square\, K_2$. Furthermore, each vertex $22x$ of $\mathcal{P}_n^{22\bullet}$ has exactly one neighbor in $\mathcal{P}_n^{1\bullet}$, that is, the vertex $11x$. What we have just described is the *fundamental decomposition* of Π_n.

The fundamental decomposition of Π_4 is illustrated in Fig. 9.5. The blue edges are the matching edges between the subgraphs induced by $\mathcal{P}_4^{0\bullet}$ and $\mathcal{P}_4^{1\bullet}$, respectively, each of them isomorphic to Π_3. The red edges are the matching edges from $\mathcal{P}_4^{22\bullet}$ to $\mathcal{P}_4^{11\bullet}$.

Recall that for a given connected graph G, the eccentricity $\mathrm{ecc}_G(u)$ of $u \in V(G)$ is the maximum distance between u and any other vertex of G, and that the diameter $\mathrm{diam}(G)$ and the radius $\mathrm{rad}(G)$ of G is the maximum, respectively minimum, eccentricity among vertices of G. The *center* $C(G)$

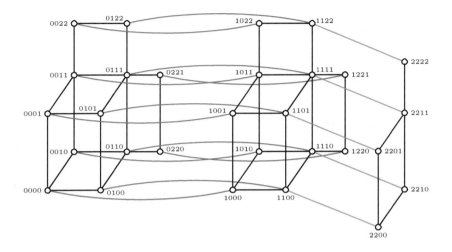

Fig. 9.5 The Pell graph Π_4 and its fundamental decomposition

of G is the set of vertices u with minimum eccentricity, that is,

$$C(G) = \{u \in V(G) : \mathrm{ecc}_G(u) = \mathrm{rad}(G)\}.$$

As it happens, the subgraph of a Pell graph induced by its center is just a Fibonacci cube. More precisely, we have the following result.

Theorem 9.20. [80, Propositions 4 and 5] *If $n \geq 1$, then*

$$\Pi_n[C(\Pi_n)] \cong \Gamma_n.$$

Proof. We first claim that $\mathrm{rad}(\Pi_n) = n$. Let $t = t_1 \dots t_n$ be an arbitrary vertex of Π_n, that is, an arbitrary Pell string. Suppose that $|t|_2 = 2k$. Then $|t|_0 + |t|_1 = n - 2k$. Consider now the Pell string t' obtained from t by exchanging the role of 0 and 1 and by replacing all the occurrences of 2 by 0. As we can change the substring 22 to 00 in three (but no less) moves, say $22 \to 11 \to 10 \to 00$, we infer that $d_{\Pi_n}(t, t') = 3k + (n - 2k) = n + k \geq n$. Hence $\mathrm{rad}(\Pi_n) \geq n$. On the other hand, we easily see that $\mathrm{ecc}(1^n) = n$, hence we conclude that $\mathrm{rad}(\Pi_n) = n$.

It remains to determine which vertices besides 1^n belong to $C(\Pi_n)$. First, if $t \in V(\Pi_n)$ contains at least one 2 (in which case, of course, t contains at least two 2s), then the above argument implies that $\mathrm{ecc}_{\Pi_n}(t) > n$, so $t \notin C(\Pi_n)$. Suppose hence in the rest that $t \in V(\Pi_n)$ is a binary (Pell) string. In the first subcase assume that t contains two consecutive 0s. Let t' be the string obtained from t by replacing two fixed consecutive 0s by

22, and by binary complementing all the other bits of t. Then, using the argument from the first paragraph again, we infer that $d_{\Pi_n}(t, t') \geq n+1$ and hence also in this case $t \notin C(\Pi_n)$. In the second subcase let $t \in V(\Pi_n)$ be a binary (Pell) string which contains no two consecutive 0s. Then we infer that $\mathrm{ecc}_{\Pi_n}(f) \leq n$ and as $\mathrm{rad}(\Pi_n) = n$ we have $t \in C(\Pi_n)$. We conclude that

$$C(\Pi_n) = \{t = t_1 \ldots t_n : t_i \in \mathcal{B}, 1 \in \{t_i, t_{i+1}\} \text{ for } i \in [n-1]\}.$$

To complete the proof just observe that $C(\Pi_n)$ induced a subgraph of Π_n isomorphic to Γ_n because taking the binary complement of each (binary) string from $C(\Pi_n)$ yields the vertex set of Γ_n, while the adjacencies are inherited. □

Fig. 9.6 shows an example illustrating Theorem 9.20. The center of Π_4 is highlighted. Note that it is isomorphic to Γ_4. As stated at the end of the proof of Theorem 9.20, the standard labeling of this Γ_4 is obtained by reversing the roles of 0 and 1.

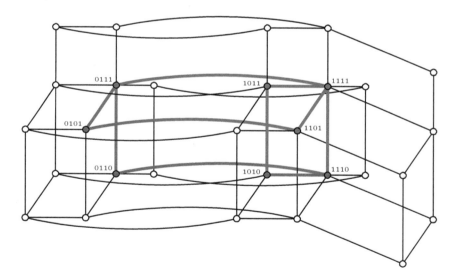

Fig. 9.6   The Fibonacci cube Γ_4 as a subgraph of the Pell graph Π_4

The center of the Pell graph Π_n is thus isomorphic to the Fibonacci cube Γ_n. On the other hand, we also find Pell graphs inside Fibonacci cubes as the next result asserts.

Theorem 9.21. [80, Theorem 7] *If $n \geq 1$, then Π_n is a subgraph of Γ_{2n-1}.*

Proof. Let $n \geq 1$, and define a mapping α on the set $V(\Pi_n) = \mathcal{P}_n$ as follows. Let $p = p_1 \ldots p_n \in V(\Pi_n)$ and proceed from left to right by replacing each 0 by 10, each 1 by 00, and each substring 22 by 0100. Denote the obtained string by p'. For instance, if $p = 12200120$, then $p' = 00\,0100\,0100\,10\,10\,00\,0100\,10$. Clearly $p' \in \mathcal{B}_{2n}$. Note that p' ends by 0. Define now $\alpha(p)$ to be the string obtained from p' be removing the last 0. Then $\alpha(p) \in \mathcal{B}_{2n-1}$. Moreover, it is clear by the construction that $\alpha(p)$ contains no two consecutive 1s, hence we have defined a mapping

$$\alpha : V(\Pi_n) \to V(\Gamma_{2n-1}).$$

From the definition of α we also infer that α is injective. Hence the theorem will be proved by demonstrating that α maps edges to edges.

Let $pq \in E(\Pi_n)$, where $p = p_1 \ldots p_n$ and $q = q_1 \ldots q_n$. Suppose first that p and q differ in one position, say i. Then we may without loss of generality assume that $p_i = 0$ and $q_i = 1$. Then $\alpha(p)_{2i-1} = 1$ and $\alpha(q)_{2i-1} = 0$, while $\alpha(p)_j = \alpha(q)_j$ holds for every $j \in [2n]$, $j \neq 2i - 1$. Hence $\alpha(p)$ is adjacent to $\alpha(q)$ in Γ_{2n-1}. Suppose second that p and q are adjacent in Π_n because $p_i = p_{i+1} = 1$ and $q_i = q_{i+1} = 2$ hold for some $i \in [n-1]$. Then we see that $\alpha(p)_{2i} = 0$ and $\alpha(q)_{2i} = 1$, while in all the other positions $\alpha(p)$ and $\alpha(q)$ are equal. We conclude that also in this case $\alpha(p)$ is adjacent to $\alpha(q)$ in Γ_{2n-1}. $\square$

In Section 6.3 we have seen that a central insight into Fibonacci cubes, which allows them to be quickly recognized, is the fact that they are median graphs. As it happens, Pell graphs are median graphs as well. One way to see this is as follows.

Let $\mathcal{F}_{2n}^*$ be the set of Fibonacci strings u of length $2n$ without a final 1 such that u cannot be written as $u = v0101w$ with v and w of even length. For example 00101000 belongs to $\mathcal{F}_8^*$ but not 00010100. Let further Γ_{2n}^* denote the subgraph of Q_{2n} induced by the strings from $\mathcal{F}_{2n}^*$. Then, using the mapping α from the proof of Theorem 9.21, we deduce (see [80, Theorem 8]) that $\Pi_n \cong \Gamma_{2n}^*$. Considering $\Pi_n \cong \Gamma_{2n}^*$ as a subgraph of Q_{2n}, we can then proceed along the same lines as we did in the proof of Theorem 6.3 to establish the following result.

Theorem 9.22. [80, Theorem 10] *Π_n is a median graph for $n \geq 1$.*

Another way to derive Theorem 9.22 is to use the fundamental decomposition of Π_n. By induction, Π_{n-1} is median, and hence $\Pi_{n-1} \,\square\, \Pi_{n-1}$

is median. But Π_n can be obtained from $\Pi_{n-1} \,\square\, \Pi_{n-1}$ by a (peripheral) convex expansion and hence, by the Mulder's convex expansion theorem mentioned in Section 6.3.3, Π_n is indeed a median graph.

In addition to what we have outlined so far, a number of other interesting properties of Pell graphs have been identified. We will present only a short list of these properties.

In [80, Theorem 17] a recurrence for the cube polynomials of Pell graphs is determined, leading to corresponding generating functions that can be expressed in terms of the so-called Delannoy polynomials. This in turn enables to express the number of k-cubes in Π_n as

$$\sum_{i=k}^{n} \binom{i}{k} \sum_{j=0}^{n} \binom{i}{j}\binom{n-j}{i}.$$

For $k = 0$ this result implies

$$n(\Pi_n) = P_{n+1} = \sum_{i=k}^{n} \sum_{j=0}^{n} \binom{i}{j}\binom{n-j}{i},$$

while for $k = 1$ it yields the following formula for the size of Pell graphs:

$$m(\Pi_n) = \sum_{i=1}^{n} i \sum_{j=0}^{n} \binom{i}{j}\binom{n-j}{i}.$$

As a conclusion to this section, we would like to add that in the article [84], Özer, E. Saygı and Z. Saygı investigated domination parameters of Pell graphs along the directions that we presented in Chapter 7 on domination in Fibonacci cubes. Among other things, they also used integer linear programming there.

Pell graphs are explored further in Section 9.8.

9.5 k-Fibonacci Cubes

For any given $k > 0$, a variant of Fibonacci cubes called k-*Fibonacci cubes* (or k-Fibonacci graphs) are obtained as subgraphs of Fibonacci cubes by eliminating certain edges during the fundamental recursion phase of their construction. These graphs have the same number of vertices as Fibonacci cubes, but their edge sets are determined by the parameter k.

The edge elimination which defines k-Fibonacci cubes is carried out at the step analogous to where the fundamental recursion is used to construct Γ_n from the two previous cubes by the perfect matching between $10\Gamma_{n-2}$ and its copy $00\Gamma_{n-2}$ in $0\Gamma_{n-1}$. The edges in the matching have a natural ordering induced by the labels of (either) ends of the edges. In k-Fibonacci cubes, only the first k of these edges are used as link edges, and the others discarded. The eliminated edges in Γ_n^k then recursively propagate according to the resulting fundamental construction. We denote k-Fibonacci cubes by Γ_n^k and follow the treatment of Eğecioğlu, E. Saygı and Z. Saygı from [32].

Let $\Gamma_0^k = \Gamma_0$ and $\Gamma_1^k = \Gamma_1$. As long as $F_n \le k$, the construction for the k-Fibonacci cube Γ_n^k for $n \ge 2$ in terms of Γ_{n-1}^k and Γ_{n-2}^k is identical to the construction of the Fibonacci cubes with the same initial graphs, and therefore for $F_n \le k$ we have $\Gamma_n^k = \Gamma_n$. Let $n_0 = n_0(k)$ be the smallest integer for which $F_{n_0} > k$. Using the Binet formula for the Fibonacci numbers, it can be shown that

$$n_0 = n_0(k) = 1 + \left\lfloor \log_\varphi(\sqrt{5}k + \sqrt{5} - \tfrac{1}{2}) \right\rfloor$$

where φ is the golden ratio.

Fig. 9.7 shows the steps of the construction of the k-Fibonacci cubes Γ_4^k from Γ_3^k and Γ_2^k for $k \in [3]$.

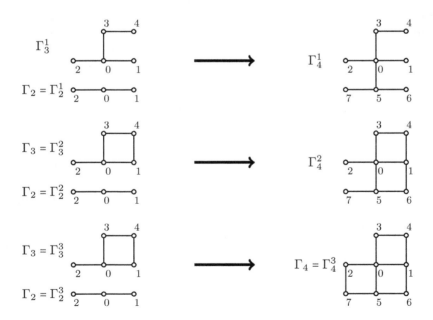

Fig. 9.7 The construction of Γ_4^k from Γ_3^k and Γ_2^k for $k = 1, 2, 3$

9.5.1   *Examples for Small k*

For $k = 1$, the graphs Γ_n^1 are all trees, as shown in the first column of Fig. 9.8 for $n \in \{0, 1, \ldots, 6\}$. If we think of them as rooted at the all zero vertex, then the next tree is obtained by making the root of the previous tree a child of the root of the present tree, i.e., by making the previous tree a principal subtree of the current one. Note that this is different from the usual definition of Fibonacci trees which was defined and studied in Section 4.2, where the two previous trees are made left and right principal subtrees of a new root vertex.

The number of vertices in Γ_n^1 is $n(\Gamma_n) = F_{n+2}$. The height h_n of Γ_n^1 satisfies $h_0 = 0$, $h_1 = 1$ and $h_n = \min\{h_{n-1}, 1 + h_{n-2}\}$. Therefore the height is given by $h_n = \lceil n/2 \rceil$. Indeed, k-Fibonacci cubes for $k = 1$ are the "Fibonacci Trees" (we have written "Fibonacci Trees" here because this is not about Fibonacci trees from Section 4.1) as given in Hsu's original paper [51].

Examples of k-Fibonacci cubes for small n and k are shown in Fig. 9.8. For $n \geq 3$, Γ_n^2 consists of $F_n - 1$ squares (Q_2's, or 4-cycles) glued by their edges and F_{n-1} pendant vertices. For $n \geq 4$, Γ_n^3 is constructed from $F_{n+1} - 2$ squares and for $n \geq 4$, Γ_n^4 is constructed from $2F_n - 3$ squares in the manner shown in Fig. 9.8. The graphs of Γ_{12}^4 and Γ_{12}^{13} on 144 vertices are shown in Fig. 9.9.

9.5.2   *Basic Properties*

By definition, $n(\Gamma_n^k) = n(\Gamma_n) = F_{n+2}$. The size satisfies $m(\Gamma_n^k) = m(\Gamma_n)$ for $n < n_0$ and the recursion

$$m(\Gamma_n^k) = m(\Gamma_{n-1}^k) + m(\Gamma_{n-2}^k) + \min\{k, F_n\}. \tag{9.6}$$

For $n \geq n_0$, the recursion in (9.6) reduces to

$$m(\Gamma_n^k) = m(\Gamma_{n-1}^k) + m(\Gamma_{n-2}^k) + k. \tag{9.7}$$

Using (9.7) and induction on n, we obtain

Proposition 9.23. *The size of Γ_n^k is given by*

$$m(\Gamma_n^k) = (k + m(\Gamma_{n_0-2})) F_{t+3} + (m(\Gamma_{n_0-1}) - m(\Gamma_{n_0-2})) F_{t+2} - k,$$

where $t = n - n_0$.

By using the classical identity $L_t = F_{t-1} + F_{t+1}$ along with Proposition 9.23 and the expression for $m(\Gamma_n)$ given in Proposition 3.2, the following closed form is obtained.

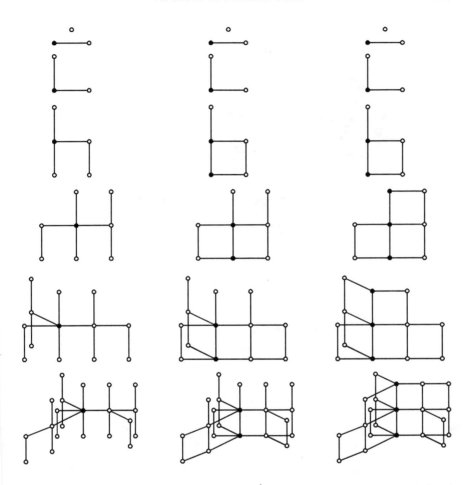

Fig. 9.8 The first seven k-Fibonacci cubes Γ_n^k for $k = 1, 2, 3$: the rows are indexed $n = 0, 1, \ldots, 6$ from top to bottom; the columns are indexed with $k = 1, 2, 3$ from left to right

Corollary 9.24. *If $n \geq n_0$, then $m(\Gamma_n^k)$ is given in closed form by*

$$m(\Gamma_n^k) = \tfrac{1}{2}(L_t + 3F_t)\,m(\Gamma_{n_0-1}) + \tfrac{1}{2}(L_t + F_t)m(\Gamma_{n_0-2}) + (L_t + 2F_t - 1)k$$
$$= \tfrac{1}{5}\left(n_0 F_{n_0-1}L_{t+1} + (n_0 - 1)F_{n_0}L_{t+2}\right) + (F_{t+3} - 1)k\,,$$

where $t = n - n_0$.

We note that there is an edge between the vertices $x1y$ and $x0y$ in Γ_n^k if and only if y is either the null-word, or it is the Fibonacci encoding of a number in $\{0, 1, \ldots, k-1\}$.

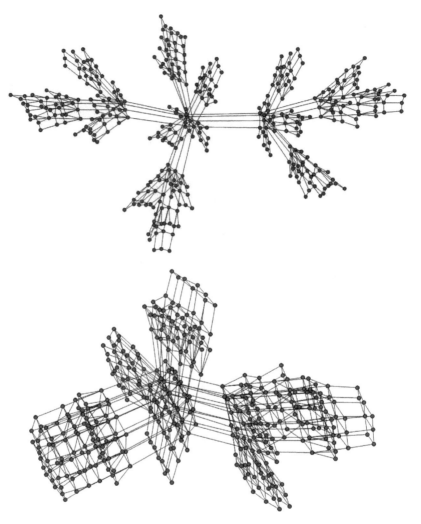

Fig. 9.9   The structure of Γ_{12}^4 (top) and Γ_{12}^{13} (bottom)

9.5.3   *Degree Polynomials of* Γ_n^k

For the degree sequence of Γ_n^k we need a refinement of Theorem 3.4. Define the bivariate degree enumerator polynomial $D_n^k(x,y)$ for Γ_n^k in which the degrees of the k vertices with labels $0, 1, \ldots, k-1$ are kept track of by the variable y, while the others are kept track of by the variable x. Thus

$$D_n^k(x, y) = \sum_{i=0}^{k-1} y^{d_i} + \sum_{i=k}^{F_{n+2}-1} x^{d_i} ,$$

where d_i is the degree of the vertex labeled i. This polynomial can be seen as a refinement of the boundary enumerator polynomial $\mathbb{D}_{n,0}$ given in [94, Section 3].

As examples we have $D_2^2(x, y) = y^2 + y + x$ and $D_3^2(x, y) = y^3 + y^2 + 2x^2 + x$. Using $D_2^2(x, y)$ and $D_3^2(x, y)$ we can now develop $D_4^2(x, y)$ as follows: By the definition of Γ_4^2 there are $k = 2$ link edges between Γ_3^2 and Γ_2^2. The first one is the edge between the vertices labeled $0 \in \Gamma_3^2$ and $0 \in \Gamma_2^2$, whereas the second one is the edge between the vertices labeled $1 \in \Gamma_3^2$ and $1 \in \Gamma_2^2$. Therefore, only the degrees of these first 2 vertices in Γ_3^2 and first 2 vertices in Γ_2^2 increase by 1 in Γ_4^2. The degrees of the other vertices remain the same. The vertices labeled $0, 1 \in \Gamma_4^2$ are the vertices $0, 1 \in \Gamma_3^2$ whose degree information in $D_4^2(x, y)$ should be kept track of by the variable y. This means

$$D_4^2(x, y) = yD_3^2(0, y) + D_3^2(x, 0) + xD_2^2(0, x) + D_2^2(x, 0)$$
$$= y^4 + y^3 + x^3 + 3x^2 + 2x .$$

By generalizing the above idea for fixed k, one obtains the following result on degree enumerator polynomial $D_n^k(x, y)$ for Γ_n^k.

Theorem 9.25. *Assume that* $D_{n_0-1}^k(x, y) = p_{n_0-1}(y) + q_{n_0-1}(x)$ *and* $D_{n_0-2}^k(x, y) = p_{n_0-2}(y) + q_{n_0-2}(x)$. *Then the degree enumerator polynomial* $D_n^k(x, y)$ *for* Γ_n^k *satisfies the recursion*

$$D_n^k(x, y) = y^{t+1}p_{n_0-1}(y) + F_{t+2}q_{n_0-1}(x) + F_{t+1}q_{n_0-2}(x)$$
$$+ F_{t+1}xp_{n_0-2}(x) + xp_{n_0-1}(x) \sum_{i=0}^{t} F_{t-i}x^i$$

for $n \geq n_0$ *with* $t = n - n_0$.

Using Theorem 9.25 with the initial conditions from Theorem 3.4 we obtain the following special cases.

Corollary 9.26. *For* $k \in \{1, 2, 3\}$ *the degree enumerator polynomials*

$D_n^k(x, y)$ for Γ_n^k are given by

$$D_n^1(x, y) = y^n + F_{n+1}x + \sum_{i=2}^{n-1} F_{n-i}x^i$$

$$D_n^2(x, y) = y^n + y^{n-1} + F_{n-1}x + \sum_{i=2}^{n-1} F_{n-i+1}x^i$$

$$D_n^3(x, y) = y^n + y^{n-1} + y^{n-2} + F_1 x^{n-1} + L_{n-1}x^2 + 2\sum_{i=3}^{n-2} F_{n-i}x^i .$$

9.5.4   Number of Hypercubes in Γ_n^k

In this section we count the number $c_d(\Gamma_n^k)$ of d-dimensional hypercubes Q_d induced in Γ_n^k. We know that for $d = 0$ and $d = 1$ these numbers are equal to the order and size of Γ_n^k respectively.

We first consider the number of squares (Q_2s) in Γ_n^k, i.e., the case where $d = 2$.

Definition 9.27. Let $Z(i)$ denote the number of 1s in the Zeckendorf representation of i for $i \geq 0$ and define for $m \geq 0$, the partial sums

$$P(m) = \sum_{i=0}^{m} Z(i) .$$

These sequences start as

$$0, 1, 1, 1, 2, 1, 2, 2, 1, 2, 2, 2, 3, 1, 2, 2, 2, 3, 2, 3, 3, 1, \ldots$$

for $Z(i)$ and

$$0, 1, 2, 3, 5, 6, 8, 10, 11, 13, 15, 17, 20, 21, 23, 25, 27, 30, 32, 35, 38, 39, \ldots$$

for $P(m)$.

Let $S(n) = c_2(\Gamma_n)$ denote the number of Q_2s in Γ_n and $S_k(n) = c_2(\Gamma_n^k)$ denote the number of Q_2s in Γ_n^k for $k \geq 2$. From [58] we know that

$$S(n) = \tfrac{1}{50}\left((5n + 1)(n - 2)F_n + 6nF_{n-2}\right) .$$

For $n < n_0$ we have $S_k(n) = S(n)$. By the fundamental decomposition of Γ_n^k, the number of Q_2s in Γ_n^k is the sum of three quantities: the number of Q_2s in Γ_{n-1}^k, the number of Q_2s in Γ_{n-2}^k and the number of Q_2s that are created by the addition of k link edges between Γ_{n-1}^k and Γ_{n-2}^k involving the vertices with labels $0, 1, \ldots, k - 1$.

The number of Q_2s of the last type above is equal to the size of the subgraph of Γ_n^k induced by the first k vertices $0, 1, \ldots, k - 1$.

Lemma 9.28. *The size of the subgraph of Γ_n^k induced by the first k vertices $0, 1, \ldots, k - 1$ is $P(k - 1)$.*

Proof. For a vertex i in Γ_n^k with $i \in \{0, 1, \ldots, k-1\}$, switching a 1 in the Zeckendorf representation to a 0 gives an adjacent vertex to i in $\{0, 1, \ldots, k-1\}$. So i has $Z(i)$ neighbors in the subgraph induced by the vertices 0 through $k-1$. Summing the contributions over i gives the lemma. $\square$

It follows that $S_k(n)$ satisfies the recursion

$$S_k(n) = S_k(n-1) + S_k(n-2) + P(k-1). \qquad (9.8)$$

Using (9.8) and induction on n we directly obtain that for $n \geq n_0$

$$S_k(n) = (P(k-1) + S(n_0 - 2)) F_{t+3} \qquad (9.9)$$
$$+ (S(n_0 - 1) - S(n_0 - 2)) F_{t+2} - P(k-1),$$

where $t = n - n_0$.

Numerical values of the number of Q_2s for small values of k and n can be found in Table 9.2, where the entries given in boldface are the number of Q_2s in the Fibonacci cube Γ_n itself. Note that this sequence for $n \geq 0$ is $0, 0, 0, 1, 3, 9, 22, 51, 111, 233, 474, 942, \ldots$, and these numbers are the triple convolution of the Fibonacci numbers.

$k \backslash n$	3	4	5	6	7	8	9	10	Closed form	$n_0(k)$
2	1	2	4	7	12	20	33	54	$F_{n-1} + F_{n-2} - 1$	4
3	1	**3**	6	11	19	32	53	87	$3F_{n-2} + 4F_{n-3} - 2$	5
4	1	**3**	7	13	23	39	65	107	$4F_{n-2} + 4F_{n-3} - 3$	5
5	1	**3**	**9**	17	31	53	89	147	$8F_{n-3} + 12F_{n-4} - 5$	6
6	1	**3**	**9**	18	33	57	96	159	$9F_{n-3} + 12F_{n-4} - 6$	6
7	1	**3**	**9**	20	37	65	110	183	$11F_{n-3} + 12F_{n-4} - 8$	6
8	1	**3**	**9**	**22**	41	73	124	207	$19F_{n-4} + 31F_{n-5} - 10$	7
9	1	**3**	**9**	**22**	42	75	128	214	$20F_{n-4} + 31F_{n-5} - 11$	7
10	1	**3**	**9**	**22**	44	79	136	228	$22F_{n-4} + 31F_{n-5} - 13$	7
11	1	**3**	**9**	**22**	46	83	144	242	$24F_{n-4} + 31F_{n-5} - 15$	7
12	1	**3**	**9**	**22**	48	87	152	256	$26F_{n-4} + 31F_{n-5} - 17$	7
13	1	**3**	**9**	**22**	**51**	93	164	277	$42F_{n-5} + 73F_{n-6} - 20$	8
14	1	**3**	**9**	**22**	**51**	94	166	281	$43F_{n-5} + 73F_{n-6} - 21$	8

Table 9.2 Counting Q_2s in Γ_n^k

Let $c_d(\Gamma_n^k)$ denote the number of Q_d in Γ_n^k. Then $c_1(\Gamma_n^k) = m(\Gamma_n^k)$ and $c_2(\Gamma_n^k) = S_k(n)$ as they appear in (9.6) and (9.8), respectively. Let $P_d(k-1, n)$ denote the number of Q_d contained in the subgraph of Γ_n^k induced by the vertices with labels $0, 1, \ldots, k-1$. Note that with this notation,

$P_1(k-1,n) = P(k-1)$ as it appears in recursion (9.9) and $P_0(k-1,n) = k$, as it appears as the non-homogeneous part of recursion (9.7).

Proposition 9.29. $c_d(\Gamma_n^k)$ *satisfies the recurrence relation*

$$c_d(\Gamma_n^k) = c_d(\Gamma_{n-1}^k) + c_d(\Gamma_{n-2}^k) + P_{d-1}(k-1),$$

where

$$P_{d-1}(k-1) = \sum_{i=0}^{k-1} \binom{Z(i)}{d-1}.$$

Proof. There are three types of Q_d that contribute to $c_d(\Gamma_n^k)$: those coming from Γ_{n-1}^k, those coming from Γ_{n-2}^k, and the ones formed by the k link vertices used in the construction of Γ_n^k. The d-dimensional hypercubes of the last type are counted by the number of $(d-1)$-dimensional hypercubes contained in the subgraph of Γ_{n-1}^k induced by the vertices with labels $0, 1, \ldots, k-1$. For any of these vertices i we need to select $d-1$ ones among the $Z(i)$ ones in i. Then by varying these $d-1$ ones we obtain 2^{d-1} vertices with labels in $\{0, 1, \ldots, k-1\}$ each giving a $(d-1)$-dimensional hypercube in Γ_{n-1}^k. Therefore, a simple generalization of Lemma 9.28 gives the number of such hypercubes as

$$P_{d-1}(k-1,n-1) = \sum_{i=0}^{k-1} \binom{Z(i)}{d-1}.$$

We can denote the above quantity as $P_{d-1}(k-1)$ as the sum on the right does not depend on n. This completes the proof. $\qquad\square$

The number of Q_d in Γ_n and its q-analogue are determined in Theorem 5.3 and Proposition 5.20, respectively. Using these result we have the following

Corollary 9.30. *Let* $c_d(\Gamma_n)$ *denote the number of* Q_d *in* Γ_n. *Then* $c_d(\Gamma_n)$ *is given explicitly by*

$$c_d(\Gamma_n) = \sum_{i=d}^{\lfloor \frac{n+1}{2} \rfloor} \binom{n-i+1}{i}\binom{i}{d}.$$

In particular, we have the formulas for the first few dimensions d as follows:

$$c_1(\Gamma_n) = m(\Gamma_n) = \tfrac{1}{5}\left(2(n+1)F_n + nF_{n+1}\right),$$
$$c_2(\Gamma_n) = S(n) = \tfrac{1}{50}\left((5n+1)(n-2)F_n + 6nF_{n-2}\right),$$
$$c_3(\Gamma_n) = \tfrac{1}{150}n(n-2)\left(4(n-4)F_{n-3} + 3(n-3)F_{n-4}\right).$$

Using Corollary 9.30 and by solving the recurrence relation satisfied by $c_d(\Gamma_n^k)$ given in Proposition 9.29 by induction, similar to the case of Proposition 9.23 and (9.9), we obtain

Theorem 9.31. *Let* $c_d(\Gamma_n^k)$ *denote the number of* Q_d *in* Γ_n^k. *Then*

$$c_d(\Gamma_n^k) = (P_{d-1}(k-1) + c_d(\Gamma_{n_0-2})) F_{t+3}$$
$$+ (c_d(\Gamma_{n_0-1}) - c_d(\Gamma_{n_0-2})) F_{t+2} - P_{d-1}(k-1),$$

for $n \geq n_0$ *with* $t = n - n_0$, *where* $c_d(\Gamma_n)$ *is the number of* Q_d *in* Γ_n.

9.5.5 *Diameter and Radius*

The diameter and the radius of Γ_n^k are directly related to the same properties of the Fibonacci cubes themselves. We start by noting the following nested structure of k-Fibonacci cubes.

For non-negative integers n and k we know that Γ_n^k can be obtained directly from Γ_n. It is either equal to Γ_n, or for $n \geq n_0$, it is obtained from Γ_n by removing certain edges. Furthermore, for $n \geq n_0$, Γ_n^k can also be obtained from Γ_n^{k+1} by removing edges. Therefore

$$\Gamma_n^1 \subseteq \cdots \subseteq \Gamma_n^k \subseteq \cdots \subseteq \Gamma_n. \tag{9.10}$$

Γ_n^1 is a tree with root 0^n (the vertex with integer label 0). It follows that for $u, v \in V(\Gamma_n^1)$

$$d(u, v) \leq d(u, 0^n) + d(v, 0^n) = |u|_1 + |v|_1. \tag{9.11}$$

We have $\mathrm{diam}(\Gamma_n) = n$ as given in [51]. For $n < n_0$ we have $\mathrm{diam}(\Gamma_n^k) = \mathrm{diam}(\Gamma_n) = n$. For $n \geq n_0$, we know that Γ_n^k is a subgraph of Γ_n, the vertices of Γ_n^k and Γ_n are the same and Γ_n^k has fewer edges. Therefore, $\mathrm{diam}(\Gamma_n^k) \geq \mathrm{diam}(\Gamma_n) = n$. On the other hand, using (9.10) and (9.11) for any $u, v \in V(\Gamma_n^k)$ we have

$$d(u, v) \leq d(u, 0^n) + d(v, 0^n) = |u|_1 + |v|_1 \leq n.$$

Therefore, we have $\mathrm{diam}(\Gamma_n^k) = n$.

By a similar argument one can show that the radius of Γ_n^k is equal to the radius of Γ_n, which is obtained in [82] as $\lceil \frac{n}{2} \rceil$.

9.5.6 *Domination-Type Invariants*

Using the definition of Γ_n^k and the recursion $\Gamma_n^k = 0\Gamma_{n-1}^k + 10\Gamma_{n-2}^k$ the following bounds on $\gamma(\Gamma_n^k)$ and $\gamma_t(\Gamma_n^k)$ can be obtained.

Theorem 9.32. [33, Theorem 4.1] *If n and k are positive integer, then*

$$\gamma(\Gamma_n^{k+1}) \le \gamma(\Gamma_n^k) \le \gamma(\Gamma_{n-1}^k) + \gamma(\Gamma_{n-2}^k), \quad and$$

$$\gamma_t(\Gamma_n^{k+1}) \le \gamma_t(\Gamma_n^k) \le \gamma_t(\Gamma_{n-1}^k) + \gamma_t(\Gamma_{n-2}^k).$$

Proof. By the definition of k-Fibonacci cubes, Γ_n^k can be obtained from Γ_n^{k+1} by removing certain edges. This means that a (total) dominating set for Γ_n^k is also a (total) dominating set for Γ_n^{k+1}, which gives $\gamma(\Gamma_n^{k+1}) \le \gamma(\Gamma_n^k)$ and $\gamma_t(\Gamma_n^{k+1}) \le \gamma_t(\Gamma_n^k)$.

Consider the fundamental decomposition of Γ_n^k into the subgraphs induced by the vertices that start with 0 and 10, which are isomorphic to the graphs Γ_{n-1}^k and Γ_{n-2}^k, respectively. We have $\gamma(\Gamma_n^k) \le \gamma(\Gamma_{n-1}^k) + \gamma(\Gamma_{n-2}^k)$ and $\gamma_t(\Gamma_n^k) \le \gamma_t(\Gamma_{n-1}^k) + \gamma_t(\Gamma_{n-2}^k)$. $\square$

Next we use the integer linear programming formulation used in [8, 54] that we described in Section 7.1 to obtain $\gamma(\Gamma_n)$ and $\gamma_t(\Gamma_n)$. We recall that if each vertex $v \in V(\Gamma_n^k)$ is associated with a binary variable x_v, then the problems of determining $\gamma(\Gamma_n^k)$ and $\gamma_t(\Gamma_n^k)$ can be expressed as a problem of minimizing the objective function

$$\sum_{v \in V(\Gamma_n^k)} x_v$$

subject to the following constraints for every $v \in V(\Gamma_n^k)$:

$$\sum_{a \in N_{\Gamma_n^k}[v]} x_a \ge 1 \text{ (for the domination number)},$$

$$\sum_{a \in N_{\Gamma_n^k}(v)} x_a \ge 1 \text{ (for the total domination number)}.$$

The optimal value of the objective function gives $\gamma(\Gamma_n^k)$ and $\gamma_t(\Gamma_n^k)$ respectively. The values in Table 9.3 and Table 9.4 are taken from [33].

Using Theorem 9.32 and the results in Tables 9.3 and 9.4, the following upper bounds on $\gamma(\Gamma_n^k)$ and $\gamma_t(\Gamma_n^k)$ can be obtained.

Corollary 9.33. [33, Corollary 4.2] *We have the following upper bounds on $\gamma(\Gamma_n^k)$.*

(i) *If $n \ge 13$ and $k \in \{1, 2\}$, then $\gamma(\Gamma_n^k) \le F_n$.*
(ii) *If $n \ge 13$ and $k \in \{3, 4\}$, then $\gamma(\Gamma_n^k) \le 42F_{n-8} - 16F_{n-10}$.*
(iii) *If $n \ge 13$ and $k = 5$, then $\gamma(\Gamma_n^k) \le 37F_{n-8} - 14F_{n-10}$.*
(iv) *If $n \ge 13$ and $k \in \{6, 7, 8\}$, then $\gamma(\Gamma_n^k) \le F_{n-1}$.*
(v) *If $n \ge 13$ and $k \in \{9, 10, 11\}$, then $\gamma(\Gamma_n^k) \le 32F_{n-8} - 12F_{n-10}$.*

$k\backslash n$	1	2	3	4	5	6	7	8	9	10	11	12
1		2	3	5	8	13	21	34	55	89	144	
2				3	5	8	13	21	34	55	89	144
3				4	6	10	16	26	42	68	110	
4					4	6	10	16	26	42	68	110
5						6	9	14	23	37	60	97
6						5	8	13	21	34	55	89
7						5	8	13	21	34	55	89
8							8	13	21	34	55	89
9							8	13	20	32	52	84
10							8	13	20	32	52	84
11							8	13	20	32	52	84
12							8	12	19	31	50	81

Table 9.3   Known domination numbers $\gamma(\Gamma_n^k)$ of k-Fibonacci cubes

$k\backslash n$	1	2	3	4	5	6	7	8	9	10	11	12
1		2	3	5	8	13	21	34	55	89	144	
2				3	5	8	13	21	34	55	89	144
3					5	8	13	21	34	55	89	144
4					5	8	13	21	34	55	89	144
5						7	10	16	26	42	68	110
6						7	10	16	26	42	68	110
7						7	10	16	26	42	68	110
8							10	15	23	37	60	97
9							10	14	22	36	58	94
10							10	14	22	36	58	94
11							10	14	22	36	58	94
12							10	14	22	35	57	92

Table 9.4   Known total domination numbers $\gamma_t(\Gamma_n^k)$ of k-Fibonacci cubes

(vi) If $n \geq 13$ and $k \geq 12$, then $\gamma(\Gamma_n^k) \leq 31F_{n-8} - 12F_{n-10}$.

Proof. We give the proof only for the case $k \in [2]$ and note that the same proof is valid for all of the other stated cases. From Table 9.3 we know that $\gamma(\Gamma_{11}^k) = F_{11}$ and $\gamma(\Gamma_{12}^k) = F_{12}$ where $k \in [2]$. Then for $n \geq 13$, using Theorem 9.32 we have $\gamma(\Gamma_n^k) \leq \gamma(\Gamma_{n-1}^k) + \gamma(\Gamma_{n-2}^k) \leq F_n$. □

Corollary 9.34. [33, Corollary 4.3] *We have the following upper bounds on* $\gamma_t(\Gamma_n^k)$.

    (i) *If* $n \geq 13$ *and* $k \in \{1, 2, 3, 4\}$, *then* $\gamma_t(\Gamma_n^k) \leq F_n$.
    (ii) *If* $n \geq 13$ *and* $k \in \{5, 6, 7\}$, *then* $\gamma_t(\Gamma_n^k) \leq 42F_{n-8} - 16F_{n-10}$.
    (iii) *If* $n \geq 13$ *and* $k = 8$, *then* $\gamma_t(\Gamma_n^k) \leq 37F_{n-8} - 14F_{n-10}$.
    (iv) *If* $n \geq 13$ *and* $k \in \{9, 10, 11\}$, *then* $\gamma_t(\Gamma_n^k) \leq 36F_{n-8} - 14F_{n-10}$.
    (v) *If* $n \geq 13$ *and* $k \geq 12$, *then* $\gamma_t(\Gamma_n^k) \leq 35F_{n-8} - 13F_{n-10}$.

The exact values of domination and total domination numbers of Γ_n^k for $k \in \{1, 2\}$ can also be determined.

Proposition 9.35. [33, Proposition 4.4] *If* $n \geq 2$ *and* $k \in \{1, 2\}$, *then* $\gamma(\Gamma_n^k) = \gamma_t(\Gamma_n^k) = F_n$.

9.6   Fibonacci-run Graphs

Another set of binary strings which are counted by Fibonacci numbers are those with a restriction on the runlengths. Induced subgraphs of the hypercube on the latter strings as vertices define *Fibonacci-run graphs*. These were introduced and studied by Eğecioğlu and Iršič [30, 31]. Fibonacci-run graphs have the same number of vertices as Fibonacci cubes, but fewer edges and different graph theoretical properties.

    We start by noting that a Fibonacci cube can equivalently be defined by adding 00 to the end of the binary representation of every vertex, essentially embedding Γ_n into Q_{n+2}. We can call such binary strings *extended Fibonacci strings*. Actually, in an extended Fibonacci string, the rightmost zero corresponds to the Fibonacci number f_0 and the second to last zero corresponds to f_1 in the encoding of the Zeckendorf representation of Section 1.5. Here f_0 is not needed since it is zero, and f_1 is not used to preserve the uniqueness of the representation. We call this representation with the two additional 0s the *extended Zeckendorf representation*.

    With this interpretation

$$V(\Gamma_n) = \{w00 \mid w \in \mathcal{F}_n\}$$

and two vertices are adjacent if they differ in exactly one coordinate. Extended Fibonacci strings together with the null-word λ and the singleton

0, are generated freely (as a monoid) by the infinite alphabet

$$F = \{0, 100, 10100, 1010100, \ldots\}.$$

This means that every $v \in V(\Gamma_n)$ can be written uniquely as a concatenation of zero or more strings from F.

We now consider *run-constrained binary strings*, which are strings of 0s and 1s in which every run of 1s is immediately followed by a strictly longer run of 0s. Such run-constrained strings, together with the null-word λ and the singleton 0, are generated freely by the letters from the alphabet

$$R = \{0, 100, 11000, 1110000, \ldots\} \tag{9.12}$$

Note that run-constrained strings of length $n \geq 2$ must end with 00.

The *Fibonacci-run graph* $\mathcal{R}_n$ is defined as follows:

$$V(\mathcal{R}_n) = \{w00 : w00 \text{ is a run-constrained string of length } n + 2\},$$
$$E(\mathcal{R}_n) = \{\{u00, v00\} : H(u, v) = 1\}.$$

Clearly, $\mathcal{R}_n$ is a subgraph of Q_{n+2}, but it is more natural to see it as a subgraph of Q_n (after suppressing the tailing 00 in the vertices of $\mathcal{R}_n$). We can view the vertices of a Fibonacci-run graph without the trailing pair of zeros as

$$V(\mathcal{R}_n) = \{w : w00 \text{ is a run-constrained binary string of length } n + 2\}.$$

This is the same kind of a convention as viewing Γ_n as a subgraph of Q_{n+2} if we think of the vertices as extended Fibonacci strings, or as a subgraph of Q_n as usual by suppressing the trailing 00 of the vertex labels in the extended Zeckendorf representation.

Additionally, we define $\mathcal{R}_0 = K_1$, its only vertex corresponding to the label 00, which after the removal of the trailing pair of zeros corresponds to the null-word.

9.6.1 *Order and Decomposition*

Lemma 9.36. [30, Lemma 3.1] *If $n \geq 1$, then $n(\mathcal{R}_n) = F_{n+2}$.*

Proof. It suffices to provide a bijection between vertex sets of Γ_n and $\mathcal{R}_n$. For the purpose of this proof, we view both vertex sets with additional 00 at the end of each string. First define $\Phi : F \to R$ by setting $\Phi((10)^i 0) = 1^i 0^{i+1}$ for $i \geq 0$, and then extend Φ to full words via the unique factorization. So for example, starting with the extended Fibonacci string $w = 10010100001010100100$,

$$\Phi(w) = \Phi\big((100)(10100)(0)(0)(1010100)(100)\big)$$
$$= (100)(11000)(0)(0)(1110000)(100)$$
$$= 10011000001110000100.$$

This clearly yields a bijection, thus $n(\mathcal{R}_n) = n(\Gamma_n) = F_{n+2}$. □

Corollary 9.37. [30, Corollary 3.2] *The number of vertices in $\mathcal{R}_n$ of Hamming weight w, $0 \le w \le \lceil n/2 \rceil$ is $\binom{n-w+1}{w}$.*

Proof. The bijection Φ preserves the number of 1s in a string. Therefore the corollary is a consequence of Proposition 3.1. □

There is a certain decomposition of the Fibonacci-run graphs. It is shown in [30, Lemma 4.1] that $V(\mathcal{R}_n)$ can be partitioned as

$$\bigcup_{k=0}^{\lceil n/2 \rceil - 1} 1^k 0^{k+1} V(\mathcal{R}_{n-(2k+1)}) \cup 1^{\lceil n/2 \rceil} 0^{\lfloor n/2 \rfloor} V(\mathcal{R}_0)$$

so that $\mathcal{R}_n$ contains the following graphs as subgraphs

$$0\mathcal{R}_{n-1}, 100\mathcal{R}_{n-3}, 11000\mathcal{R}_{n-5}, 1110000\mathcal{R}_{n-7}, \ldots$$

The last graph in this sequence is $1^{m-1}0^m\mathcal{R}_1$ if $n = 2m$, and $1^{m-1}0^m\mathcal{R}_0$ if $n = 2m - 1$. We augment this list by one more subgraph of $\mathcal{R}_n$ consisting of a single vertex: $1^m 0^m \mathcal{R}_0$ if $n = 2m$, and $1^m 0^{m-1} \mathcal{R}_0$ if $n = 2m - 1$. If we denote this partition into subgraphs with $+$, then we obtain the following for $n \in [8]$:

$$\mathcal{R}_1 = 0\mathcal{R}_0 + 1\mathcal{R}_0$$
$$\mathcal{R}_2 = 0\mathcal{R}_1 + 10\mathcal{R}_0$$
$$\mathcal{R}_3 = 0\mathcal{R}_2 + 100\mathcal{R}_0 + 110\mathcal{R}_0$$
$$\mathcal{R}_4 = 0\mathcal{R}_3 + 100\mathcal{R}_1 + 1100\mathcal{R}_0$$
$$\mathcal{R}_5 = 0\mathcal{R}_4 + 100\mathcal{R}_2 + 11000\mathcal{R}_0 + 11100\mathcal{R}_0$$
$$\mathcal{R}_6 = 0\mathcal{R}_5 + 100\mathcal{R}_3 + 11000\mathcal{R}_1 + 111000\mathcal{R}_0$$
$$\mathcal{R}_7 = 0\mathcal{R}_6 + 100\mathcal{R}_4 + 11000\mathcal{R}_2 + 1110000\mathcal{R}_0 + 1111000\mathcal{R}_0$$
$$\mathcal{R}_8 = 0\mathcal{R}_7 + 100\mathcal{R}_5 + 11000\mathcal{R}_3 + 1110000\mathcal{R}_1 + 11110000\mathcal{R}_0$$

Fibonacci-run graphs $\mathcal{R}_1, \ldots, \mathcal{R}_5$ and their decompositions as indicated above are shown color-coded in Fig. 9.10. A schematic representation of the decompositions of $\mathcal{R}_6$ and $\mathcal{R}_7$ appears in Fig. 9.11.

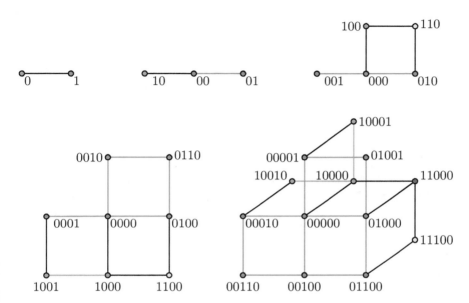

Fig. 9.10 The graphs $\mathcal{R}_n$, for $n \in [5]$, with their decomposition schematically shown using colors. As an example, in $\mathcal{R}_5 = 0\mathcal{R}_4 + 100\mathcal{R}_2 + 11000\mathcal{R}_0 + 11100\mathcal{R}_0$, the induced subgraphs $\mathcal{R}_4$, $\mathcal{R}_2$, R_0, and $\mathcal{R}_0$ of the decomposition from left to right are shown using the colors red, green, blue, and yellow, respectively

9.6.2 *Size*

We have the first few sizes by inspection: $m(\mathcal{R}_1) = 1$, $m(\mathcal{R}_2) = 2$, $m(\mathcal{R}_3) = 5$, and $m(\mathcal{R}_4) = 10$. For $n \geq 5$, we can use the decomposition to obtain

$$m(\mathcal{R}_n) = \sum_{k=0}^{\lceil n/2 \rceil - 1} m(\mathcal{R}_{n-(2k+1)}) + n(\mathcal{R}_{n-3}) + 2 \sum_{k=2}^{\lceil n/2 \rceil - 1} n(\mathcal{R}_{n-(2k+1)}) + 2. \quad (9.13)$$

Lemma 9.38. [30, Lemma 4.2] *If $n \geq 4$, then*

$$m(\mathcal{R}_n) = m(\mathcal{R}_{n-1}) + m(\mathcal{R}_{n-2}) + F_{n-1} + F_{n-3}.$$

Proof. Set $e_n = m(\mathcal{R}_n)$. If $n \geq 7$, we can use the recursion from (9.13) for n and $n - 2$:

$$e_n = e_{n-1} + \sum_{k=1}^{\lceil n/2 \rceil - 1} e_{n-(2k+1)} + n(\mathcal{R}_{n-3}) + 2n(\mathcal{R}_{n-5})$$

$$+ 2 \sum_{k=3}^{\lceil n/2 \rceil - 1} n(\mathcal{R}_{n-(2k+1)}) + 2$$

$$= e_{n-1} + F_{n-1} + F_{n-3} + e_{n-2},$$

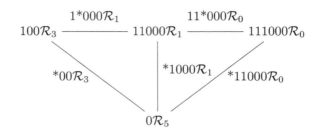

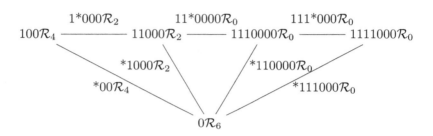

Fig. 9.11 The decomposition of $\mathcal{R}_6$ (above) and $\mathcal{R}_7$ (below). The edges are symbolically marked with the lines indicating the edges present between the parts

where we used $n(\mathcal{R}_n) = F_{n+2}$. For $n \in \{4, 5, 6\}$, we can determine e_n from (9.13), and directly check that $e_n = e_{n-1} + e_{n-2} + F_{n-1} + F_{n-3}$. □

Note that the result of Lemma 9.38 can be simplified to $m(\mathcal{R}_n) = m(\mathcal{R}_{n-1}) + m(\mathcal{R}_{n-2}) + L_{n-2}$, where L_{n-2} is the Lucas number. This compares nicely to the expression $m(\Gamma_n) = m(\Gamma_{n-1}) + m(\Gamma_{n-2}) + F_n$, which follows directly from the fundamental decomposition of Γ_n.

Corollary 9.39. [30, Corollary 4.3] *If $n \geq 5$, then*

$$m(\mathcal{R}_n) = m(\Gamma_n) - m(\Gamma_{n-4}) = (3n + 4)F_{n-6} + (5n + 6)F_{n-5}.$$

It would be satisfying to find a proof of this difference result for the size combinatorially, without using the decomposition of $\mathcal{R}_n$. Note that the count of edges shows that Γ_n and $\mathcal{R}_n$ are never isomorphic for $n \geq 5$ as noted in [30, Corollary 3.4]. It is also known that $\mathcal{R}_n$ is a partial cube if and only if $n \leq 6$ [30, Proposition 8.1] and it is not a median graph for $n \geq 5$.

9.6.3 *Diameter*

Determining the diameter of Fibonacci-run graphs turns out to be a rather difficult task. Clearly, $\text{diam}(\mathcal{R}_n) = n$ for $n \in [4]$. The exact values of the diameter computed by brute force in [30] are shown in Fig. 9.12 for $n \le 30$. Using the computer, the following values were also obtained in [30]: $\text{diam}(\mathcal{R}_n) = n - 1$ for $5 \le n \le 13$, and $\text{diam}(\mathcal{R}_n) = n - 2$ for $14 \le n \le 22$.

We start with the following lemma.

Lemma 9.40. [30, Lemma 5.1] *If* $n = \frac{1}{2}(r^2 + 3r - 2)$, *then* $\text{diam}(\mathcal{R}_n) \ge n - \lfloor \frac{r-1}{2} \rfloor$.

Proof. It suffices to find two vertices $u, v \in V(\mathcal{R}_n)$ with $d(u, v) = n - \lfloor \frac{r-1}{2} \rfloor$.

If r is even, take

$$u = 10^2 1^3 0^4 \ldots 1^{r-1} 0^r 1^{r/2} 0^{r/2+1},$$
$$v = 01^2 0^3 1^4 \ldots 0^{r-1} 1^r 0^{r+1},$$

where the trailing 00 in the representation of the vertices is not omitted. In this case,

$$n = 1 + 2 + \cdots + r + (r - 1) = \tfrac{1}{2}(r^2 + 3r - 2),$$
$$d(u, v) = 1 + 2 + \cdots + r + \frac{r}{2} = n - \left(\frac{r}{2} - 1\right) = n - \left\lfloor \frac{r-1}{2} \right\rfloor.$$

If r is odd, then we take

$$u = 10^2 1^3 0^4 \ldots 1^r 0^{r+1},$$
$$v = 01^2 0^3 1^4 \ldots 0^r 1^{(r+1)/2-1} 0^{(r+1)/2+1},$$

where again the suffix 00 is not omitted. In this case, we get

$$n = 1 + 2 + \cdots + r + (r - 1) = \tfrac{1}{2}(r^2 + 3r - 2),$$
$$d(u, v) = 1 + 2 + \cdots + r + \frac{r-1}{2} = n - \left(\frac{r-1}{2}\right) = n - \left\lfloor \frac{r-1}{2} \right\rfloor.$$

$\square$

Corollary 9.41. [30, Corollary 5.2] *If* $n = \frac{1}{2}(r^2 + 3r - 2)$, *then* $\text{diam}(\mathcal{R}_n) \ge n - \sqrt{\frac{n}{2}}$.

Proof. This can be verified simply by checking that $\sqrt{\frac{n}{2}} \ge \frac{r-1}{2} \ge \lfloor \frac{r-1}{2} \rfloor$. $\square$

Theorem 9.42. [30, Theorem 5.3] *If* $n \ge 1$, *then* $\text{diam}(\mathcal{R}_n) > n - \sqrt{2n}$.

Proof. If $n = \frac{1}{2}(r^2 + 3r - 2)$ for some integer r, then the result holds. Otherwise, we have

$$\tfrac{1}{2}(r^2 + 3r - 2) < n < \tfrac{1}{2}((r+1)^2 + 3(r+1) - 2),$$

which implies

$$n = \tfrac{1}{2}(r^2 + 3r - 2) + \delta, \quad \text{with } 1 \le \delta \le r + 1.$$

We again aim to construct vertices $u, v \in V(\mathcal{R}_n)$ which differ on at least $n - \sqrt{2n}$ coordinates. The idea is to extend the last run of $r + 1$ zeros in u or v from the proof of Lemma 9.40, and add the maximum allowed number of 1s followed by appropriate number of 0s in the other vertex.

If r is even, then let

$$u = 10^2 1^3 0^4 \ldots 1^{r-1} 0^r 1^{\lceil (\delta + r - 1)/2 \rceil} 0^{\lfloor (\delta + r + 3)/2 \rfloor},$$
$$v = 01^2 0^3 1^4 \ldots 0^{r-1} 1^r 0^{\delta + r + 1},$$

while if r is odd, let

$$u = 10^2 1^3 0^4 \ldots 1^r 0^{\delta + r + 1},$$
$$v = 01^2 0^3 1^4 \ldots 0^r 1^{\lceil (\delta + r - 1)/2 \rceil} 0^{\lfloor (\delta + r + 3)/2 \rfloor}.$$

In both cases, we obtain

$$n = 1 + 2 + \cdots + r + (r + \delta - 1) = \tfrac{1}{2}(r^2 + 3r - 2) + \delta,$$
$$d(u,v) = 1 + 2 + \cdots + r + \left\lceil \frac{r + \delta - 1}{2} \right\rceil = n - \left\lfloor \frac{r + \delta - 1}{2} \right\rfloor.$$

Now it suffices to prove that $n - \lfloor \frac{r+\delta-1}{2} \rfloor > n - \sqrt{2n}$. This holds, if we can prove that $\sqrt{2n} > \frac{r+\delta-1}{2}$, with $n = \frac{1}{2}(r^2 + 3r - 2) + \delta$ for some $r \ge 1$, and $1 \le \delta \le r+1$. But since $\delta \ge 1$, we have $\sqrt{2n} \ge \sqrt{r^2 + 3r} > r$, and since $\delta \le r+1$, we get $\frac{r+\delta-1}{2} \le r$. Thus $\sqrt{2n} > \frac{r+\delta-1}{2}$, and indeed $d(u,v) > n - \sqrt{2n}$. $\qquad\square$

The exact values of $\operatorname{diam}(\mathcal{R}_n)$ together with the corresponding values of the lower bound of Theorem 9.42 are shown in Fig. 9.12. We see that in the range given, the values for $n = 4, 8, 13, 19, 26$ corresponding to $r = 2, 3, 4, 5, 6$ of Lemma 9.40 are actually exact. Based on this observation and the values in Fig. 9.12, it is conjectured in [30] that

$$\operatorname{diam}(\mathcal{R}_n) = n - \left\lfloor \sqrt{1 + \frac{n}{2}} - \frac{3}{4} \right\rfloor.$$

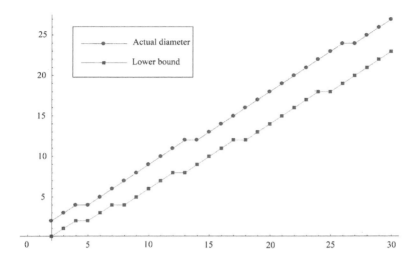

Fig. 9.12 The exact values and the lower bound given by Theorem 9.42 for diam($\mathcal{R}_n$) for $n \le 30$

9.6.4 *Hamiltonicity, Radius and Center*

Since $\mathcal{R}_n$ is bipartite, it can only be Hamiltonian if both parts are of equal cardinality. Let Δ_n denote the number of vertices of even Hamming weight minus the number of vertices of odd Hamming weight in $\mathcal{R}_n$. Using Corollary 9.37,

$$\Delta_n = \begin{cases} 1 & \text{if } n \equiv 0, 5 \,(\mathrm{mod}\,6), \\ 0 & \text{if } n \equiv 1, 4 \,(\mathrm{mod}\,6), \\ -1 & \text{if } n \equiv 2, 3 \,(\mathrm{mod}\,6). \end{cases}$$

Therefore if $n \not\equiv 1 \pmod 3$, then $\mathcal{R}_n$ cannot contain a Hamiltonian cycle.

Based on the decomposition in Fig. 9.11 and computational evidence, it was conjectured in [30] that $\mathcal{R}_n$ is Hamiltonian if and only if $n \equiv 1 \pmod 3$ and that every $\mathcal{R}_n$ has a Hamiltonian path.

It turns out that the Hamiltonian path problem can be approached using Gray codes, and has recently been resolved by Baril, Kirgizov and Vajnovszki [11]. We record this result as Theorem 9.43 and refer the reader to the original paper for the proof.

Theorem 9.43. [11, Corollary 8] *Every Fibonacci-run graph has a Hamiltonian path.*

As a consequence of Theorem 9.43 we have

Corollary 9.44. [30, Corollary 9.3] *If* $n \geq 1$, *then* $\alpha(\mathcal{R}_n) = \lceil \frac{1}{2} F_{n+2} \rceil$.

Another conjecture in [31] on the determination of the radius of $\mathcal{R}_n$ was settled recently by Wei [114], who also determined the center $C(\mathcal{R}_n)$.

Theorem 9.45. [114, Theorem 3.5] *The radius and the center of* $\mathcal{R}_n$ *are given by* $\mathrm{rad}(\mathcal{R}_n) = \lceil \frac{n}{2} \rceil$ *and* $C(\mathcal{R}_n) = \{0^n\} \cup U_n$, *where*

$$U_n = \begin{cases} \{0^t 10^{n-t-1} : 0 \leq t \leq \frac{n-1}{2}\} & \text{if } n \text{ is odd}, \\ \varnothing & \text{if } n \text{ is even}. \end{cases}$$

9.6.5   *Up-Degrees and Down-Degrees*

Since each neighbor of $v \in V(\mathcal{R}_n)$ is obtained either by changing a 0 in v into a 1 or by changing a 1 in v into a 0, we can distinguish between the *up-degree* $\deg_{\mathrm{up}}(v)$, and *down-degree* $\deg_{\mathrm{down}}(v)$ of the vertex v. The first is the number of up-neighbors of v while the second is the number of down-neighbors of v. Clearly, $\deg(v) = \deg_{\mathrm{up}}(v) + \deg_{\mathrm{down}}(v)$. Note that in $\mathcal{R}_n$, $\deg_{\mathrm{down}}(v)$ is not necessarily equal to the Hamming weight of v because of the constraints on the run-lengths that must hold.

We keep track of the degree sequences of our graphs $\mathcal{R}_n$ as the coefficients of a polynomial. This polynomial is called the *degree enumerator polynomial* of the graph. The coefficient of x^i in the degree enumerator polynomial is the number of vertices of degree i in $\mathcal{R}_n$. Similar polynomials are defined to keep track of the up- and down-degree sequences as well.

The nature of the distribution of the up-degrees and the down-degrees are most easily seen from the Hasse diagram of $\mathcal{R}_n$ for which $\deg_{\mathrm{up}}(v)$ and $\deg_{\mathrm{down}}(v)$ are simply the number of edges emanating up and down from $v \in \mathcal{R}_n$, respectively.

Using the variable d to keep track of the down-degrees and u to keep track of the up-degrees and using Fig. 9.13, the down-degree enumerator polynomial of $\mathcal{R}_4$ is given by

$$1 + 4d + 3d^2, \tag{9.14}$$

and its up-degree enumerator polynomial by

$$3 + 2u + 2u^2 + u^4. \tag{9.15}$$

The degree-enumerator polynomial of $\mathcal{R}_4$ is

$$5x^2 + 2x^3 + x^4. \tag{9.16}$$

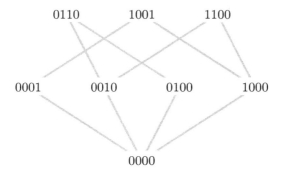

Fig. 9.13 The Hasse diagram of the Fibonacci-run graph $\mathcal{R}_4$ viewed as a partially ordered set

First, we consider the generating function of the down-degree enumerator polynomials for $\mathcal{R}_n$.

Proposition 9.46. [30, Proposition 7.1] *The generating function of down-degree enumerator polynomials of Fibonacci-run graphs is*

$$\sum_{n\geq 1} t^n \sum_{v\in\mathcal{R}_n} d^{\deg_{\text{down}}(v)} = \frac{t(1 + d + dt + (d^2 - 1)t^2 + d(d - 1)t^3 + d(d - 1)t^4)}{1 - t - t^2 - (d - 1)t^3 - d(d - 1)t^5}.$$

Proof. We first consider the contributions of the strings from the alphabet R of (9.12). The string 100 contributes dt^3, but longer strings $1^k 0^{k+1}$ of length n contribute $d^2 t^n$, since both the first and the last 1 appearing can be switched to 0. Thus keeping track of the total length as the exponent of t, the strings from R give

$$t + dt^3 + d^2 t^5 + d^2 t^7 + \cdots = t + dt^3 + \frac{d^2 t^5}{1 - t^2}.$$

Therefore the generating function of the free monoid, which includes vertices $V(\mathcal{R}_n), n \geq 1$, is

$$\frac{1}{1 - t - dt^3 - \frac{d^2 t^5}{1 - t^2}}.$$

From this we need to subtract the terms $1, t, t^2$, which correspond to the null-word, 0 and 00 respectively. This gives

$$\frac{1}{1 - t - dt^3 - \frac{d^2 t^5}{1 - t^2}} - 1 - t - t^2 = \frac{t^3(1 + d + dt + (d^2 - 1)t^2 + d(d - 1)t^3 + d(d - 1)t^4)}{1 - t - t^2 - (d - 1)t^3 - d(d - 1)t^5}.$$

Finally, we divide by t^2 to effectively shorten the length by 2 and get rid of the contribution to the length of the last two zeros in each run-constrained string generated to obtain the desired result. $\qquad\square$

First few terms given by the generating function in Proposition 9.46 are

$$(1 + d)t + (1 + 2d)t^2 + (1 + 3d + d^2)t^3 + (1 + 4d + 3d^2)t^4$$
$$+ (1 + 5d + 7d^2)t^5 + (1 + 6d + 12d^2 + 2d^3)t^6 + \cdots$$

Since the sum of down-degrees of the vertices in $\mathcal{R}_n$ is the total number of edges, we can obtain the generating function of the sequence $(m(\mathcal{R}_n))_{n \geq 0}$ by differentiating the expression in Proposition 9.46 with respect to d, and then setting $d = 1$.

Along similar lines we obtain

Proposition 9.47. [30, Proposition 7.2] *The generating function of up-degree enumerator polynomials of Fibonacci-run graphs is*

$$\sum_{n \geq 1} t^n \sum_{v \in \mathcal{R}_n} u^{\deg_{up}(v)} = \frac{t(1 + u - (u - 2)t - 2ut^2 + t^3 - (u - 1)t^5 - (u - 1)t^6)}{1 - ut - 2t^2 + (2u - 1)t^3 + t^4 - (u - 1)t^5 + (u - 1)t^7}.$$

First few terms of the power series expansion of the generating function in Proposition 9.47 are

$$(1 + u)t + (2 + u^2)t^2 + (2 + 2u + u^3)t^3 + (3 + 2u + 2u^2 + u^4)t^4$$
$$+ (5 + 2u + 3u^2 + 2u^3 + u^5)t^5 + (6 + 6u + 2u^2 + 4u^3 + 2u^4 + u^6)t^6 + \cdots$$

9.6.6 q-Cube Polynomial

Proposition 9.46 can be used to compute the generating function of the q-cube polynomials $C_{\mathcal{R}_n}(x, q)$.

Proposition 9.48. [30, Proposition 8.2] $\sum_{n \geq 1} C_{\mathcal{R}_n}(x, q)t^n$ *is given by*

$$\frac{t(1 + q + x + (q + x)t + ((q + x)^2 - 1)t^2 + (q + x)(q + x - 1)t^3 + (q + x)(q + x - 1)t^4)}{1 - t - t^2 - (q + x - 1)t^3 - (q + x)(q + x - 1)t^5}.$$

Proof. To each hypercube Q_k in $\mathcal{R}_n$ we associate the monomial $q^d x^k$, where d is the distance of the Q_k to the all zero vertex $0^n \in V(\mathcal{R}_n)$. For every vertex $v \in \mathcal{R}_n$, select k 1s in its string representation that can be replaced with a 0. Note that the number of such 1s is at most $\deg_{down}(v)$. By flipping these 1s to 0s in all possible ways, we obtain the vertices of a copy of Q_k in $\mathcal{R}_n$. The distance of this hypercube to 0^n is $w - k$, where $w = |v|_1$ is the Hamming weight of the vertex v. So from every vertex of Hamming weight w and down-degree r, we obtain $\binom{r}{k}$ different copies of Q_k, with the associated monomial $q^{w-k} x^k$ for each.

The generating function can now be obtained from Proposition 9.46 by replacing each d^r that appears in the series expansion by $(q+x)^r$. The reason for this is that the term d^r arises from a vertex v with down-degree r, and its contribution to the monomials making up the generating function is

$$\sum_{k=0}^{r} \binom{r}{k} q^{r-k} x^k = (q+x)^r .$$

Thus this replacement is the same as if we replace d by $q+x$ in the generating function in Proposition 9.46, and this substitution gives the generating function of the proposition. $\qquad\square$

The coefficients of the generating function in Proposition 9.48 for $n \in [6]$ are

$$1 + q + x,$$
$$1 + 2q + 2x,$$
$$1 + 3q + q^2 + (3 + 2q)x + x^2,$$
$$1 + 4q + 3q^2 + (4 + 6q)x + 3x^2,$$
$$1 + 5q + 7q^2 + (5 + 14q)x + 7x^2,$$
$$1 + 6q + 12q^2 + 2q^3 + (6 + 24q + 6q^2)x + (12 + 6q)x^2 + 2x^3.$$

So for example, the term $(12 + 6q)x^2$ in the last polynomial in this list indicates that in $\mathcal{R}_6$, there are 12 squares (Q_2's) that contain the all zero vertex, and 6 squares whose distance to the all zero vertex is one.

9.6.7 *Up-Down Degree Enumerator Polynomial*

The bivariate up-down degree enumerator polynomial of $\mathcal{R}_n$ is

$$\sum_{v \in \mathcal{R}_n} u^{\deg_{\mathrm{up}}(v)} d^{\deg_{\mathrm{down}}(v)} .$$

For example, for $n = 4$, this polynomial is

$$3d^2 + 2du + 2du^2 + u^4 , \tag{9.17}$$

as can be verified by inspecting $\mathcal{R}_4$ in Fig. 9.13. The polynomial in (9.17) specializes to (9.14) for $u = 1$, to (9.15) for $d = 1$, and to (9.16) for $u = d = x$. Thus the generating function of the up-down degree enumerator polynomials for $\mathcal{R}_n$ would give Proposition 9.46 and Proposition 9.47 as corollaries, and provide the generating function of the degree enumerator polynomials itself for $u = d = x$. The derivation of this general case is of was studied in detail by Eğecioğlu and Iršič in [31].

We can only give the main results of [31] without proof here. The proofs make use of the elements formal languages of Chapter 2 and rather intricate generating function arguments.

We recall that the generating function of the sequence of the up-down degree enumerator polynomials is defined as

$$GF = \sum_{n \geq 1} t^n \sum_{v \in \mathcal{R}_n} u^{\deg_{\text{up}}(v)} d^{\deg_{\text{down}}(v)},$$

(where the dependence on u, v and t on the left is supressed).

Theorem 9.49. [31, Theorem 5.1] *The generating function of the up-down degree enumerator polynomials of the graphs $\mathcal{R}_n$ is given by $GF = \text{Num}/\text{Den}$ where*

$$\text{Num} = (d + u)t - d(u - 2)t^2 + (d^2 - d - 2u)t^3 - (d - 2)d(u - 2)t^4$$
$$- (d - 1)(u - d + du)t^5 - d(d + u - 2)t^6 + d(1 - 2d + 2d^2 + du - 2d^2u)t^7$$
$$- 2(d - 1)d^2(u - 1)t^8 - (d - 1)d^2(d + 1)(u - 1)t^9 - (d - 1)^2d^2(u - 1)t^{10}$$
$$- (d - 1)^2d^2(u - 1)t^{11},$$

and

$$\text{Den} = 1 - ut - 2t^2 + (2u - d)t^3 + t^4 + (2d - d^2 - u)t^5 + d(du - 1)t^7$$
$$+ 2(d - 1)d^2(u - 1)t^9 + (d - 1)^2d^2(u - 1)t^{11}.$$

The generating function given in Theorem 9.49 indeed specializes to the generating function of the down-degree enumerator polynomials of $\mathcal{R}_n$ in Proposition 9.46 for $u = 1$, and to the generating function of the up-degree enumerator polynomials of $\mathcal{R}_n$ in Proposition 9.47 for $d = 1$.

For instance, the degree enumerator polynomial $g_{10}(x)$ for $\mathcal{R}_{10}$ (computed by Mathematica) is as follows:

$$g_{10}(x) = x^{10} + 2x^9 + 10x^8 + 18x^7 + 30x^6 + 32x^5 + 39x^4 + 10x^3 + 2x^2.$$

Making the substitutions $u \to x$ and $d \to x$ in the generating function of the up-down degree enumerator polynomials, we find the generating function of the degree enumerator polynomials of $\mathcal{R}_n$.

Theorem 9.50. [31, Theorem 6.1] *The generating function of the degree enumerator polynomials of Fibonacci-run graphs is given in closed form as*

$$\sum_{n \geq 1} g_n(x)t^n = \text{Num}/\text{Dem},$$

where

$$\text{Num} = xt\Big(2 - (x-2)t + (x-3)t^2 - (x-2)^2t^3 - x(x-1)t^4 - 2(x-1)t^5$$
$$- (x-1)(2x^2 - x + 1)t^6 - 2x(x-1)^2t^7 - x(x-1)^2(x+1)t^8$$
$$- x(x-1)^3t^9 - x(x-1)^3t^{10}\Big)$$

and

$$\text{Den} = 1 - xt - 2t^2 + xt^3 + t^4 - x(x-1)t^5 + x(x-1)(x+1)t^7$$
$$+ 2x^2(x-1)^2t^9 + x^2(x-1)^3t^{11}.$$

9.7 Cube-Complement of Fibonacci Cubes

Definition 9.51. Let $\mathcal{F}_n^{\text{co}}$ be the set of binary strings of length n with 11 as substring. We will call the strings in $\mathcal{F}_n^{\text{co}}$ *non-Fibonacci strings of length n*. The cube-complement of Γ_n is the subgraph of Q_n induced by $\mathcal{F}_n^{\text{co}}$. We denote this graph by Γ_n^{co}.

Two small examples of the cube-complement of Fibonacci cubes are depicted in Fig. 9.14.

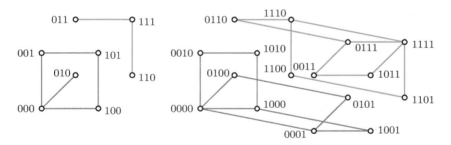

Fig. 9.14 Γ_3 and Γ_4, and the corresponding cube-complements Γ_3^{co} and Γ_4^{co}

More generally, in [109] Vesel introduced the concept of the cube-complement of an arbitrary induced subgraph of Q_n as follows. Let G be an induced subgraph of Q_n. Then the *cube-complement* of G in Q_n is the subgraph of Q_n induced by $\{v \in \mathcal{B}_n : v \notin V(G)\}$. When n is clear from the context, the cube-complement of G is denoted by G^{co}.

Among other results, Vesel obtained the following two theorems about the cube-complement of generalized Fibonacci cubes.

Theorem 9.52. [109, Theorem 3] *Let f be a binary string and d, t positive integers. The cube-complement $Q_n(f)^{co}$ is a partial cube if and only if*

(i) $f \in \{1^d, 0^d, 1^d 0, 10^d, 0^d 1, 01^d\}$ *or*

(ii) $f \in \{1^d 0^t, 0^d 1^t\}$ *and $n \le 2\min(t, d) + \max(d, t)$.*

Theorem 9.53. [109, Theorem 4] *Let f be a binary string and d, t positive integers. The cube-complement $Q_n(f)^{co}$ is a median graph if and only if*

(i) $f \in \{1^d, 0^d\}$ *and $n \le 2d$, or*

(ii) $f \in \{1^d 0^t, 0^d 1^t\}$ *and $n \le 2\min(t, d) + \max(d, t)$.*

We will consider the cube-complement of daisy cubes in Section 9.8.

Let us now focus on Γ_n^{co}. Note that Γ_n^{co} is connected since there is always a path between any vertex $x \in V(\Gamma_n^{co})$ and 1^n. Clearly the order of Γ_n^{co} is

$$n(\Gamma_n^{co}) = 2^n - F_{n+2}.$$

The size of Γ_n^{co} is obtained by an interesting bijective proof.

Proposition 9.54. [76, Proposition 5.1] *If $n \ge 1$, then*

(i) $m(Q_n)$ *is the total number of 0s in binary strings of length n,*

(ii) $m(\Gamma_n^{co})$ *is the total number of 0s in non-Fibonacci strings of length n,*

(iii) $m(\Gamma_n)$ *is the total number of 1s in Fibonacci strings of length n.*

Proof. We start by the observation that an edge of Q_n can be viewed as a couple (s, i), where s belongs to $\mathcal{B}_n$ and $i \in [n]$ is the changed coordinate.

Let e be an edge of Q_n and let x, y such that $e = xy$ with $x_i = 0$ and $y_i = 1$. Define the mappings $\phi(xy) = (x, i)$ and $\psi(xy) = (y, i)$. The key observation now is that the mapping ϕ is a one to one mapping between $E(Q_n)$ and $\{(s, i) : s \in \mathcal{B}_n, s_i = 0\}$, that is, the set of 0s appearing in strings of $\mathcal{B}_n$. Likewise, ψ is a bijection between $E(Q_n)$ and $\{(s, i) : s \in \mathcal{B}_n, s_i = 1\}$, that is, the set of 1s appearing in strings of $\mathcal{B}_n$.

Changing a 0 to 1 in a string s of $\mathcal{F}_n^{co}$ gives a string of $\mathcal{F}_n^{co}$. Therefore the restriction of ϕ to the edges of Γ_n^{co} defines a one-to-one mapping between $E(\Gamma_n^{co})$ and $\{(s, i) : s \in \mathcal{F}_n^{co}, s_i = 0\}$.

Likewise, since changing a 1 to 0 in a string of $\mathcal{F}_n$ gives a string of $\mathcal{F}_n$, the restriction of ψ to the edges of Γ_n defines a one-to-one mapping between $E(\Gamma_n)$ and $\{(s, i) : s \in \mathcal{F}_n, s_i = 1\}$. $\square$

Proposition 9.55. [76, Proposition 5.2] *The total number of 0s in Fibonacci strings of length n is $\sum_{i=1}^{n} F_{i+1} F_{n-i+2}$.*

Proof. Let $s \in \mathcal{F}_n$ and $i \in [n]$. Then $s_1 s_2 \ldots s_{i-1}$ and $s_{i+1} s_{i+2} \ldots s_n$ are Fibonacci strings. Conversely, if u and v are Fibonacci strings, then $u0v$ is also a Fibonacci string. Therefore the mapping defined by

$$\theta((s,i)) = (s_1 s_2 \ldots s_{i-1}, s_{i+1} s_{i+2} \ldots s_n)$$

is a one-to-one correspondence between $\{(s,i) : s \in \mathcal{F}_n, s_i = 0\}$ and the Cartesian product $\mathcal{F}_{i-1} \times \mathcal{F}_{n-i}$. The identity follows. $\square$

Theorem 9.56. [76, Theorem 5.3] *The size of Γ_n^{co} is given as:*

(i) $m(\Gamma_n^{co}) = n2^{n-1} - \sum_{i=1}^{n} F_{i+1} F_{n-i+2}$,

(ii) $m(\Gamma_n^{co}) = n2^{n-1} - \frac{1}{5}(4nF_{n+1} + (3n-2)F_n)$.

Proof. Since $m(Q_n) = n2^{n-1}$, combining the first two identities of Proposition 9.54 with Proposition 9.55 the first expression follows.

The second expression can be obtained from the evaluation of $\sum_{i=1}^{n} F_{i+1} F_{n-i+2}$ by one of the methods used in Section 3.5. An alternative proof is to consider the set of edges Z_n of Q_n, incident to exactly one vertex of Γ_n. The n edges of Q_n incident to a vertex of Γ_n belong to $E(\Gamma_n)$ or to Z_n. Summing over all vertices of Γ_n, the edges in $E(\Gamma_n)$ are obtained two times. Therefore $nF_{n+2} = |Z_n| + 2m(\Gamma_n)$. From the partition relation

$$m(Q_n) = m(\Gamma_n^{co}) + |Z_n| + m(\Gamma_n),$$

we deduce $m(\Gamma_n^{co})$. $\square$

The degree sequence of Γ_n^{co} is simpler than that of Γ_n. Indeed there are only three possible degrees. To deduce this fact, we need the following interpretation of the edges of Γ_n.

Proposition 9.57. *Let $e = xy$ be an edge of Γ_n with $x_i \neq y_i$ and let $\theta(e) = (x_1 \ldots x_{i-1}, x_{i+1} \ldots x_n)$. Then θ is a one-to-one mapping between the edges of Γ_n using the coordinate i and the Cartesian product $\mathcal{F}_{i-1}^{\bullet 0} \times \mathcal{F}_{n-i}^{0 \bullet}$.*

Proof. A 0 can be changed in 1 in $\mathcal{F}_n$ if and only if it is not preceded or succeeded by a 1. Assume first $1 < i < n$. We have then $x_1 \ldots x_{i-1} \in \mathcal{F}_{i-1}^{\bullet 0}$ and $x_{i+1} \ldots x_n \in \mathcal{F}_{n-i}^{0 \bullet}$. Conversely any $(x_1 \ldots x_{i-1}, x_{i+1} \ldots x_n) \in \mathcal{F}_{i-1}^{\bullet 0} \times \mathcal{F}_{n-i}^{0 \bullet}$ is the image by θ of an edge. The proof extends immediately to the case $i = 1$ or $i = n$, keeping in mind that by our convention the empty string belongs to $\mathcal{F}_0^{0 \bullet}$ and $\mathcal{F}_0^{\bullet 0}$ (see Section 3.3). $\square$

Theorem 9.58. [76, Theorem 5.5] *The degree of a vertex in Γ_n^{co} is n, $n-1$, or $n-2$. Moreover, there are*

(i) $m(\Gamma_{n-1})$ *vertices of degree* $n-2$,

(ii) $m(\Gamma_{n-2})$ *vertices of degree* $n-1$, *and*

(iii) $\displaystyle\sum_{k=0}^{n-4} 2^k m(\Gamma_{n-k-3})$ *vertices of degree* n.

Proof. Here a maximal substring of consecutive 1s of length at least 2 in a binary string will be called a *block*. Therefore, a string in Γ_n^{co} is a string with a least one block. The proof of Theorem 9.58 is based on the study of the possible blocks of a string of $\mathcal{F}_n^{co}$:

The vertices of degree $n-2$ are the strings that contain a unique block, and furthermore this block is of length 2. Indeed let x be such a string of $\mathcal{F}_n^{co}$ and assume that this block is $x_i x_{i+1}$ with $i \in [n-1]$. Then for $j \in \{i, i+1\}$, the string $x + \delta_j$ is a Fibonacci string. For j distinct from i and $i+1$, $x + \delta_j$ is a string of $\mathcal{F}_n^{co}$. Therefore $\deg_{\Gamma_n^{co}}(x) = n - 2$. Furthermore we can associate to x the pair of strings $(x_1 \ldots x_{i-1}, x_{i+2} \ldots x_n)$ that belongs to $\mathcal{F}_{i-1}^{\bullet 0} \times \mathcal{F}_{n-i-1}^{0\bullet}$. By Proposition 9.57, the number of such vertices is $m(\Gamma_{n-1})$.

The vertices of degree $n-1$ are the strings with a unique block, and this block is of length 3. In this case the central 1 of the block cannot be changed to 0.

If there exist at least two blocks or a block of length at least 4, the vertex is of degree n. Indeed, in this case all 1s can be changed to 0s.

In the last two cases the arguments for the cardinality are similar to the first case. See [76] for details. □

The sequence $0, 0, 0, 1, 4, 13, 36, \ldots$ formed by the number of vertices of degree n in $\Gamma_n^{co}, n \geq 1$, appears in OEIS [98, A235996] as "sequence of the number of length n binary words that contain at least one pair of consecutive 0s followed by (at some point in the word) at least one pair of consecutive 1s." This is clearly the same sequence. Indeed let s be a string of length $n \geq 4$ involved in this sequence. Considering the leftmost pair of consecutive 0s and the rightmost pair of consecutive 1s, the string s can be uniquely written as $\bar{a}00b11c$ where $a \in \mathcal{F}_i^{\bullet 0}$, $b \in \mathcal{B}_j$, and $c \in \mathcal{F}_k^{0\bullet}$, where i, j, k are non-negative integers with $i + j + k = n - 4$. On the other hand, from the characterization of vertices of degree n in Γ_n^{co} in terms of blocks, those vertices can be uniquely written as $a11b11c$, where $a \in \mathcal{F}_i^{\bullet 0}$, $b \in \mathcal{B}_j$, and $c \in \mathcal{F}_k^{0\bullet}$, where i, j, k are non-negative integers with $i + j + k = n - 4$. The two sequences are thus identical for $n \geq 4$ (and null for $n \leq 3$).

As we can notice in Fig. 9.14, Γ_4 is isomorphic to the cube-complement Γ_4^{co}. Our last result completes the general case of this observation.

Theorem 9.59. [76, Theorem 5.7] *If $n \geq 4$, then Γ_n is isomorphic to an induced subgraph of Γ_n^{co}.*

Proof. Define a mapping between binary strings of length $n \geq 4$ by $\theta(x) = \theta(x_1 x_2 \ldots x_n) = \overline{x}_4 \overline{x}_2 \overline{x}_3 \overline{x}_1 \overline{x}_5 \overline{x}_6 \ldots \overline{x}_n$. Let σ be the permutation on $[n]$ defined by $\sigma(1) = 4$, $\sigma(4) = 1$, and $\sigma(i) = i$ for $i \notin \{1,4\}$.

Note first that $x \in \mathcal{F}_n$ implies $\theta(x) \in \mathcal{F}_n^{co}$. Indeed since $x_2 x_3 \neq 11$ we can consider the following three cases.

   (i) If $x_2 x_3 = 00$, then $\overline{x}_2 \overline{x}_3 = 11$ is a substring of $\theta(x)$.
   (ii) If $x_2 x_3 = 10$, then $x_1 = 0$ and $\overline{x}_3 \overline{x}_1 = 11$ is a substring of $\theta(x)$.
   (iii) If $x_2 x_3 = 01$, then $x_4 = 0$ and $\overline{x}_4 \overline{x}_2 = 11$ is a substring of $\theta(x)$.

Therefore θ maps vertices of Γ_n to vertices in Γ_n^{co}.

Let $x(x + \delta_i)$ be an edge of Γ_n. Then by construction we have $\theta(x + \delta_i) = \theta(x) + \delta_{\sigma(i)}$ and therefore $\theta(x)$ and $\theta(x + \delta_i)$ are adjacent in Γ_n^{co}.

Since $\sigma^2 = \mathrm{Id}$, we have also for all $i \in [n]$ that $\theta(x) + \delta_i = \theta(x + \delta_{\sigma(i)})$. Therefore, if $\theta(x)\theta(y)$ is an edge in the subgraph induced by $\theta(\Gamma_n)$, then $\theta(y) = \theta(x) + \delta_i = \theta(x + \delta_{\sigma(i)})$ for some i. Applying the involution θ, we obtain $y = x + \delta_{\sigma(i)}$ and thus $xy \in E(\Gamma_n)$. $\qquad\square$

9.8 Daisy Cubes

We have already encountered the property of Fibonacci strings that changing 1s to 0s in a string of $\mathcal{F}_n$ always produces a string of $\mathcal{F}_n$. A natural generalization of Fibonacci cubes is to consider subgraphs of Q_n induced by sets of binary strings that satisfy this property.

Klavžar and Mollard introduced daisy cubes in the following fashion [64].

Let $\leq$ be a partial order on $\mathcal{B}_n$ defined with $u_1 \ldots u_n \leq v_1 \ldots v_n$ if $u_i \leq v_i$ holds for all $i \in [n]$. For $X \subseteq \mathcal{B}_n$ we define the graph $Q_n(X)$ as the following induced subgraph of Q_n:
$$Q_n(X) = Q_n[\{u \in \mathcal{B}_n : u \leq x \text{ for some } x \in X\}]$$
and say that $Q_n(X)$ is a *daisy cube (generated by X)*.

Vertex sets of daisy cubes are in extremal combinatorics known as *hereditary* or *downwards closed sets*, see [56, Section 10.2].

9.8.1 *Examples, Properties, Characterizations*

Let G be a graph isomorphic to a daisy cube and θ an isometric embedding of G into Q_n. Let $\theta(V(G)) \subset \mathcal{B}_n$ be the set of labels of the vertices of G.

Then the embedding is a *proper labeling* and G is *properly embedded* if G is isomorphic to $Q_n(\theta(V(G)))$.

Before given general properties of daisy cubes let us list some of their important subclasses.

(i) If $X = \{1^n\}$, then $Q_n(X) = Q_n$.

(ii) If $X = \{u_1 \ldots u_n : u_i u_{i+1} = 0, i \in [n-1]\}$, then $Q_n(X) = \Gamma_n$. More generally for $k \geq 2$ the generalized Fibonacci cube $Q_n(1^k)$ is a daisy cube.

(iii) If $X = \{u_1 \ldots u_n : u_i u_{i+1} = 0, i \in [n-1], \text{and } u_1 u_n = 0\}$, then $Q_n(X)$ is the Lucas cube Λ_n.

(iv) If $X = \{u_1 \ldots u_n : u_i u_{i+1} = 0, i \in [n-1], \text{and } u_n u_{n-2} = 0\}$, then $Q_n(X)$ is the alternate Lucas cube $\mathcal{L}_n$ (see Section 8.10).

(v) If $X = \{110^{n-2}, 0110^{n-3}, \ldots, 0^{n-2}11, 10^{n-1}1\}$, then $Q_n(X) = BW_n$, where BW_n is a bipartite wheel also known as a gear graph.

(vi) If $X = \{u : |w|_1 \leq n-1\}$, then $Q_n(X) = Q_n^-$, the vertex-deleted cube.

Note that if $x, y \in X$ and $y \leq x$, then $Q_n(X) = Q_n(X \setminus \{y\})$. More generally, if $\widehat{X}$ is the antichain consisting of the maximal elements of the poset $(X, \leq)$, then $Q_n(\widehat{X}) = Q_n(X)$. Hence, for a given set $X \subseteq \mathcal{B}_n$ it is enough to consider the antichain $\widehat{X}$; we call the vertices of $Q_n(X)$ from $\widehat{X}$ the *maximal vertices* of $Q_n(X)$.

As an example let $X = \{u \in \mathcal{B}_n : w(u) \leq k\}$. Then X induces a daisy cube and the maximal vertices of $Q_n(X)$ are the vertices u with $|u|_1 = k$. In particular, the vertex-deleted n-cube Q_n^- can be represented as

$$Q_n^- = Q_n(\{u : |u|_1 = n-1\}).$$

Using the decomposition of Fibonacci strings (Proposition 5.8), the maximal vertices of Γ_n with Hamming weight k are the strings $u = 0^{l_0} 10^{l_1} \ldots 10^{l_i} \ldots 10^{l_k}$ where $\sum_{i=0}^{k} l_i = n-k$, $l_0, l_k \in \mathcal{B}$, and $l_i \in [2]$ for $i \in [k-1]$ (see also Lemma 5.9). It is immediate that the class of daisy cubes is closed under the Cartesian product, a fact which further extends the richness of this class. We have defined the cube-complement of G in Q_n as the subgraph of Q_n induced by $\{v \in \mathcal{B}_n : v \notin V(G)\}$. When n is clear from the context we will drop it and denote the cube-complement of G by G^{co} (see Section 9.7). Additionally the *binary complement* of an induced subgraph G of Q_n is defined as the subgraph of Q_n induced by $\{\overline{v} : v \in V(G)\}$. Here $\overline{b}$ denotes the complement of $b \in \mathcal{B}_n$.

Proposition 9.60. [109, Proposition 10] *Let G be an induced subgraph of Q_n. Then G is a daisy cube if and only if Q_n does not admit a pair of* *vertices* $u \in V(G)$, $v \in V(G^{co})$ *with* $v \leq u$.

Proof. If G is a daisy cube, then $G = Q_n(V(G))$ and the assertion follows. Suppose now that G does not admit a pair of vertices $u \in V(G)$, $v \in V(G^{co})$ such that $v \leq u$. If $u \in V(G)$ then by the assumption, for any $w \in V(Q_n)$ with $w \leq u$ we have $w \in V(G)$. Since this holds for every $u \in V(G)$ we obtain that $G = Q_n(V(G))$. $\qquad\square$

Proposition 9.61. [109, Proposition 1] *Let G be an induced subgraph of Q_n. Then the binary complement of G is isomorphic to G.*

Proof. The mapping $v \mapsto \bar{v}$ is the required graph isomorphism between $V(G)$ and $\{\bar{v} : v \in V(G)\}$. $\qquad\square$

Theorem 9.62. [109, Theorem 2] *Let G be an induced subgraph of Q_n. If G is a daisy cube, then the cube-complement of G in Q_n is isomorphic to a daisy cube.*

Proof. Let H be the cube-complement of G and let G' and H' be the binary complements of G and H, respectively. Note that H' is also the cube complement in Q_n of G'. We first show that H' is a daisy cube. Assume the contrary. Then by Proposition 9.60 there exist $x \in H'$ and $y \in (H')^{co} = G'$ with $y \leq x$. Therefore $\bar{x} \leq \bar{y}$. Since $\bar{x}$ belongs to $(H')' = H$ and $\bar{y}$ belongs to $(G')' = G$, this contradicts the assumption that G is a daisy cube.

Therefore H' is a daisy cube. By Proposition 9.61 H is isomorphic to the daisy cube H'. $\qquad\square$

Taranenko [103] characterized daisy cubes by means of special kind of peripheral expansions.

A graph isomorphic to a daisy cube can have isometric embeddings in Q_n that are not proper. An algorithm which finds, in linear time, a proper labeling of a graph isomorphic to a daisy cube was given by Vesel in [110].

9.8.2 *Distance Cube Polynomial*

In Section 9.1 we have introduced the interval $I_G(u, v)$ between vertices u and v of a graph G as the set of vertices lying on shortest u, v-paths. We may also write $I(u, v)$ when G is clear from the context. If $k \in [n]$, then the interval between two vertices at distance k in Q_n induces a Q_k. Recall further from Section 5.1 that $c_k(G)$, $k \geq 0$, denotes the number of induced subgraphs of G isomorphic to Q_k and that the cube polynomial $C_G(x)$ of G is as defined in (5.1).

For a given property, say an identity P, a usual technique is to consider the q-analogue of P, a generalization involving a new parameter q, such that setting $q = 1$ gives the original identity. Of course a q-analogue of an enumerator polynomial such as $C_G(x)$ is only interesting if it counts something. The cube polynomial of Γ_n satisfies the recursion

$$C_{\Gamma_n}(x) = C_{\Gamma_{n-1}}(x) + (1+x)C_{\Gamma_{n-2}}(x) \quad (n \geq 2)$$

and its q-analogue, the q-cube polynomial, the recursion

$$C_{\Gamma_n}(x,q) = C_{\Gamma_{n-1}}(x,q) + (q+x)C_{\Gamma_{n-2}}(x,q) \quad (n \geq 2).$$

We have already met the q-cube polynomial of Γ_n in Section 5.4. This bivariate polynomial has the remarkable property that it is the enumerator polynomial of the number of induced subgraphs isomorphic to Q_k at distance d from the vertex 0^n. In the same way the q-cube polynomials of Λ_n and $\mathcal{L}_n$ are obtained as q-analogues of their cube polynomials. We will see that this holds in general for daisy cubes.

We first introduce a generalization of this enumerator polynomial to arbitrary graphs as follows.

If u is a vertex of a graph G and $k, d \geq 0$, then let $c_{k,d,u}(G)$ be the number of induced subgraphs of G isomorphic to Q_k at distance d from u. The *distance cube polynomial* of G with respect to u is

$$D_{G,u}(x,y) = \sum_{k,d \geq 0} c_{k,d,u}(G)x^k y^d.$$

Note that we have changed the name of the polynomial and used y instead of q since it is not always obtained as a q-analogue. By definition of $D_{G,u}$ we have $D_{G,u}(x,1) = C_G(x)$ for any vertex u. We also point out that if G is vertex-transitive, then $D_{G,u}(x,y)$ is independent of u. Moreover, since the polynomials C and D are multiplicative for Cartesian product of graphs,

$$C_{Q_n}(x) = (2+x)^n \tag{9.18}$$

and more generally, for any $u \in V(Q_n)$,

$$D_{Q_n,u}(x,y) = D_{Q_n,0^n}(x,y) = (1+x+y)^n. \tag{9.19}$$

Let H be an induced hypercube of Q_n. Let us recall (see Proposition 5.1) that there exists a unique vertex of H with maximum weight, the top vertex of H denoted $t(H)$. Similarly, H contains a unique vertex with minimum weight, $b(H)$, the base vertex of H. Furthermore $H = Q_n[I(b(H), t(H))]$.

We are now ready for the main result of this section.

Theorem 9.63. [64, Theorem 3.4] *If G is a daisy cube, then $D_{G,0^n}(x,y) = C_G(x+y-1)$.*

Proof. Let $G = Q_n(X)$ and $\hat{X} = \{x_1, \ldots, x_p\}$ be the maximal vertices of G. We thus have $V(G) = \bigcup_{i \in [p]} I(0^n, x_i)$.

An induced k-cube H of Q_n is an induced k-cube of G if and only if $t(H) \in V(G)$. Similarly, an induced k-cube H of Q_n is an induced k-cube of $Q_n[I(0^n, x)]$ if and only if $t(H) \in I(0^n, x)$.

For any k-cube H of Q_n and any subset T of $V(Q_n)$, let $\mathbb{1}_H(T) = 1$ if $t(H) \in T$, and $\mathbb{1}_H(T) = 0$ otherwise. Let $\mathbb{H}_{k,d}$ denote the set of induced k-cubes of Q_n that are at distance d from 0^n, and let $\mathbb{H}_k$ be the set of induced k-cubes of Q_n. Using this notation we can write

$$D_{G,0^n}(x,y) = \sum_k \sum_d \sum_{H \in \mathbb{H}_{k,d}} \mathbb{1}_H(V(G)) x^k y^d \qquad (9.20)$$

and

$$C_G(z) = \sum_k \sum_{H \in \mathbb{H}_k} \mathbb{1}_H(V(G)) z^k . \qquad (9.21)$$

By the inclusion-exclusion principle for the union of sets $A_1, \ldots, A_p$ we deduce

$$\mathbb{1}_H\left(\bigcup_{i \in [p]} A_i\right) = \sum_{J \subset [p], J \neq \varnothing} (-1)^{|J|-1} \mathbb{1}_H\left(\bigcap_{i \in J} A_i\right).$$

Therefore,

$$\mathbb{1}_H(V(G)) = \mathbb{1}_H\left(\bigcup_{i \in [p]} I(0^n, x_i)\right) = \sum_{J \subset [p], J \neq \varnothing} (-1)^{|J|-1} \mathbb{1}_H\left(\bigcap_{i \in J} I(0^n, x_i)\right).$$

Changing the order of summation in (9.20) and (9.21) we obtain

$$D_{G,0^n}(x,y) = \sum_{J \subset [p], J \neq \varnothing} (-1)^{|J|-1} D_{Q_n[\bigcap_{i \in J} I(0^n, x_i)], 0^n}(x,y)$$

and

$$C_G(z) = \sum_{J \subset [p], J \neq \varnothing} (-1)^{|J|-1} C_{Q_n[\bigcap_{i \in J} I(0^n, x_i)]}(z) .$$

Note that for arbitrary vertices u, v of Q_n we have $I(0^n, u) \cap I(0^n, v) = I(0^n, u \wedge v)$, where $(u \wedge v)_i = 1$ if and only if $u_i = 1$ and $v_i = 1$. The same property extends to the intersection of an arbitrary number of intervals. So $\bigcap_{i \in J} I(0^n, x_i)$ is an interval that induces a hypercube with base vertex 0^n. From (9.18) and (9.19) we see that the assertion of the theorem holds if G is an induced hypercube with base vertex 0^n. Therefore,

$$D_{Q_n[\bigcap_{i \in J} I(0^n, x_i)], 0^n}(x,y) = C_{Q_n[\bigcap_{i \in J} I(0^n, x_i)]}(x+y-1)$$

and we are done. $\qquad \square$

Theorem 9.63 has the following pleasing consequence.

Corollary 9.64. *If G is a daisy cube, then $D_{G,0^n}(x,y) = D_{G,0^n}(y,x)$.*

In words, this corollary says that for any integers k and d, the number of induced k-cubes at distance d from 0^n in a daisy cube G is equal to the number of induced d-cubes at distance k from 0^n.

To obtain another consequence of Theorem 9.63 we introduce the enumerator polynomial of the number of vertices at a given distance from a vertex u as follows.

If u is a vertex of a graph G and $d \geq 0$, then let $w_{d,u}(G)$ denote the number of vertices of G at distance d from u. Set

$$W_{G,u}(x) = \sum_{d \geq 0} w_{d,u}(G)x^d.$$

Note that $W_{G,u}(x) = D_{G,u}(0,x)$. With this definition in hand we can state the following important consequence of Theorem 9.63.

Corollary 9.65. *If G is a daisy cube then*

$$D_{G,0^n}(x,y) = W_{G,0^n}(x+y) \quad and \quad C_G(x) = W_{G,0^n}(x+1).$$

Proof. From Theorem 9.63 we get $C_G(x) = D_{G,0^n}(0,x+1)$. By the definition of the polynomials $D_{G,0^n}(0,x) = W_{G,0^n}(x)$ holds, and consequently $D_{G,0^n}(0,x+1) = W_{G,0^n}(x+1)$. We conclude that $C_G(x) = W_{G,0^n}(x+1)$.

Using Theorem 9.63 again and the already proved second assertion of the corollary we get

$$D_{G,0^n}(x,y) = C_G(x+y-1) = W_{G,0^n}(x+y),$$

which is the first assertion. $\qquad\qquad\qquad\qquad\qquad\qquad\qquad\qquad\qquad\qquad\square$

So if G is a daisy cube, then the polynomials $D_{G,0^n}$ and C_G are completely determined by $W_{G,0^n}(x) = D_{G,0^n}(x,0) = D_{G,0^n}(0,x)$.

Corollary 9.65 gives an easy way for proving some of the results previously given in this book. Consider for example the Fibonacci cube Γ_n. The number of vertices at distance k from 0^n is $\binom{n-k+1}{k}$. Therefore

$$W_{\Gamma_n,0^n}(x) = \sum_{k=0}^{\lfloor \frac{n+1}{2} \rfloor} \binom{n-k+1}{k} x^k$$

and we deduce that

$$C_{\Gamma_n}(x) = \sum_{k=0}^{\lfloor \frac{n+1}{2} \rfloor} \binom{n-k+1}{k} (1+x)^k,$$

which is Theorem 5.3. Also

$$D_{\Gamma_n,0^n}(x,y) = \sum_{i=0}^{\lfloor \frac{n+1}{2} \rfloor} \binom{n-i+1}{i}(x+y)^i$$

$$= \sum_{k=0}^{\lfloor \frac{n+1}{2} \rfloor} \sum_{d=0}^{\lfloor \frac{n+1}{2} \rfloor} \binom{n-k-d+1}{k+d}\binom{k+d}{d}x^k y^d,$$

a result obtained in [92, Proposition 3].

We already noticed that Lucas cubes and alternate Lucas cubes are daisy cubes. By Proposition 8.2 and Proposition 8.61, $W_{\Lambda_n,0^n}(x) = W_{\Gamma_n,0^n}(x)$. Therefore their q-cube polynomials are identical.

Fibonacci cubes are median graphs (see Theorem 6.3) but not all daisy cubes are median. For example the vertex-deleted cube Q_3^- is not median and more generally, the generalized Fibonacci cube $Q_n(1^k)$ is median only for $k = 2$ [52, Proposition 6.4]. It is well-known that median graphs are partial cubes. Soltan and Chepoi [99] and independently Škrekovski [97] proved that if G is a median graph then $C_G(-1) = 1$. This equality in particular generalizes the fact that $n(T) - m(T) = 1$ holds for any tree T. Hence if a daisy cube G is median (say a Fibonacci cube), then by Theorem 9.63 we have $D_{G,0^n}(x,-x) = 1$. As the next result asserts, this equality holds for every daisy cube and every vertex.

Theorem 9.66. [64, Theorem 4.1] *If G is a daisy cube, then $D_{G,u}(x,-x) = 1$ holds for every vertex u in G.*

The following immediate consequence by Theorem 9.63 extends the class of partial cubes G for which $C_G(-1) = 1$ holds.

Corollary 9.67. *If G is a daisy cube, then $C_G(-1) = 1$.*

9.8.3 *Pell Graphs as Daisy Cubes*

An interesting subfamily of daisy cubes is provided by Pell graphs Π_n. Let us recall (Section 9.4) that the Pell strings are the ternary strings over the alphabet $\{0,1,22\}$. The vertex set of Π_n is $\mathcal{P}_n$, the set of Pell strings of length n. Two vertices of Π_n are adjacent if either one of them can be obtained from the other by replacing one 0 with 1 (or vice versa), or by replacing one substring 11 with 22 (or vice versa).

Let us also recall the construction of the mapping α from $\mathcal{P}_n$ to a subset of $\mathcal{F}_{2n-1}$. For $p \in \mathcal{P}_n$, proceed from left to right by replacing each 0 by 10, each 1 by 00, and each substring 22 by 0100. We obtain a string p' in $\mathcal{F}_{2n}$

ending with 0. Let $\psi(p) = p'$. Note that if p is the concatenation of two Pell strings, $p = qr$, then $\psi(p) = \psi(q)\psi(r)$. Removing the trailing 0 gives $\alpha(p)$. Let $K = \{\psi(p) : p \in \mathcal{P}_n\}$, in other words K is the image of $\mathcal{P}_n$ under ψ. We have already seen in Section 9.4 that $K = \mathcal{F}_{2n}^*$ but we need only to remark here that by construction the elements of K are Fibonacci strings that ends with 0.

Munarini proved [80, Theorem 11] that the mapping α preserves distances and thus that Π_n is an isometric subgraph of Q_{2n-1}. Since $\psi(p) = \alpha(p)0$ we have also $d_{Q_n}(\psi(p), \psi(q)) = d_{\Pi_n}(p, q)$ for any pair of strings of $\mathcal{P}_n$.

We can now prove that Pell graphs are daisy cubes.

Theorem 9.68. *The Pell graph Π_n can be isometrically embedded as a daisy cube in Q_{2n-1}. The maximal vertices of this daisy cube are the images of the vertices of Π_n without 1s under the embedding. The image of the vertex 1^n of Π_n is the vertex 0^{2n-1} of Q_{2n-1}.*

Proof. We will first prove that the subgraph of Q_{2n} induced by K, the image of $\mathcal{P}_n$ over ψ, is a daisy cube. Since all vertices in this image are strings ending with 0, this subgraph will be a daisy cube of Q_{2n-1}. It is immediate that $\psi(1^n) = 0^{2n}$ and thus $\alpha(1^n) = 0^{2n-1}$.

Let A be the set of Pell strings in $\mathcal{P}_n$ without 1 and assume $u \in \mathcal{P}_n$. If there exists an occurrence of 1 in the ternary string u, then $u = x1y$ where x and y are Pell strings. Note that $u_1 = x0y$ also belongs to $\mathcal{P}_n$. Then $\psi(u) = \psi(x)00\psi(y)$ and $\psi(u_1) = \psi(x)10\psi(y)$. Thus $\psi(u) \leq \psi(u_1)$.

Assume that some 1 remains in u_1. By the same argument there exists u_2 in $\mathcal{P}_n$ with one fewer occurrence of 1 with $\psi(u_1) \leq \psi(u_2)$. Therefore $\psi(u) \leq \psi(u_2)$.

Repeating this process we obtain a Pell string u_m without 1, thus in A, such that $\psi(u) \leq \psi(u_m)$. Therefore $K \subset \{u \in \mathcal{B}_n : u \leq \psi(a) \text{ for some } a \in A\}$.

Consider now $a \in A$ and let x be any binary string with $x \leq \psi(a)$. Note that $\psi(a)$ is a word over the alphabet $\{10, 0100\}$. Since x is obtained by changing some occurrences of 1 to 0, x is a word over $\{00, 10, 0100\}$. Therefore x is the image by ψ of a Pell string. This gives the other inclusion. Thus

$$K = \{u \in \mathcal{B}_n : u \leq \psi(a) \text{ for some } a \in A\}.$$

We infer that Π_n is isometrically embedded by ψ as the daisy cube $Q_{2n}(\psi(A))$, thus by α as a daisy cube of Q_{2n-1}.

We have to prove that the elements of $\psi(A)$ are maximal. Assume $x \le y$ with $x \in \psi(A)$ and $y \in K$. Let $z \in \psi(A)$ such that $y \le z$. By transitivity $x \le z$. Since x and z are words over the alphabet $\{10, 0100\}$ and $x \le z$, if x starts 10 (respectively 0100), then so does z. Processing from left to right, we deduce $x = z$. Thus the elements of $\alpha(A)$ are maximal and we are done. $\qquad\square$

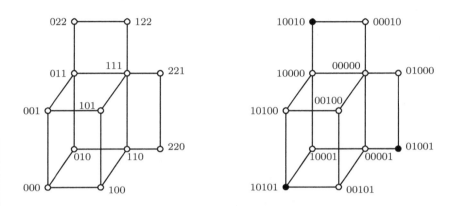

Fig. 9.15 The Pell graph $\varPi_3$ and its maximal vertices as a daisy cube of Q_5

9.8.4 *Maximal Hypercubes and an Application*

Maximal hypercubes are easy do determine in daisy cubes.

Proposition 9.69. *Let $Q_n(X)$ be a daisy cube. The number of maximal hypercubes of dimension k in $Q_n(X)$ is the number of maximal vertices of Hamming weight k.*

Proof. Let H be a hypercube in $Q_n(X)$ with base vertex b and top vertex t. Since $Q_n(X)$ is a daisy cube there exists a maximal vertex a with $t \le a$. Then $H = I(b,t) \subset I(0^n, t) \subset I(0^n, a)$. By the construction of daisy cubes, $I(0^n, a)$ is a maximal hypercube. $\qquad\square$

As an example, we already proved in this section that the maximal vertices of Γ_n of Hamming weight k are the strings $u = 0^{l_0} 10^{l_1} \ldots 10^{l_i} \ldots 10^{l_k}$ where $\sum_{i=0}^{k} l_i = n - k$, $l_0, l_k \in \mathcal{B}$, and $l_i \in [2]$ for $i \in [k-1]$. We obtain again Lemma 5.9.

Consider now the Pell graph Π_n. The maximal vertices of Π_n are the images by its embedding in Q_{2n-1} of the vertices of Π_n without 1. Let a be such a Pell string with r occurrences of 0 and s of 22, thus with $r + 2s = n$. The image of a is a binary string of Hamming weight $r + s$. Setting $r + s = k$ we deduce $r = 2k - n$ and $s = n - k$. Therefore, the number of maximal vertices of Hamming weight k is the number of ways of choosing the places of the r 0s among $r + s$ substrings 0 or 22. This number is $\binom{r+s}{s} = \binom{k}{n-k}$. We have obtained the following theorem.

Theorem 9.70. *If $0 \le k \le n$, and $h_k(\Pi_n)$ is the number of maximal k-cubes in Π_n, then*

$$h_k(\Pi_n) = \binom{k}{n-k}.$$

By Pascal's identity we have the relation

$$h_k(\Pi_n) = h_{k-1}(\Pi_{n-1}) + h_{k-1}(\Pi_{n-2}) \tag{9.22}$$

for $n \ge 2$ and $k \ge 1$. Let $H_{\Pi_n}(x)$ denote the enumerator polynomial of $h_k(\Pi_n)$. By direct inspection, the first $H_{\Pi_n}(x)$ are as follows:

$$H_{\Pi_0}(x) = 1,$$
$$H_{\Pi_1}(x) = x,$$
$$H_{\Pi_2}(x) = x + x^2,$$
$$H_{\Pi_3}(x) = 2x^2 + x^3,$$
$$H_{\Pi_4}(x) = x^2 + 3x^3 + x^4.$$

From (9.22) we infer that for $n \ge 2$,

$$H_{\Pi_n}(x) = x(H_{\Pi_{n-1}}(x) + H_{\Pi_{n-2}}(x)).$$

Therefore, the generating function of H_{Π_n} is

$$\sum_{n \ge 1} H_{\Pi_n}(x)t^n = \frac{1}{1 - xt - xt^2}.$$

As an immediate consequence, the sum of coefficients of $H_{\Pi_n}(x)$ is $H_{\Pi_n}(1) = F_{n+1}$.

9.8.5   Wiener Index and Mostar Index

In this section we will prove that the Wiener index and the Mostar index of daisy cubes are easy to determine. Furthermore, they are linked by the following result due to Mollard, which we will prove below.

Theorem 9.71. [78, Theorem 3.1] *If G is a daisy cube, then*

$$2W(G) - \mathrm{Mo}(G) = n(G)m(G).$$

By construction, daisy cubes are partial cubes. Therefore the Wiener index of a daisy cube can be determined by Theorem 7.5. This can be reformulated for an embedded partial cube as follows.

Theorem 9.72. *Let G be a partial cube of dimension n isometrically embedded into Q_n. Then*

$$W(G) = \sum_{i=1}^{n} |W_{(i,0)}(G)| \cdot |W_{(i,1)}(G)|,$$

where $W_{(i,\chi)}(G) = \{u = u_1 u_2 \ldots u_n \in V(G) : u_i = \chi\}$ for $\chi \in \mathcal{B}$.

Proposition 9.73. *If $i \in [n]$, then $|W_{(i,0)}(G)| \geq |W_{(i,1)}(G)|$.*

Proof. Let $u = u_1 u_2 \ldots u_n$ belong to $W_{(i,1)}(G)$, and consider $\theta(u) = u_1 \ldots u_{i-1} 0 u_{i+1} \ldots u_n$. Note that $\theta(u) \leq u$ and since u is a vertex of G there exists $x \in X$ with $u \leq x$. Therefore $\theta(u) \leq x$ and $\theta(u) \in V(G)$. By this way we construct an injective mapping from $W_{(i,1)}(G)$ to $W_{(i,0)}(G)$. $\square$

For $i \in [n]$, let E_i be the set of edges of our daisy cube G using the coordinates i.

Proposition 9.74. *If $i \in [n]$, then $|E_i| = |W_{(i,1)}(G)|$.*

Proof. Indeed, let $u = u_1 u_2 \ldots u_n$ belong to $W_{(i,1)}(G)$, and let $v = u_1 \ldots u_{i-1} 0 u_{i+1} \ldots u_n$. Using the same argument as in the previous proof, it is clear that v is a vertex of G and that the edge uv belongs to E_i. Reciprocally exactly one of the extremities of a given edge of E_i belongs to $W_{(i,1)}(G)$. We thus obtain a one-to-one mapping between $W_{(i,1)}(G)$ and E_i. $\square$

Lemma 9.75. [78, Lemma 3.1] *Let G be a daisy cube of dimension n properly embedded into Q_n. Then*

$$\mathrm{Mo}(G) = \sum_{i=1}^{n} |W_{(i,1)}(G)|(|W_{(i,0)}(G)| - |W_{(i,1)}(G)|).$$

Proof. Let $e = uv$ be an edge of E_i with $u_i = 0$. By Proposition 9.73 we have $n_u = |W_{(i,0)}(G)| \geq |W_{(i,1)}(G)| = n_v$. The contribution of the edge e to $\sum_{uv \in E(G)} |n_u - n_v|$ is thus $|W_{(i,0)}(G)| - |W_{(i,1)}(G)|$. Therefore

$$\mathrm{Mo}(G) = \sum_{i=1}^{n} \sum_{uv \in E_i} (|W_{(i,0)}(G)| - |W_{(i,1)}(G)|)$$

$$= \sum_{i=1}^{n} |E_i|(|W_{(i,0)}(G)| - |W_{(i,1)}(G)|).$$

The conclusion follows from Proposition 9.74. $\square$

We can now proceed to the proof of Theorem 9.71. By Theorem 9.72 we have

$$W(G) = \sum_{i=1}^{n} |W_{(i,0)}(G)| \cdot |W_{(i,1)}(G)|.$$

Since $|W_{(i,0)}(G)| + |W_{(i,1)}(G)| = n(G)$, we deduce from Lemma 9.75 that $2W(G) - \mathrm{Mo}(G)$ is equal to

$$\sum_{i=1}^{n} |W_{(i,1)}(G)|(2|W_{(i,0)}(G)| - |W_{(i,0)}(G)| + |W_{(i,1)}(G)|)$$
$$= \sum_{i=1}^{n} |W_{(i,1)}(G)|n(G).$$

Since $E(G)$ is the disjoint union $E(G) = \bigcup_{i=1}^{n} E_i$, we deduce from Proposition 9.74 that $\sum_{i=1}^{n} |W_{(i,1)}(G)| = m(G)$ and Theorem 9.71 follows.

The Wiener and Mostar indices of daisy cubes are thus completely determined by $n(G)$ and the sequence $(|E_i|)_{i \in [n]}$ of the number of edges that use the coordinate i. Indeed, from Theorem 9.72 and Lemma 9.75 we have the relation

$$W(G) - \mathrm{Mo}(G) = \sum_{i=1}^{n} |W_{(i,1)}(G)|^2.$$

Combining this identity with that of Theorem 9.71 we obtain the following assertion.

Corollary 9.76. [78, Corollary 4.1] *Let G be a daisy cube properly embedded into Q_n. For $i \in [n]$ let E_i be the set of edges that use coordinate i. Then the Wiener and the Mostar indices of G are*

$$W(G) = n(G)m(G) - \sum_{i=1}^{n} |E_i|^2$$

$$\mathrm{Mo}(G) = n(G)m(G) - 2\sum_{i=1}^{n} |E_i|^2.$$

In the set of daisy cubes embedded into Q_n with the same numbers of vertices and edges, $W(G)$ and $\mathrm{Mo}(G)$ are thus maximum for graphs in which the edges are equidistributed among coordinates.

9.8.6 *Applications in Chemistry and Quantum Physics*

We conclude the section on daisy cubes with their application in mathematical chemistry. Before this some preparation is needed.

In Theorem 6.2 we have proved that if H is a fibonaccene with $n \geq 1$ hexagons, then its resonance graph $R(H)$ is isomorphic to Γ_n. An important generalization of fibonaccenes in theoretical chemistry is the following. A graph G is a *catacondensed even ring system* (shortly *CERS*) if G is a bipartite, 2-connected, outerplanar graph with all vertices of degree 2 or 3. A CERS is thus a plane graph such that all its inner faces are even and every pair of inner faces are either disjoint or share exactly one edge. Further, by the degree condition, no three faces share a vertex. Clearly, fibonaccenes are CERSs. For another example of a CERS, see Fig. 9.16.

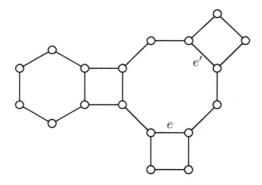

Fig. 9.16 A CERS which is not regular

The *distance between two edges* of a graph G is the distance between the edges in the line graph of G. Suppose that F, F', and F'' are three inner faces of a CERS such that F and F' intersect in edge e, and F' and F'' intersect in edge e'. The triple (F, F', F'') is an *adjacent triple of faces*, and the edges e, e' are its *intersecting edges*. A CERS is regular if it has at most two inner faces or the intersecting edges of an arbitrary adjacent triple of faces are at an even distance. Note that in a fibonaccene, each pair of intersecting edges are at distance 2, hence every fibonaccene is a regular CERS. Note also that the CERS from Fig. 9.16 is not regular because the intersection edges e and e' are at distance 3.

After this preparation, we can state the following attractive application of daisy cubes due to Brezovnik, Tratnik and Žigert Pleteršek.

Theorem 9.77. [15, Theorem 4.2] *Let G be a CERS. Then G is regular if and only if $R(G)$ is a daisy cube.*

Finally, let us mention a surprising appearance of daisy cubes in quantum physics [26]. Very roughly, in this paper two families of constrained models described by certain Hamiltonians and with different choices of projectors are considered. Projectors are further restricted such that it must always be possible to de-excite an atom. As it happens, all the corresponding graphs considered are daisy cubes.

9.9 Fibonacci *p*-Cubes

Very recently, Wei and Yang [115] proposed a new line of research by introducing Fibonacci p-cubes in the following way. If $p \geq 1$ and $n \geq 1$, then the *Fibonacci p-string of length n* is a binary string which contains no substring of the form $10^s 1$, where $s < p$. That is, a Fibonacci p-string of length n is a binary string of length n such that between any two 1s there exist at least p consecutive 0s. The *Fibonacci p-cube of dimension n* is then the subgraph of Q_n induced by the Fibonacci p-strings of length n. Let us denote this graph by $\Gamma_n^{[p]}$. (In [115] the notation Γ_n^p is used, but we already used this notation for p-Fibonacci cubes of dimension n.)

The seminal paper [115] provides a wealth of interesting results on Fibonacci p-cubes. Their recursive structure is described along the lines of the fundamental decomposition; their order, size, diameter and radius are determined. It is proved that $\Gamma_n^{[p]}$ are median graphs as soon as $n \geq p$; the generating functions of their cube polynomials presented; and more.

On the other hand, it would be interesting to derive many additional features of Fibonacci p-cubes, several of them are listed at the end of the seminal paper. Let us recall two of them. Is there a closed formula for the Wiener index of $\Gamma_n^{[p]}$? For what values of n and p does $\Gamma_n^{[p]}$ have a Hamiltonian cycle or a Hamiltonian path?

In [115] the *Lucas p-cube of dimension n* is also defined as expected, that is, its vertices are binary strings of length n with at least p consecutive 0s in a circular manner between any two 1s. Many results are also proved for this interesting family of graphs.

Chapter 10

Asymptotic Properties

In recent decades large graphs became a topic of great interest—not only in mathematics but also in computer science and its many applications to daily life—and hence it seems justified to consider the asymptotic behavior of relevant families of graphs, such as Fibonacci and Lucas cubes and their variants. Here we consider the asymptotic behavior of a selected number of parameters associated with these graph families.

First of all, one of the reasons the golden ratio φ appears in some patterns in nature is an asymptotic result. Indeed, as remarked in Chapter 1, the ratio of successive Fibonacci numbers converges to φ:

$$\lim_{n \to \infty} \frac{F_{n+1}}{F_n} = \frac{1 + \sqrt{5}}{2} = \varphi .$$

From the Binet formula (1.7) for F_n and the fact that $\left| \frac{1-\sqrt{5}}{2} \right| < 1$, we find that

$$F_n \sim \frac{1}{\sqrt{5}} \left(\frac{1 + \sqrt{5}}{2} \right)^n = \frac{1}{\sqrt{5}} \varphi^n . \tag{10.1}$$

10.1 Order

Let us start with a few immediate considerations. From (10.1), the order of the Fibonacci cube is asymptotically given by

$$n(\Gamma_n) \sim \frac{1}{\sqrt{5}} \varphi^{n+2} . \tag{10.2}$$

A similar argument applied to the Binet formula for Lucas numbers (1.9) gives

$$n(\Lambda_n) \sim \varphi^n . \tag{10.3}$$

The two variants of these families, k-Fibonacci cubes Γ_n^k (Section 9.5) and Fibonacci-run graphs $\mathcal{R}_n$ (Section 9.6) have the same number of vertices as Γ_n and therefore $n(\Gamma_n^k)$ and $n(\mathcal{R}_n)$ are both asymptotically given by (10.2).

Alternate Lucas cubes (Section 8.10) have the same number of vertices as Lucas cubes. Therefore $n(\mathcal{L}_n) \sim \varphi^n$ by (10.3).

Using the Binet formula, we find that the Pell number P_n is given explicitly by

$$P_n = \frac{1}{2\sqrt{2}} \left((1 + \sqrt{2})^n - (1 - \sqrt{2})^n \right) .$$

Since $|1 - \sqrt{2}| < 1$, using (9.5) we obtain

$$n(\Pi_n) \sim \frac{1}{2\sqrt{2}} \left(1 + \sqrt{2} \right)^{n+1} .$$

10.2   Size

From Propositions 3.2, 8.3, 8.60 and Corollary 9.39, we have the following closed formulas for the sizes.

$$m(\Gamma_n) = \tfrac{1}{5} \left(n F_{n+1} + 2(n + 1) F_n \right)$$

$$m(\Lambda_n) = m(\mathcal{L}_n) = n F_{n-1} ,$$

$$m(\mathcal{R}_n) = (3n + 4) F_{n-6} + (5n + 6) F_{n-5} .$$

From these we immediately obtain their asymptotic behavior using (10.1).

Proposition 10.1. *The asymptotic sizes of* Γ_n, Λ_n, $\mathcal{L}_n$ *and* $\mathcal{R}_n$ *are given by*

$$m(\Gamma_n) \sim \tfrac{1}{10}(1 + \sqrt{5}) n \varphi^n ,$$

$$m(\Lambda_n) = m(\mathcal{L}_n) \sim \tfrac{1}{10}(5 - \sqrt{5}) n \varphi^n ,$$

$$m(\mathcal{R}_n) \sim \tfrac{1}{10}(5 - \sqrt{5}) n \varphi^n .$$

10.3   Average Degree and Average Eccentricity

The *average degree* and the *average eccentricity* of a graph G are respectively defined as:

$$\overline{\deg}(G) = \frac{1}{n(G)} \sum_{u \in V(G)} \deg_G(u) ,$$

$$\overline{\mathrm{ecc}}(G) = \frac{1}{n(G)} \sum_{u \in V(G)} \mathrm{ecc}_G(u) .$$

The asymptotic average degree of Γ_n and Λ_n were computed in [63, Theorem 5.1]. We have

Theorem 10.2.

$$\lim_{n\to\infty} \frac{\overline{\deg}(\Gamma_n)}{n} = \lim_{n\to\infty} \frac{\overline{\deg}(\Lambda_n)}{n} = \lim_{n\to\infty} \frac{\overline{\deg}(\mathcal{L}_n)}{n} = \tfrac{1}{5}(5 - \sqrt{5}).$$

Proof. By Proposition 3.2, $m(\Gamma_n) = \tfrac{1}{5}(nF_{n+1} + 2(n+1)F_n)$, hence

$$\overline{\deg}(\Gamma_n) = \frac{1}{n(\Gamma_n)} 2\, m(\Gamma_n) = \frac{2}{5\, F_{n+2}} (nF_{n+1} + 2(n+1)F_n).$$

Therefore,

$$\begin{aligned}
\lim_{n\to\infty} \frac{\overline{\deg}(\Gamma_n)}{n} &= \lim_{n\to\infty} \frac{2}{5} \left(\frac{F_{n+1}}{F_{n+2}} + \frac{2F_n}{F_{n+2}} + \frac{2}{n} \frac{F_n}{F_{n+2}} \right) \\
&= \frac{2}{5} \left(\varphi^{-1} + 2\varphi^{-2} \right) = \tfrac{1}{5}(5 - \sqrt{5}).
\end{aligned}$$

For the Lucas cubes we recall that $m(\Lambda_n) = nF_{n-1}$ by Proposition 8.3 and that $n(\Lambda_n)L_n = F_{n-1} + F_{n+1}$ by (1.10). Hence $\overline{\deg}(\Lambda_n) = 2nF_{n-1}/(F_{n-1} + F_{n+1})$ and

$$\lim_{n\to\infty} \frac{\overline{\deg}(\Lambda_n)}{n} = \lim_{n\to\infty} \frac{2F_{n-1}}{F_{n-1} + F_{n+1}} = \frac{2}{1 + \varphi^2} = \tfrac{1}{5}(5 - \sqrt{5}). \tag{10.4}$$

Alternate Lucas cube $\mathcal{L}_n$ has the same order and size as Lucas cubes by Proposition 8.60. Therefore (10.4) holds for $\mathcal{L}_n$ as well. $\qquad\square$

We will determine now the asymptotic average eccentricity of Fibonacci and Lucas cubes. It is intuitively rather "obvious" that, here also, in both cases the result should be the same. We begin with:

Theorem 10.3. [63, Theorem 2.1]

$$\lim_{n\to\infty} \frac{\overline{\mathrm{ecc}}(\Gamma_n)}{n} = \tfrac{1}{10}(5 + \sqrt{5}).$$

Proof. Let $f_{n,k}$ denote the number of vertices of Γ_n with eccentricity k. Denote the generating function (4.2) already computed in Theorem 4.7 by $F(x,t)$. If e_n is the sum of the eccentricities of all vertices of Γ_n, i.e.,

$$e_n = \sum_{v \in V(\Gamma_n)} \mathrm{ecc}_{\Gamma_n}(v),$$

then

$$\left. \frac{\partial F(x,t)}{\partial x} \right|_{x=1} = \sum_{n,k\geq 0} k f_{n,k} t^n = \sum_{n\geq 0} e_n t^n.$$

On the other hand,

$$\left.\frac{\partial F(x,t)}{\partial x}\right|_{x=1} = \frac{2t + t^2}{(1 - t - t^2)^2}.$$

Using from the generating function of the Fibonacci sequence we have

$$\sum_{n\geq 0} F_{n+1} t^n = \frac{1}{1 - t - t^2},$$

$$\sum_{n\geq 0} n F_{n+1} t^n = \frac{t + 2t^2}{(1 - t - t^2)^2} \quad \text{and} \quad \sum_{n\geq 0} n F_n t^n = \frac{t + t^3}{(1 - t - t^2)^2}.$$

From the decomposition

$$\frac{2t + t^2}{(1 - t - t^2)^2} = \frac{1}{5}\left(3\frac{t}{1 - t - t^2} + 4\frac{t + 2t^2}{(1 - t - t^2)^2} + 3\frac{t + t^3}{(1 - t - t^2)^2}\right)$$

we obtain

$$\sum_{n\geq 0} e_n t^n = \frac{1}{5}\left(3\sum_{n\geq 0} F_n t^n + 4\sum_{n\geq 0} n F_{n+1} t^n + 3\sum_{n\geq 0} n F_n t^n\right)$$

and thus

$$e_n = \frac{3F_n + 4nF_{n+1} + 3nF_n}{5} = \frac{3F_n + nF_{n+1} + 3nF_{n+2}}{5}.$$

Therefore,

$$\overline{ecc}(\Gamma_n) = \frac{3F_n + nF_{n+1} + 3nF_{n+2}}{5F_{n+2}}.$$

We conclude that

$$\lim_{n\to\infty} \frac{\overline{ecc}(\Gamma_n)}{n} = \frac{3}{5} + \lim_{n\to\infty} \frac{1}{5}\frac{F_{n+1}}{F_{n+2}} = \frac{3}{5} + \frac{1}{5}\varphi^{-1} = \frac{1}{10}\left(5 + \sqrt{5}\right).$$

$\square$

Note that $(5 + \sqrt{5})/10 \approx 0.7236$ which should be compared with the (trivial) fact that for hypercubes we have

$$\lim_{n\to\infty} \frac{\overline{ecc}(Q_n)}{n} = 1.$$

Following the same idea but with a rather different computation sequence, the analogous result for Lucas cubes is obtained.

Theorem 10.4. [63, Theorem 2.2]

$$\lim_{n\to\infty} \frac{\overline{ecc}(\Lambda_n)}{n} = \frac{1}{10}\left(5 + \sqrt{5}\right).$$

Now we consider k-Fibonacci graphs Γ_n^k. and Fibonacci-run graphs $\mathcal{R}_n$. We have proved in Theorem 10.2 that

$$\lim_{n \to \infty} \frac{\overline{\deg(\Gamma_n)}}{n} = \tfrac{1}{5}(5 - \sqrt{5}).$$

It follows that the average degree of a vertex in Γ_n is asymptotically about $0.553n$. For the analogous problem for Γ_n^k for a fixed k, we have the following.

Proposition 10.5. *For a fixed k, the average degree of a vertex in Γ_n^k is asymptotically given by*

$$\tfrac{1}{5}\left(3 + \sqrt{5}\right) + \left(1 - \frac{1}{\sqrt{5}}\right) \log_\varphi \left(\sqrt{5}k + \sqrt{5} - \frac{1}{2}\right).$$

Proof. By the properties of the Fibonacci numbers we have

$$\lim_{n \to \infty} \frac{F_{n-n_0+3}}{F_{n+2}} = \varphi^{1-n_0}, \qquad \lim_{n \to \infty} \frac{F_{n-n_0+2}}{F_{n+2}} = \varphi^{-n_0}. \tag{10.5}$$

For k fixed, using Proposition 9.23 and (10.5), the average degree of a vertex in Γ_n^k is given by

$$\lim_{n \to \infty} \frac{2m(\Gamma_n^k)}{F_{n+2}} = 2\varphi^{-n_0}\big((k + m(\Gamma_{n_0-2}))\varphi + m(\Gamma_{n_0-1}) - m(\Gamma_{n_0-2})\big)$$

$$= 2\varphi^{-n_0}\left(\varphi k + \frac{n_0}{10}(5 - \sqrt{5})F_{n_0-1} + \frac{n_0 - 1}{\sqrt{5}}F_{n_0}\right), \tag{10.6}$$

where we used the expression for $m(\Gamma_n)$ for $n = n_0 - 1$ and $n = n_0 - 2$. To obtain the rate of growth of the exact formula for the asymptotic average degree given in (10.6), we further use the approximations

$$F_{n_0} \approx \frac{\varphi^{n_0}}{\sqrt{5}}, \qquad n_0 \approx 1 + \log_\varphi \left(\sqrt{5}k + \sqrt{5} - \frac{1}{2}\right).$$

$\square$

It is interesting that for a fixed k, the average asymptotic degree of a vertex in Γ_n^k is independent of n.

It was shown in [51] that Γ_n contains about $\frac{4}{5}$ the number of edges of the hypercube for the same number of vertices. The analogous ratio goes to zero with increasing n for Γ_n^k since the average degree is independent of n.

By Corollary 9.39, the size of the Fibonacci-run graph $\mathcal{R}_n$ is

$$m(\mathcal{R}_n) = m(\Gamma_n) - m(\Gamma_{n-4})$$

for $n \geq 5$. Since for large n we have $m(\mathcal{R}_n) < m(\Gamma_n)$, it is natural to consider the asymptotic behavior of the quotient $m(\mathcal{R}_n)/m(\Gamma_n)$. From the formula for $m(\Gamma_n)$ in Proposition 3.2 and the asymptotic behavior of Fibonacci numbers we find

$$\lim_{n\to\infty} \frac{m(\mathcal{R}_n)}{m(\Gamma_n)} = 1 - \lim_{n\to\infty} \frac{m(\Gamma_{n-4})}{m(\Gamma_n)} = \tfrac{1}{2}(3\sqrt{5}-5) \approx 0.85. \tag{10.7}$$

So asymptotically, $\mathcal{R}_n$ has about four-fifths the number of edges of Γ_n.

From Theorem 10.2,

$$\lim_{n\to\infty} \frac{\overline{\deg}(\Gamma_n)}{n} = \tfrac{1}{5}(5-\sqrt{5}) \approx 0.55.$$

Using this result and (10.7), we obtain the asymptotic average degree of the Fibonacci-run graph $\mathcal{R}_n$ as

$$\lim_{n\to\infty} \frac{\overline{\deg}(\mathcal{R}_n)}{n} = 2\left(\sqrt{5}-2\right) \approx 0.47,$$

a slightly lower value than 0.55.

10.4 Average Distance

As mentioned at the beginning of Section 7.2, the Wiener index can be also be studied as the average distance in a graph, where for a connected graph G, its *average distance* $\mu(G)$ of G is defined as

$$\mu(G) = \frac{1}{\binom{n(G)}{2}} W(G).$$

We thus have the following result.

Corollary 10.6. [62, Corollary 3.3] *The asymptotic behavior of the average distance of Fibonacci cubes is given by*

$$\lim_{n\to\infty} \frac{\mu(\Gamma_n)}{n} = \frac{2}{5}.$$

Proof. Since $\lim_{n\to\infty} \frac{F_{n+1}}{F_n} = \varphi$ and $n(\Gamma_n) = F_{n+2}$, Theorem 7.7 yields

$$\lim_{n\to\infty} \frac{\mu(\Gamma_n)}{n} = 2\left(\frac{4}{25\varphi^4} + \frac{9}{25\varphi^3} + \frac{6}{25\varphi^2}\right).$$

From $\varphi^2 = \varphi + 1$ we deduce $\varphi^4 = 3\varphi + 2$ and thus

$$\frac{4}{25\varphi^4} + \frac{9}{25\varphi^3} + \frac{6}{25\varphi^2} = \frac{4+9\varphi+6\varphi^2}{25\varphi^4} = \frac{5\varphi^4}{25\varphi^4} = \frac{1}{5}.$$

$\square$

Using Theorem 8.57 and its counterpart (10.3) for $n(\Lambda_n)$ we obtain a result for the average distance of Lucas cubes:

Corollary 10.7. *The asymptotic behavior of the average distance of Lucas cubes is given by*

$$\lim_{n\to\infty} \frac{\mu(\Lambda_n)}{n} = \frac{2}{5}.$$

The closed formula for the Wiener index of alternate Lucas cubes in Theorem 8.76 allows us to determine the asymptotic behavior of $\mu(\mathcal{L}_n)$. From (8.24)

$$W(\mathcal{L}_n) \sim \tfrac{1}{5}nL_{2n}.$$

Using the Binet formula (1.9) for Lucas numbers gives $W(\mathcal{L}_n) \sim \tfrac{1}{5}n\varphi^{2n}$, and consequently we have the following result.

Corollary 10.8. *The asymptotic behavior of the average distance of alternate Lucas cubes is given by*

$$\lim_{n\to\infty} \frac{\mu(\mathcal{L}_n)}{n} = \frac{2}{5}.$$

This of course is identical to that of Lucas cubes in Corollary 10.7 above.

These corollaries should be compared to the case of hypercubes for which

$$\lim_{n\to\infty} \frac{\mu(Q_n)}{n} = \frac{1}{2}.$$

10.5 Mostar Index

We have the closed formulas

$$\mathrm{Mo}(\Gamma_n) = \tfrac{1}{25}\left((3n-2)F_{2n+2} + nF_{2n+1} + (3n+2)(-1)^n\right),$$
$$\mathrm{Mo}(\Lambda_n) = nF_nF_{n-1},$$
$$\mathrm{Mo}(\mathcal{L}_n) = \tfrac{1}{25}\left(16L_{2n} + (5n-28)L_{2n-1} - (15n-40)(-1)^n\right),$$

that were obtained in Theorems 7.16, 8.59, and 8.74, respectively. Binet formulas and standard limit operations provide the asymptotic behavior of the Mostar indices of Γ_n, Λ_n, and $\mathcal{L}_n$. Using the Binet formulas and (1.7) and (1.9), we obtain the following asymptotic results for the Mostar index in terms of the golden ratio:

Corollary 10.9. *The asymptotic behavior of the Mostar indices of Γ_n, Λ_n and $\mathcal{L}_n$ are given by*

$$\mathrm{Mo}(\Gamma_n) \sim \tfrac{1}{25}n\varphi^{2n+3}, \quad \mathrm{Mo}(\Lambda_n) \sim \tfrac{1}{5}n\varphi^{2n-1} \quad and \quad \mathrm{Mo}(\mathcal{L}_n) \sim \tfrac{1}{5}n\varphi^{2n-1}.$$

10.6 Irregularity

We have already calculated formulas in closed form for the irregularity of a number of families of graphs, including Fibonacci cubes, Lucas cubes and alternate Lucas cubes. From Theorem 7.8 and Corollaries 8.55 and 8.68, respectively, we have

$$\mathrm{irr}(\Gamma_n) = \frac{2}{5}\left((n-1)F_n + 2nF_{n-1}\right),$$
$$\mathrm{irr}(\Lambda_n) = 2nF_{n-2},$$
$$\mathrm{irr}(\mathcal{L}_n) = 2\left(F_{n-1} + (n-1)F_{n-2}\right).$$

Using these formulas we easily obtain the following asymptotic results.

Proposition 10.10. *The asymptotic irregularity of* Γ_n, Λ_n *and* $\mathcal{L}_n$ *are given by*

$$\mathrm{irr}(\Gamma_n) \sim \frac{2}{5}n\varphi^n,$$
$$\mathrm{irr}(\Lambda_n) \sim \left(\frac{3}{\sqrt{5}} - 1\right)n\varphi^n,$$
$$\mathrm{irr}(\mathcal{L}_n) \sim \left(\frac{3}{\sqrt{5}} - 1\right)n\varphi^n.$$

Proof. These results are consequences of (10.1). □

10.7 Boundary of Hypercubes

Theorem 5.23 can be used to find asymptotic results on average behavior of the boundary of hypercubes in Γ_n. To see how to go about this, we note that the expression

$$\frac{\frac{\partial}{\partial d}\mathbb{D}_{n,k}(d)}{\mathbb{D}_{n,k}(d)}\bigg|_{d=1} \tag{10.8}$$

is the average boundary of k-dimensional hypercubes Q_k in Γ_n. This is because the numerator at $d = 1$ is the total boundary of all of the k-dimensional hypercubes in Γ_n and the denominator at $d = 1$ is simply their number.

The case $d = 0$ is simply the average degree of a vertex in Γ_n, and we compute that

$$\lim_{n\to\infty} \frac{\frac{\partial}{\partial d}\mathbb{D}_{n,k}(d)}{n\mathbb{D}_{n,k}(d)}\bigg|_{d=0}$$

is equal to the asymptotic result given in Theorem 10.2.

We demonstrate this method for 1-dimensional hypercubes in Γ_n. These are simply the edges of Γ_n. We know that the size of Γ_n is as given in Proposition 3.2, so that

$$\mathbb{D}_{n,1}(1) = m(\Gamma_n) = \tfrac{1}{5}\left(nF_{n+1} + 2(n+1)F_n\right).$$

For the numerator in (10.8), we take the partial derivative of the generating function $\mathbb{D}_1(d,t)$ given in Theorem 5.23 with respect to d, and then set $d = 1$. This gives the generating function

$$\frac{2t^2(1+3t-t^2)}{(1-t-t^2)^3}.$$

The coefficients of the series above are the quantities we need in the numerator of (10.8). We use the expansion

$$\frac{1}{(1-t-t^2)^3} = \sum_{n\geq 0} c_n t^n,$$

where $\{c_n\}_{n\geq 0}$ is the sequence [98, A001628] given by

$$c_n = \tfrac{1}{50}\left((5n+6)(n+1)F_{n+2} + (5n+17)(n+2)F_{n+1}\right).$$

A Mathematica calculation finds

$$\lim_{n\to\infty} \frac{2c_{n-2} + 6c_{n-3} - 2c_{n-4}}{nm(\Gamma_n)} = 2 - \frac{2}{\sqrt{5}},$$

so that the average boundary of a Q_1 in Γ_n is asymptotically given by

$$2\left(1 - \frac{1}{\sqrt{5}}\right)n \approx 1.106n.$$

Chapter 11

Further Avenues of Research

In the course of the book, we have already encountered several graph problems such as the domination number that have not yet been solved on Fibonacci cubes. There are many other open problems related to Fibonacci cubes and their variants that we have alluded to in this book. The topic is very rich and its study by no means complete. Undoubtedly many beautiful relationships between the Fibonacci cube variants are still waiting to be discovered.

Here we mention a number of additional classical concepts for which a complete solution for Fibonacci cubes is yet to be determined.

The first one of these is related to vertex colorability of Fibonacci cubes. Even though the chromatic number is trivial to calculate, the chromatic polynomial of Γ_n is yet to be determined in a satisfactory way. This is followed by the problem of the isoperimetric number and the bisection width. These are two classical problems that have been extensively studied for various families of graphs. Finally we consider the computation of the independence polynomial of Fibonacci cubes. This involves the enumeration of the number of independent sets of vertices of a given cardinality in Γ_n.

11.1 Chromatic Polynomial

By a *proper (vertex) coloring* of a graph G we mean an assignment of colors from a coloring kit with k colors to the vertices of G in such a way that no adjacent vertices are given the same color. The smallest number of colors required to properly color G is its *chromatic number*, denoted by $\chi(G)$. The chromatic number of a bipartite graph is 2, therefore $\chi(\Gamma_0) = 1$ and $\chi(\Gamma_n) = 2$ for $n \geq 1$.

If G is a graph and k a non-negative integer, then let $P(G, k)$ be the number of colorings of G with k colors. The chromatic polynomial $p(G, x)$ of G is a polynomial which evaluated at each $k \geq 0$ has the value $P(G, k)$. It is well-known that $p(G, x)$ is unique and is of degree $n(G)$. Evidently, $\chi(G)$ is the smallest positive integer x such that $p(G, x) > 0$.

One way to calculate the chromatic polynomial of G is the recursion

$$p(G, x) = p(G - e, x) - p(G/e, x), \tag{11.1}$$

where $e \in E(G)$, the graph $G - e$ is obtained from G by removing the edge e, and G/e is obtained from G by contracting the edge e. In contraction we progressively shrink e until the end points collapse into a single vertex. If multiple edges are created by this process, we collapse them into single edges. However it requires exponential time in general to compute $p(G, x)$ [29, Chapter 8].

The chromatic polynomials of Γ_n, $n \in [5]$, as computed by the ChromaticPolynomial functionality of Mathematica are as follows:

$p(\Gamma_0, x) = x$

$p(\Gamma_1, x) = x(x - 1)$

$p(\Gamma_2, x) = x(x - 1)^2$

$p(\Gamma_3, x) = x(x - 1)^2(x^2 - 3x + 3)$

$p(\Gamma_4, x) = x(x - 1)(x^2 - 3x + 3)^3$

$p(\Gamma_5, x) = x(x - 1)(x^{11} - 19x^{10} + 171x^9 - 960x^8 + 3732x^7 - 10544x^6$
$\qquad\qquad + 22088x^5 - 34314x^4 + 38774x^3 - 30408x^2 + 14942x - 3499)$.

It is clear that $x(x - 1)$ is always a factor of $p(\Gamma_n, x)$ for $n \geq 1$.

While the chromatic polynomials of Fibonacci cubes are not yet known, it is possible to give closed form expressions for the chromatic polynomials of k-Fibonacci cubes Γ_n^k for $k \in [2]$. This was done in [33] and presented in the following. For this sake, we need the following lemma on chromatic polynomials.

Lemma 11.1. [33, Lemma 3.1] *If G_1 and G_2 are subgraphs of a graph G, and the subgraph of G induced by $V(G_1) \cap V(G_2)$ is isomorphic to K_r, $r \geq 1$, then*

$$p(G, x) = \frac{p(G_1, x)p(G_2, x)}{x(x - 1)\cdots(x - r + 1)}.$$

For $k = 1$, the graphs Γ_n^1 are all trees with $n(\Gamma_n^1) = F_{n+2}$. Since the chromatic polynomial of a tree with N vertices is $x(x - 1)^{N-1}$, we have

$$p(\Gamma_n^1, x) = x(x - 1)^{F_{n+2}-1}.$$

For $k = 2$, $\Gamma_n^2 = \Gamma_n$ for $n \le 2$ and for $n \ge 3$, Γ_n^2 consists of $F_n - 1$ $(1, 2, 4, 7, 12, \ldots)$ squares (4-cycles or Q_2s) glued by their edges and F_{n-1} pendant vertices as shown in [32].

Theorem 11.2. [33, Theorem 3.2] *If $n \ge 1$, then*

$$p(\Gamma_n^2, x) = x(x-1)^{F_{n-1}+1}(x^2 - 3x + 3)^{F_n - 1}.$$

Proof. For $n \in [2]$, the graphs Γ_n^2 are trees on two and three vertices respectively. Therefore $p(\Gamma_1^2, x) = x(x-1)$ and $p(\Gamma_2^2, x) = x(x-1)^2$.

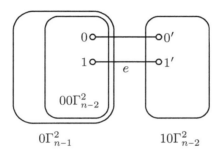

Fig. 11.1 The construction of Γ_n^2 from Γ_{n-1}^2 and Γ_{n-2}^2 by adding $k = 2$ link edges

For $n \ge 3$, Γ_n^2 is constructed from Γ_{n-1}^2 and Γ_{n-2}^2 as symbolically indicated in Fig. 11.1. The vertices labeled 0 and 1 are the vertices with labels $0 \ldots 00$ and $0 \ldots 01$ in Γ_{n-1}^2 (and also in Γ_n^2), whereas the labels $0'$ and $1'$ are the vertices labeled $0 \ldots 00$ and $0 \ldots 01$ in Γ_{n-2}^2, which are labeled as $10 \ldots 00$ and $10 \ldots 01$ in Γ_n^2 after the addition of the link edges. Let e denote the link edge from 1 to $1'$ as shown in Fig. 11.1 and put $G = \Gamma_n^2$. $G - e$ consists of the union of two graphs G_1 and G_2, where G_1 is obtained from Γ_{n-1}^2 by adding the vertex $0'$ and the edge $\{0, 0'\}$; G_2 is obtained from Γ_{n-2}^2 by adding the vertex 0 and the edge $\{0, 0'\}$. Then

$$p(G_1, x) = p(\Gamma_{n-1}^2, x)(x-1), \quad p(G_2, x) = p(\Gamma_{n-2}^2, x)(x-1),$$

and therefore by Lemma 11.1,

$$p(G - e, x) = \frac{p(\Gamma_{n-1}^2, x)p(\Gamma_{n-2}^2, x)(x-1)^2}{x(x-1)}$$

$$= p(\Gamma_{n-1}^2, x)p(\Gamma_{n-2}^2, x)\frac{(x-1)}{x}.$$

In G/e, denote the vertex obtained by the identification of the endpoints 1 and $1'$ of e by v. G/e consists of the union of two graphs H_1 and H_2, where

H_1 is obtained from Γ_{n-1}^2 by adding the vertex $0'$ and the edges $\{0,0'\}$ and $\{0',v\}$; H_2 is obtained from Γ_{n-2}^2 by adding the vertex 0 and the edges $\{0,0'\}$ and $\{0,v\}$. H_1 and H_2 meet at the triangle with vertices $0,0',v$. Therefore,

$$p(H_1,x) = p(\Gamma_{n-1}^2,x)(x-2), \quad p(H_2,x) = p(\Gamma_{n-2}^2,x)(x-2),$$

and again by Lemma 11.1,

$$p(G/e,x) = \frac{p(\Gamma_{n-1}^2,x)p(\Gamma_{n-2}^2,x)(x-2)^2}{x(x-1)(x-2)}$$

$$= p(\Gamma_{n-1}^2,x)p(\Gamma_{n-2}^2,x)\frac{(x-2)}{x(x-1)}.$$

By recursion (11.1),

$$p(G,x) = p(\Gamma_{n-1}^2,x)p(\Gamma_{n-2}^2,x)\left(\frac{x-1}{x} - \frac{(x-2)}{x(x-1)}\right)$$

$$= p(\Gamma_{n-1}^2,x)p(\Gamma_{n-2}^2,x)\left(\frac{x^2-3x+3}{x(x-1)}\right)$$

and the result follows by induction on n. $\square$

11.2 Isoperimetric Number

Another interesting concept which is not yet satisfactorily settled for Fibonacci cubes is the calculation of the isoperimetric number. This quantity is defined as follows.

Let G be a graph. Recall from Section 5.5 that the edge-boundary $\partial_e X$ of $X \subseteq V(G)$ is the set of edges in $E(G)$ which connect vertices in X with vertices in $V(G) \smallsetminus X$. The *isoperimetric number* $i(G)$ of G (sometimes called the Cheeger constant of G) is then defined as

$$i(G) = \min\left\{\frac{|\partial_e X|}{|X|} : X \subseteq V(G), 1 \le |X| \le \tfrac{1}{2}n(G)\right\}.$$

A set $X \subseteq V(G)$ which attains this minimum value is called an *isoperimetric set* for G.

A closely related parameter is the *bisection width* bw(G) of G. This is the minimum number of edges that must be removed from G in order to split $V(G)$ into two equal cardinality (within one if $n(G)$ is odd) subsets. The known values of $i(\Gamma_n)$ and bw(Γ_n) are given in Table 11.1, while in Fig. 11.2 isoperimetric sets in Γ_n, $n \in [5]$, are indicated.

n	$n(\Gamma_n)$	$i(\Gamma_n)$	bw(Γ_n)
1	2	1	1
2	3	1	1
3	5	1	2
4	8	3/4	3
5	13	4/5	5
6	21	7/9	8
7	34	12/16	13
8	55	20/27	20

Table 11.1 Known values of $i(\Gamma_n)$ and bw(Γ_n)

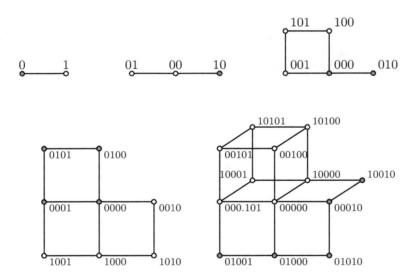

Fig. 11.2 Fibonacci cubes Γ_1 through Γ_5 with isoperimetric sets indicated

11.3 Spanning Trees

A subgraph T of a connected graph G is a *spanning tree* of G if T is a tree that contains every vertex of G. Spanning trees constitute an important graph-theoretic concept with numerous applications in various branches of science. The number of spanning trees of G is denoted by $\tau(G)$. Before we consider the case of $\tau(\Gamma_n)$, we need some preliminaries.

If G is a graph with $V(G) = \{v_1, \ldots, v_r\}$, then the adjacency matrix of G is the $r \times r$ matrix $A(G) = (a_{i,j})$, where $a_{i,j} = 1$ if $v_i v_j \in E(G)$ and $a_{i,j} = 0$ otherwise. Let $D(G)$ denote the $r \times r$ diagonal matrix with $\deg_G(v_1), \ldots, \deg_G(v_r)$ on the main diagonal. The *Laplacian matrix* of G is the matrix $L(G) = D(G) - A(G)$. A celebrated result of Kirchhoff is that $\tau(G) = \frac{1}{r}\lambda_1\lambda_2\cdots\lambda_{r-1}$, where $\lambda_1, \lambda_2, \ldots, \lambda_{r-1}$ are the non-zero eigenvalues of $L(G)$. Fortunately, this quantity can be computed without having to compute the eigenvalues, by simply taking a determinant.

We next state the following theorem which is known as the *matrix-tree theorem*. For a purely combinatorial generalization of this result, see [29, Chapter 4].

Theorem 11.3. [57] *If G is a graph, then $\tau(G)$ is given by any cofactor of $L(G)$.*

In (11.2), the number of spanning trees of Γ_n as computed by using the matrix-tree theorem are given for up to $n = 9$. The existence of relatively large primes in the prime factorizations of these numbers seems to imply that τ_n is unlikely to have a product formula for arbitrary n.

$$
\begin{aligned}
\tau_1 &= \tau_2 = 1 \\
\tau_3 &= 4 = 2^2 \\
\tau_4 &= 56 = 2^3 \times 7 \\
\tau_5 &= 16744 = 2^3 \times 7 \times 13 \times 23 \\
\tau_6 &= 592458464 = 2^5 \times 13 \times 1093 \times 1303 \\
\tau_7 &= 109129519434940800 = 2^7 \times 3 \times 5^2 \times 197 \times 199 \times 2063 \times 140557 \\
\tau_8 &= 350717222389157823952902131200000 \\
&= 2^{11} \times 5^4 \times 31 \times 229 \times 23333 \times 463319 \times 357025516223 \\
\tau_9 &= 4921753352504618717251832327371835816222162912597289861112 \\
&= 2^{16} \times 3 \times 7^2 \times 11 \times 19 \times 1321 \times 4561 \times 71429 \times 2872417 \times 57254546263 \\
&\quad \times 3453674219331286451
\end{aligned}
\tag{11.2}
$$

Evidently, τ_n grows very rapidly. We can quickly give the following simple lower bound.

Proposition 11.4. *The number τ_n of spanning trees of Γ_n satisfies $\tau_n \geq \varphi^{F_{n+1}-(n+1)}$.*

Proof. From the fundamental decomposition of Γ_n, two independently picked spanning trees of Γ_{n-1} and Γ_{n-2} together with a link edge forms a spanning tree of Γ_n. Therefore

$$\tau_n \geq F_n\, \tau_{n-1} \tau_{n-2} \tag{11.3}$$

with $\tau_1 = \tau_2 = 1$. The proof now follows by induction on n by making use of the inequality $F_n \geq \varphi^{n-2}$ which holds for $n \geq 1$. $\qquad\square$

We note that using (11.3) and induction, a sharper but more complicated looking lower bound

$$\tau_n \geq \prod_{k=1}^{n} F_k^{F_{n+1-k}}$$

can also be obtained.

We remark that directly from the recursive structure of Γ_n, the adjacency matrix $A(\Gamma_n)$ admits a block matrix decomposition. This decomposition of $A(\Gamma_n)$ in terms of $A(\Gamma_{n-1})$, $A(\Gamma_{n-2})$, and the $F_n \times F_n$ identity matrix I, is shown in Fig. 11.3.

$$A(\Gamma_n) = \begin{pmatrix} A(\Gamma_{n-1}) & \begin{array}{c} I \\ \hline 0 \end{array} \\ \hline \begin{array}{c|c} I & 0 \end{array} & A(\Gamma_{n-2}) \end{pmatrix} \qquad A(\Gamma_4) = \left(\begin{array}{ccccc|ccc} 0&1&1&1&0&1&0&0 \\ 1&0&0&0&1&0&1&0 \\ 1&0&0&0&0&0&0&1 \\ \hline 1&0&0&0&1&0&0&0 \\ 0&1&0&1&0&0&0&0 \\ \hline 1&0&0&0&0&0&1&1 \\ 0&1&0&0&0&1&0&0 \\ 0&0&1&0&0&1&0&0 \end{array} \right)$$

Fig. 11.3 The schematic decomposition of the adjacency matrix $A(\Gamma_n)$. On the right is the case for $n = 4$

11.4   Independence Polynomial

The *independence polynomial* of a graph G is the polynomial

$$I(G, x) = \sum_{i=0}^{\alpha(G)} s_i x^i$$

where s_i is the number of independent vertex sets of cardinality i in G. We have

$$I(\Gamma_0, x) = 1$$
$$I(\Gamma_1, x) = 2x + 1$$
$$I(\Gamma_2, x) = x^2 + 3x + 1$$
$$I(\Gamma_3, x) = x^3 + 5x^2 + 5x + 1$$
$$I(\Gamma_4, x) = 2x^4 + 13x^3 + 18x^2 + 8x + 1 \tag{11.4}$$
$$I(\Gamma_5, x) = x^7 + 8x^6 + 38x^5 + 97x^4 + 112x^3 + 58x^2 + 13x + 1$$
$$I(\Gamma_6, x) = x^{11} + 12x^{10} + 70x^9 + 287x^8 + 868x^7 + 1763x^6 + 2219x^5$$
$$+ 1658x^4 + 716x^3 + 172x^2 + 21x + 1$$
$$I(\Gamma_7, x) = 2x^{17} + 34x^{16} + 281x^{15} + 1514x^{14} + 6105x^{13} + 19857x^{12}$$
$$+ 53418x^{11} + 116775x^{10} + 198756x^9 + 251885x^8 + 229931x^7$$
$$+ 147880x^6 + 65845x^5 + 19892x^4 + 3954x^3 + 490x^2 + 34x + 1$$

The list in (11.4) indicates the existence of two distinct maximum independent sets of vertices for $n \in \{1, 4, 7, \ldots\}$ and a unique maximum independent set otherwise. Also, the polynomials in (11.4) are unimodal, with maximum coefficient at degree F_{n-1} term for $n \geq 2$. In other words

$$s_0 \leq s_1 \leq \cdots \leq s_{F_{n-1}} \geq s_{1+F_{n-1}} \geq \cdots \geq s_{\alpha(\Gamma_n)}.$$

A stronger condition than unimodality is log-concavity, that is, $s_{i-1}s_{i+1} \leq s_i^2$ for all $0 < i < \alpha(G)$ (see Section 5.1.1). For the independence polynomials up to $I(\Gamma_7, x)$ given here, Mathematica calculations show that the coefficient sequences are indeed log-concave.

Appendix A

The graphs of Γ_7 through Γ_{10}

In this appendix, the graphs of Γ_7 through Γ_{10} as rendered by Mathematica are presented.

Fig. A.1 Γ_7

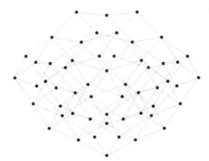

Fig. A.2 Γ_8

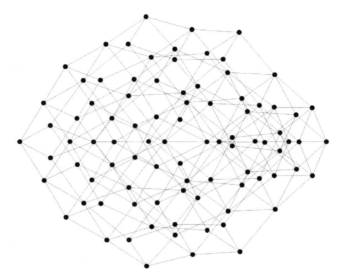

Fig. A.3 Γ_9

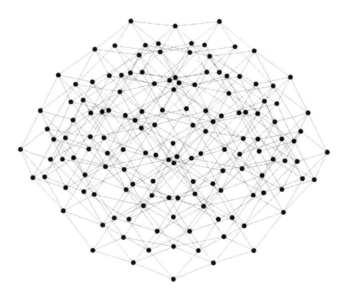

Fig. A.4 Γ_{10}

Bibliography

[1] Michael O. Albertson. The irregularity of a graph. *Ars Combin.*, 46:219–225, 1997.

[2] Yaser Alizadeh, Emeric Deutsch, and Sandi Klavžar. On the irregularity of π-permutation graphs, Fibonacci cubes, and trees. *Bull. Malays. Math. Sci. Soc.*, 43(6):4443–4456, 2020.

[3] Désiré André. Développement de sec x and tg x. *C. R. Math. Acad. Sci. Paris*, 88:965–979, 1879.

[4] Ali Reza Ashrafi, Jernej Azarija, Azam Babai, Khadijeh Fathalikhani, and Sandi Klavžar. The (non-)existence of perfect codes in Fibonacci cubes. *Inf. Process. Lett.*, 116(5):387–390, 2016.

[5] Ali Reza Ashrafi, Jernej Azarija, Khadijeh Fathalikhani, Sandi Klavžar, and Marko Petkovšek. Vertex and edge orbits of Fibonacci and Lucas cubes. *Ann. Comb.*, 20(2):209–229, 2016.

[6] Krassimir Atanassov, Vassia Attanassova, Anthony G. Shannon, and John C. Turner. *New Visual Perspectives on Fibonacci Numbers*. World Scientific, Singapore, 2002.

[7] Jernej Azarija, Sandi Klavžar, Jaehun Lee, and Yoomi Rho. Connectivity of Fibonacci cubes, Lucas cubes and generalized cubes. *Discrete Math. Theor. Comput. Sci.*, 17(1):79–88, 2015.

[8] Jernej Azarija, Sandi Klavžar, Yoomi Rho, and Seungbo Sim. On domination-type invariants of Fibonacci cubes and hypercubes. *Ars Math. Contemp.*, 14(2):387–395, 2018.

[9] Hans-Jürgen Bandelt, Victor Chepoi, and Kolja Knauer. COMs: complexes of oriented matroids. *J. Combin. Theory Ser. A*, 156:195–237, 2018.

[10] Hans-Jürgen Bandelt and Marcel van de Vel. Embedding topological median algebras in products of dendrons. *Proc. London Math. Soc. (3)*, 58(3):439–453, 1989.

[11] Jean-Luc Baril, Sergey Kirgizov, and Vincent Vajnovszki. Gray codes for Fibonacci q-decreasing words. *Theoret. Comput. Sci.*, 927:120–132, 2022.

[12] Jean-Luc Baril and Vincent Vajnovszki. Minimal change list for Lucas strings and some graph theoretic consequences. *Theor. Comput. Sci.*, 346(2-3):189–199, 2005.

[13] Norman Biggs. Perfect codes in graphs. *J. Comb. Theory Ser. B*, 15:289–296, 1973.

[14] Boštjan Brešar, Sandi Klavžar, and Riste Škrekovski. The cube polynomial and its derivatives: the case of median graphs. *Electron. J. Combin.*, 10:Research Paper 3, 11 pp. (electronic), 2003.

[15] Simon Brezovnik, Niko Tratnik, and Petra Žigert Pleteršek. Resonance graphs of catacondensed even ring systems. *Appl. Math. Comput.*, 374:125064, 9, 2020.

[16] John L. Brown. Unique representation of integers as sums of Lucas numbers. *Fibonacci Quart.*, 7:243–252, 1989.

[17] Leonard Carlitz. Fibonacci notes. III. q-Fibonacci numbers. *Fibonacci Quart.*, 12:317–322, 1974.

[18] Leonard Carlitz. Fibonacci notes. IV. q-Fibonacci polynomials. *Fibonacci Quart.*, 13:97–102, 1975.

[19] Aline Castro. *Codes de Gray généralisés à l'énumération des objets d'une structure combinatoire sous contrainte.* Thèse, Université de Grenoble, October 2012.

[20] Aline Castro, Sandi Klavžar, Michel Mollard, and Yoomi Rho. On the domination number and the 2-packing number of Fibonacci cubes and Lucas cubes. *Comput. Math. Appl.*, 61(9):2655–2660, 2011.

[21] Aline Castro and Michel Mollard. The eccentricity sequences of Fibonacci and Lucas cubes. *Discrete Math.*, 312(5):1025–1037, 2012.

[22] Johann Cigler. q-Fibonacci polynomials. *Fibonacci Quart.*, 41:31–40, 2003.

[23] Pietro Codara and Ottavio M. D'Antona. Generalized Fibonacci and Lucas cubes arising from powers of paths and cycles. *Discrete Math.*, 339(1):270–282, 2016.

[24] Bing Cong, Si-Qing Zheng, and Sanjay Sharma. On simulations of linear arrays, rings and 2D meshes on Fibonacci cube networks. In *Proceedings Seventh International Parallel Processing Symposium*, pages 748–751, 1993.

[25] Ali Dehghan and Amir Banihashemi. Counting short cycles in bipartite graphs: A fast technique/algorithm and a hardness result. *IEEE Trans. Inform. Theory*, 68:1378–1390, 12 2020.

[26] Jean-Yves Desaules, Kieran Bull, Aiden Daniel, and Zlatko Papić. Hypergrid subgraphs and the origin of scarred quantum walks in many-body Hilbert space. *Phys. Rev. B*, 105(24):245137, 2022.

[27] Tomislav Došlić, Ivica Martinjak, Riste Škrekovski, Sanja Tipurić-Spužević, and Ivana Zubac. Mostar index. *J. Math. Chem.*, 56:2995–3013, 2018.

[28] David Eppstein. Algorithms for drawing media. *Lecture Notes Comp. Sci.*, 3383:173–183, 2004.

[29] Ömer Eğecioğlu and Adriano Garsia. *Lessons in Enumerative Combinatorics.* Springer, Graduate Texts in Mathematics, 2021.

[30] Ömer Eğecioğlu and Vesna Iršič. Fibonacci-run graphs I: basic properties. *Discrete Appl. Math.*, 295:70–84, 2021.

[31] Ömer Eğecioğlu and Vesna Iršič. Fibonacci-run graphs II: Degree sequences. *Discrete Appl. Math.*, 300:56–71, 2021.

[32] Ömer Eğecioğlu, Elif Saygı, and Zülfükar Saygı. k-Fibonacci cubes: a fam-

ily of subgraphs of Fibonacci cubes. *Internat. J. Found. Comput. Sci.*, 31(5):639–661, 2020.

[33] Ömer Eğecioğlu, Elif Saygı, and Zülfükar Saygı. On the chromatic polynomial and the domination number of k-Fibonacci cubes. *Turkish J. Math.*, 44(5):1813–1823, 2020.

[34] Ömer Eğecioğlu, Elif Saygı, and Zülfükar Saygı. Alternate Lucas cubes. *Internat. J. Found. Comput. Sci.*, 32(7):871–899, 2021.

[35] Ömer Eğecioğlu, Elif Saygı, and Zülfükar Saygı. The irregularity polynomials of Fibonacci and Lucas cubes. *Bull. Malays. Math. Sci. Soc.*, 44(2):753–765, 2021.

[36] Ömer Eğecioğlu, Elif Saygı, and Zülfükar Saygı. The Mostar index of Fibonacci and Lucas cubes. *Bull. Malays. Math. Sci. Soc.*, 44(44):3677–3687, 2021.

[37] Ömer Eğecioğlu, Elif Saygı, and Zülfükar Saygı. The number of short cycles in Fibonacci cubes. *Theoret. Comput. Sci.*, 871:134–146, 2021.

[38] Ömer Eğecioğlu, Elif Saygı, and Zülfükar Saygı. Euler numbers and diametral paths in Fibonacci cubes, Lucas cubes and Alternate Lucas cubes. *arXiv:2210.13849*, 2022.

[39] Ömer Eğecioğlu, Elif Saygı, and Zülfükar Saygı. The Mostar and Wiener index of alternate Lucas cubes. *Trans. Combin.*, 12(1):37–46, 2023.

[40] Jörg Flum and Martin Grohe. The parameterized complexity of counting problems. *SIAM J. Comput.*, 33(4):892–922, 2004.

[41] Enrico Giusti and Paolo (Eds.) D'Alessandro. *Leonardi Bigolli Pisani vulgo Fibonacci: Liber Abbaci*. Biblioteca di "Nuncius", Vol. 79, Florence, 2020.

[42] Ronald L. Graham, Donald E. Knuth, and Oren Patashnik. *Concrete Mathematics*. Addison-Wesley Publishing Company Advanced Book Program, Reading, MA, 1989.

[43] Sylvain Gravier, Michel Mollard, Simon Špacapan, and Sara Sabrina Zemljič. On disjoint hypercubes in Fibonacci cubes. *Discrete Appl. Math.*, 190/191:50–55, 2015.

[44] Curtis Greene and Herbert S. Wilf. Closed form summation of C-finite sequences. *Trans. Amer. Math. Soc.*, 359:1161–1189, 2007.

[45] Harri Haanpää and Patric Östergård. Counting Hamiltonian cycles in bipartite graphs. *Math. Comp.*, 83:979–995, 03 2014.

[46] Richard Hammack, Wilfried Imrich, and Sandi Klavžar. *Handbook of Product Graphs*. Discrete Mathematics and its Applications. CRC Press, Boca Raton, FL, second edition, 2011.

[47] Richard W. Hamming. Error detecting and error correcting codes. *Bell Syst. Tech. J.*, 29(2):147–160, 1950.

[48] Teresa W. Haynes, Stephen T. Hedetniemi, and Peter J. Slater. *Fundamentals of Domination in Graphs*, volume 208 of *Monographs and Textbooks in Pure and Applied Mathematics*. Marcel Dekker, Inc., New York, 1998.

[49] Andreas Hinz, Sandi Klavžar, and Ciril Petr. *The Tower of Hanoi—Myths and Maths, Second Edition*. Birkhäuser, 2018.

[50] Alwyn Francis Horadam. Jacobsthal representation numbers. *Fibonacci Quart.*, 34:40–54, 1996.

[51] Wen-Jing Hsu. Fibonacci cubes: a new interconnection topology. *IEEE Trans. Parallel Distrib. Syst.*, 4:3–12, 1993.

[52] Aleksandar Ilić, Sandi Klavžar, and Yoomi Rho. Generalized Fibonacci cubes. *Discrete Math.*, 312(1):2–11, 2012.

[53] Aleksandar Ilić, Sandi Klavžar, and Yoomi Rho. The index of a binary word. *Theoret. Comput. Sci.*, 452:100–106, 2012.

[54] Aleksandar Ilić and Marko Milošević. The parameters of Fibonacci and Lucas cubes. *Ars Math. Contemp.*, 12(1):25–29, 2017.

[55] Wilfried Imrich and Sandi Klavžar. A convexity lemma and expansion procedures for bipartite graphs. *European J. Combin.*, 19(6):677–685, 1998.

[56] Stasys Jukna. *Extremal Combinatorics: With Applications in Computer Science*. Springer Publishing Company, Incorporated, 1st edition, 2010.

[57] Gustav Kirchhoff. über die Auflösung der Gleichungen, auf welche man bei der Untersuchung der linearen Verteilung galvanischer Ströme geführt wird. *Ann. Phys. Chem.*, 72:497–508, 1847.

[58] Sandi Klavžar. On median nature and enumerative properties of Fibonacci-like cubes. *Discrete Math.*, 299(1):145–153, 2005.

[59] Sandi Klavžar. Structure of Fibonacci cubes: a survey. *J. Comb. Optim.*, 25(4):505–522, 2013.

[60] Sandi Klavžar, Ivan Gutman, and Bojan Mohar. Labeling of benzenoid systems which reflects the vertex-distance relations. *J. Chem. Inf. Comput. Sci.*, 35(3):590–593, 1995.

[61] Sandi Klavžar and Michel Mollard. Cube polynomial of Fibonacci and Lucas cubes. *Acta Appl. Math.*, 117:93–105, 2012.

[62] Sandi Klavžar and Michel Mollard. Wiener index and Hosoya polynomial of Fibonacci and Lucas cubes. *MATCH Commun. Math. Comput. Chem.*, 68(1):311–324, 2012.

[63] Sandi Klavžar and Michel Mollard. Asymptotic properties of Fibonacci cubes and Lucas cubes. *Ann. Comb.*, 18(3):447–457, 2014.

[64] Sandi Klavžar and Michel Mollard. Daisy cubes and distance cube polynomial. *European J. Combin.*, 80:214–223, 2019.

[65] Sandi Klavžar, Michel Mollard, and Marko Petkovšek. The degree sequence of Fibonacci and Lucas cubes. *Discrete Math.*, 311(14):1310–1322, 2011.

[66] Sandi Klavžar and Iztok Peterin. Edge-counting vectors, Fibonacci cubes, and Fibonacci triangle. *Publ. Math. Debrecen*, 71(3-4):267–278, 2007.

[67] Sandi Klavžar and Sergey Shpectorov. Asymptotic number of isometric generalized Fibonacci cubes. *European J. Combin.*, 33(2):220–226, 2012.

[68] Sandi Klavžar and Petra Žigert. Fibonacci cubes are the resonance graphs of Fibonaccenes. *Fibonacci Quart.*, 43(3):269–276, 2005.

[69] Sandi Klavžar, Petra Žigert, and Gunnar Brinkmann. Resonance graphs of catacondensed even ring systems are median. *Discrete Math.*, 253(1-3):35–43, 2002.

[70] Donald E. Knuth. *The Art of Computer Programming, Vol. 4A*. Addison-Wesley, 2011.

[71] Germaine Kreweras. Les préordres totaux compatibles avec un ordre partiel. *Math. Sci. Humaines*, 53:5–30, 1976.

[72] Édouard Lucas. *Théorie des Nombres*. Gauthier-Villars, Paris, 1891.

[73] Michel Mollard. Maximal hypercubes in Fibonacci and Lucas cubes. *Discrete Appl. Math.*, 160(16-17):2479–2483, 2012.

[74] Michel Mollard. Non covered vertices in Fibonacci cubes by a maximum set of disjoint hypercubes. *Discrete Appl. Math.*, 219:219–221, 2017.

[75] Michel Mollard. The existence of perfect codes in a family of generalized Fibonacci cubes. *Inf. Process. Lett.*, 140:1–3, 2018.

[76] Michel Mollard. Edges in Fibonacci cubes, Lucas cubes and complements. *Bull. Malays. Math. Sci. Soc.*, 44(6):4425–4437, 2021.

[77] Michel Mollard. The (non-)existence of perfect codes in Lucas cubes. *Ars Math. Contemp.*, 22(3):P3.10, 2022.

[78] Michel Mollard. A relation between Wiener index and Mostar index for daisy cubes. *Discrete Math. Lett.*, 10:81–84, 2022.

[79] Martyn Mulder. The structure of median graphs. *Discrete Math.*, 24(2):197–204, 1978.

[80] Emanuele Munarini. Pell graphs. *Discrete Math.*, 342(8):2415–2428, 2019.

[81] Emanuele Munarini, Claudio Perelli Cippo, and Norma Zagaglia Salvi. On the Lucas cubes. *Fibonacci Quart.*, 39(1):12–21, 2001.

[82] Emanuele Munarini and Norma Zagaglia Salvi. Structural and enumerative properties of the Fibonacci cubes. *Discrete Math.*, 255(1):317–324, 2002.

[83] Eugen Netto. *Lehrbuch der Combinatorik*. B. G. Teubner, Leipzig, 1901.

[84] Arda Buğra Özer, Elif Saygı, and Zülfükar Saygı. Domination type parameters of Pell graphs. *Ars Math. Contemp.*, 23(1):P1.03, 2023.

[85] W. E. Patten and Solomon W. Golomb. Elementary problems and solutions: solutions: E1470. *Amer. Math. Monthly*, 69(1):61–62, 1962.

[86] David A. Pike and Yubo Zou. The domination number of Fibonacci cubes. *J. Combin. Math. Combin. Comput.*, 80:433–444, 2012.

[87] Alfred S. Posamentier and Ingmar Lehman. *The (Fabulous) Fibonacci numbers*. Prometheus Books, New York, 2007.

[88] Mark Ramras. Congestion-free routing of linear permutations on Fibonacci and Lucas cubes. *Australas. J. Comb.*, 60:1–10, 2014.

[89] Yoomi Rho and Aleksander Vesel. Linear recognition of generalized Fibonacci cubes $Q_h(111)$. *Discrete Math. Theor. Comput. Sci.*, 17(3):349–362, 2016.

[90] Elif Saygı. On the domination number and the total domination number of Fibonacci cubes. *Ars Math. Contemp.*, 16(1):245–255, 2019.

[91] Elif Saygı and Ömer Eğecioğlu. Counting disjoint hypercubes in Fibonacci cubes. *Discrete Appl. Math.*, 215:231–237, 2016.

[92] Elif Saygı and Ömer Eğecioğlu. q-Cube enumerator polynomial of Fibonacci cubes. *Discrete Appl. Math.*, 226:127–137, 2017.

[93] Elif Saygı and Ömer Eğecioğlu. q-Counting hypercubes in Lucas cubes. *Turkish J. Math.*, 42(1):190–203, 2018.

[94] Elif Saygı and Ömer Eğecioğlu. Boundary enumerator polynomial of hypercubes in Fibonacci cubes. *Discrete Appl. Math.*, 266:191–199, 2019.

[95] Zülfükar Saygı. Results on the domination number and the total domination

number of Lucas cubes. *Ars Math. Contemp.*, 19(1):25–35, 2020.

[96] Laurence E. Sigler. *Fibonacci's Liber Abaci (English translation)*. Springer-Verlag, New York, 2002.

[97] Riste Škrekovski. Two relations for median graphs. *Discrete Math.*, 226(1-3):351–353, 2001.

[98] Neil J. A. Sloane and The OEIS Foundation Inc. The On-Line Encyclopedia of Integer Sequences. 2022.

[99] Petru Soltan and Victor Chepoi. Solution of the Weber problem for discrete median metric spaces. *Trudy Tbiliss. Mat. Inst. Razmadze Akad. Nauk Gruzin. SSR*, 85:52–76, 1987.

[100] Richard P. Stanley. Log-concave and unimodal sequences in algebra, combinatorics, and geometry. In *Graph Theory and its Applications: East and West (Jinan, 1986)*, volume 576 of *Ann. New York Acad. Sci.*, pages 500–535. New York Acad. Sci., New York, 1989.

[101] Richard P. Stanley. A Survey of Alternating Permutations. *Contem. Math.*, 531:165–196, 2010.

[102] Andrej Taranenko. A new characterization and a recognition algorithm of Lucas cubes. *Discrete Math. Theor. Comput. Sci.*, 15(3):31–39, 2013.

[103] Andrej Taranenko. Daisy cubes: A characterization and a generalization. *European J. Combin.*, 85:103058, 2020.

[104] Andrej Taranenko and Aleksander Vesel. Fast recognition of Fibonacci cubes. *Algorithmica*, 49(2):81–93, 2007.

[105] Steven Vajda. *Fibonacci and Lucas Numbers, and the Golden Section: Theory and Applications*. Dover Publications, New York, 2007.

[106] Yu. L. Vasil'ev. On ungrouped, close-packed codes. *Problemy Kibernet. No.*, 8:337–339, 1962.

[107] Aleksander Vesel. Characterization of resonance graphs of catacondensed hexagonal graphs. *MATCH Commun. Math. Comput. Chem.*, 53(1):195–208, 2005.

[108] Aleksander Vesel. Linear recognition and embedding of Fibonacci cubes. *Algorithmica*, 71(4):1021–1034, 2015.

[109] Aleksander Vesel. Cube-complements of generalized Fibonacci cubes. *Discrete Math.*, 342(4):1139–1146, 2019.

[110] Aleksander Vesel. Efficient proper embedding of a daisy cube. *Ars Math. Contemp.*, 21(2):P2.07, 2021.

[111] Nicolai N. Vorobev. *Fibonacci Numbers, (Trans. Halina Moss)*. Pergamon Press, New York, 1961.

[112] Jianxin Wei. All good (bad) words consisting of 5 blocks. *Acta Math. Sin. (Engl. Ser.)*, 33(6):851–860, 2017.

[113] Jianxin Wei. The structures of bad words. *European J. Combin.*, 59:204–214, 2017.

[114] Jianxin Wei. The radius and center of Fibonacci-run graphs. *Discrete Appl. Math.*, 325:93–96, 2023.

[115] Jianxin Wei and Yujun Yang. Fibonacci and Lucas p-cubes. *Discrete Appl. Math.*, 322:365–383, 2022.

[116] Jianxin Wei, Yujun Yang, and Guangfu Wang. The self-concatenation of

isometric strings is isometric. *Discrete Math.*, 340(8):1844–1850, 2017.

[117] Jianxin Wei, Yujun Yang, and Xuena Zhu. A characterization of non-isometric binary words. *European J. Combin.*, 78:121–133, 2019.

[118] Jianxin Wei and Heping Zhang. Proofs of two conjectures on generalized Fibonacci cubes. *European J. Combin.*, 51:419–432, 2016.

[119] Jianxin Wei and Heping Zhang. A negative answer to a problem on generalized Fibonacci cubes. *Discrete Math.*, 340(2):81–86, 2017.

[120] Douglas B. West. *Introduction to Graph Theory.* Prentice Hall, Inc., Upper Saddle River, NJ, 1996.

[121] Peter M. Winkler. Isometric embedding in products of complete graphs. *Discrete Appl. Math.*, 7(2):221–225, 1984.

[122] Haiyuan Yao and Heping Zhang. Non-matchable distributive lattices. *Discrete Math.*, 338(3):122–132, 2015.

[123] Norma Zagaglia Salvi. On the existence of cycles of every even length on generalized Fibonacci cubes. *Matematiche (Catania)*, 51(suppl.):241–251 (1997), 1996.

[124] Edouard Zeckendorf. Représentation des nombres naturels par une somme de nombres de Fibonacci ou de nombres de Lucas. *Bull. Soc. R. Sci. Liège*, 41:179–182, 1972.

[125] Ioana Zelina. Hamiltonian path and cycles in Fibonacci cubes. *Carpathian J. Math.*, 24:149–155, 2008.

[126] Petra Žigert Pleteršek and Martina Berlič. Resonance graphs of armchair nanotubes cyclic polypyrenes and amalgams of Lucas cubes. *MATCH Commun. Math. Comput. Chem.*, 70(2):533–543, 2013.

Subject Index

alphabet, 19

alternate Lucas cube, 172, 236, 241

alternating permutation, 64, 182

armchair carbon nanotube, 164

asymptotic behavior
  of $Mo(\Gamma_n)$, 255
  of $Mo(\Lambda_n)$, 255
  of $Mo(\mathcal{L}_n)$, 255
  of $\mu(\Gamma_n)$, 254
  of $\mu(\Lambda_n)$, 255
  of $\mu(\mathcal{L}_n)$, 255
  of $\mu(Q_n)$, 255
  of $W(\Gamma_n)$, 254
  of $W(\Lambda_n)$, 255
  of $W(\mathcal{L}_n)$, 255
  of average degree in Γ_n, 251
  of average degree in Γ_n^k, 253
  of average degree in Λ_n, 251
  of average degree in $\mathcal{L}_n$, 251
  of average degree in $\mathcal{R}_n$, 254
  of average eccentricity, 251
  of boundary of Q_0s in Γ_n, 256
  of boundary of Q_1s in Γ_n, 257
  of boundary of hypercubes in Γ_n, 256

asymptotic irregularity
  of Γ_n, 256
  of Λ_n, 256
  of $\mathcal{L}_n$, 256

asymptotic order
  of Γ_n, 249
  of Γ_n^k, 250
  of Λ_n, 249
  of $\mathcal{L}_n$, 250
  of Π_n, 250
  of $\mathcal{R}_n$, 250

asymptotic size
  of Γ_n, 250
  of Λ_n, 250
  of $\mathcal{L}_n$, 250
  of $\mathcal{R}_n$, 250

automorphism group, 31
  of Γ_n, 45
  of Λ_n, 146

average
  boundary of Q_1s in Γ_n, 257
  boundary of hypercubes in Γ_n, 256
  degree, 251
  distance, 254
  eccentricity, 251

bad word, 188

binary
  alphabet, 32
  string, 20
  variable, 122
  word, 20

Author Index

Milošević, M., 122
Mohar, B., 125
Mollard, M., 41, 45, 55, 58, 78, 84, 86, 88, 125, 132, 168, 197, 199, 235, 244
Mulder, H.M., 115
Munarini, E., 38, 54, 141, 201, 242

Östergård, P., 60
Özer, A.B., 206

Paffenholz, P., 12
Patten, W.E., 47
Perelli Cippo, C., 38, 141
Peterin, I., 116
Petkovšek, M., 41, 46
Petr, C., 60
Pike, D., 122, 166
Pisano, L. (Fibonacci), 1

Ramras, M., 49
Rho, Y., v, 43, 45, 122, 184, 185, 191

Saygı, E., 64, 69, 88, 89, 100, 123, 129, 134, 151, 157, 165, 171, 180, 181, 206, 207
Saygı, Z., 64, 69, 123, 129, 134, 151, 171, 180, 181, 206, 207
Schur, I., 89
Sharma, S., 60
Shpectorov, S., 188
Sigler, L., 2
Sim, S., 122
Škrekovski, R., 78, 241
Soltan, P., 241
Špacapan, S., 86
Stanley, R., 64

Taranenko, A., 116, 118, 162, 237
Tratnik, N., 247

Vajnovszki, V., 149, 225
van de Vel, M., 105
Vasil'ev, Yu.L., 193
Vesel, A., 115, 116, 118, 119, 185, 231, 237

Wang, G., 188
Wei, J., 188, 189, 191, 192, 248
Wilf, H.S., 39
Winkler, P.M., 114

Yang, Y., 188, 192, 248
Yao, H., 164

Zagaglia Salvi, N., 38, 54, 63, 69, 141
Zeckendorf, E., 8
Zelina, I., 63
Zemljič, S.S., 86
Zhang, H., 164, 189, 192
Zheng, S.-Q., 60
Zhu, X., 192
Žigert Pleteršek, P., 109, 113, 164, 247
Zou, Y., 122, 166

Notation Index

$\alpha(G)$ - independence number of G, 31

$\text{Aut}(G)$ - automorphism group of G, 31

$\mathcal{B}$ - binary alphabet, 19

$\mathcal{B}^*$ - all binary words, 20

$\mathcal{B}_n$ - set of binary strings of length n, 20

$\mathcal{B}_n^{\bullet f}$ - strings of $\mathcal{B}_n$ with suffix f, 35

$\mathcal{B}_n(f)$ - strings of $\mathcal{B}_n$ without substring f, 33

$\mathcal{B}_n^{f\bullet}$ - strings of $\mathcal{B}_n$ with prefix f, 35

$|b|_1$ - Hamming weight of b, 36

$b(H)$ - bottom vertex of H, 77

$\text{bw}(G)$ - bisection width of G, 262

$C(G)$ - center of G, 203

$C_G(x)$ - cube polynomial of G, 78

$C_G(x,q)$ - q-cube polynomial of G, 89

$c_k(G)$ - number of k-cubes in G, 78

C_n - cycle of order n, 29

$\chi(G)$ - chromatic number of G, 259

D_{2n} - dihedral group on n elements, 49

$D_{G,u}$ - distance cube polynomial of G with respect to u, 238

$d_G(u,v)$ - distance between u and v in G, 30

$\mathbb{D}_{n,k}(d)$ - boundary polynomial, 96

$\deg_G(u)$ - degree of vertex u, 29

$\overline{\deg}(G)$ - average degree of G, 250

$\Delta(G)$ - maximum degree of G, 30

$\delta(G)$ - minimum degree of G, 30

δ_i - change the ith coordinate of a string, 32

$\text{diam}(G)$ - diameter of graph G, 30

$\mathcal{E}_n$ - set of Fibonacci strings of even Hamming weight, 63

E_n - n^{th} Euler number, 64

$\overline{\text{ecc}}(G)$ - average eccentricity of G, 250

$\text{ecc}_G(u)$ - eccentricity of u in G, 30

$\mathcal{F}_n$ - Fibonacci strings of length n, 6

$\mathcal{F}_n^{\bullet f}$ - strings of $\mathcal{F}_n$ with suffix f, 35

$\mathcal{F}_n^{f\bullet}$ - strings of $\mathcal{F}_n$ with prefix f, 35

$\mathcal{F}_n^{\text{co}}$ -non-Fibonacci strings of length n, 231

$\overline{f}$ - complement of the binary string f, 21

$\mathbb{F}$ - field $\mathbb{Z}_2$, 49

$\mathbb{F}^n$ - vector space of dimension n over the field $\mathbb{Z}_2$, 49

F_n - n^{th} Fibonacci number, 1

$F_n(x)$ - n^{th} Fibonacci polynomial, 25

$G[X]$ - subgraph of G induced by X, 30

$\overline{G}$ - complement of G, 32

$|w|_s$ - number of occurrences of s in
    w, 20
+ - disjoint union, 21
□ - Cartesian product of graphs, 30